McGRAW-HILL PUBLICATIONS IN THE
ZOOLOGICAL SCIENCES

E. J. Boell, Consulting Editor

MANUAL OF
COMPARATIVE ANATOMY

McGRAW-HILL PUBLICATIONS IN THE ZOOLOGICAL SCIENCES

E. J. Boell, CONSULTING EDITOR

Baitsell · HUMAN BIOLOGY

Breland · MANUAL OF COMPARATIVE ANATOMY

Chapman · ANIMAL ECOLOGY

Clausen · ENTOMOPHAGOUS INSECTS

Goldschmidt · PHYSIOLOGICAL GENETICS

Haupt · FUNDAMENTALS OF BIOLOGY

Hyman · THE INVERTEBRATES: PROTOZOA THROUGH CTENOPHORA (Vol. I)
THE INVERTEBRATES: PLATYHELMINTHES AND RHYNCHOCOELA (Vol. II)
THE INVERTEBRATES: ACANTHOCEPHALA, ASCHELMINTHES, AND ENTOPROCTA (Vol. III)

Johannsen and Butt · EMBRYOLOGY OF INSECTS AND MYRIAPODS

Leach · FUNCTIONAL ANATOMY OF THE MAMMAL

Metcalf and Flint · FUNDAMENTALS OF INSECT LIFE

Mitchell · GENERAL PHYSIOLOGY

Mitchell and Taylor · LABORATORY MANUAL OF GENERAL PHYSIOLOGY

Pearse · ANIMAL ECOLOGY

Quiring · FUNCTIONAL ANATOMY OF THE VERTEBRATES

Rogers · TEXTBOOK OF COMPARATIVE PHYSIOLOGY
LABORATORY OUTLINES IN COMPARATIVE PHYSIOLOGY

Shull · EVOLUTION
HEREDITY

Shull, LaRue, and Ruthven · PRINCIPLES OF ANIMAL BIOLOGY
LABORATORY DIRECTIONS IN PRINCIPLES OF ANIMAL BIOLOGY

Snodgrass · PRINCIPLES OF INSECT MORPHOLOGY

Storer · GENERAL ZOOLOGY
LABORATORY MANUAL FOR GENERAL ZOOLOGY

Weichert · ANATOMY OF THE CHORDATES

Welch · LIMNOLOGY

Wieman · AN INTRODUCTION TO VERTEBRATE EMBRYOLOGY

Wolcott · ANIMAL BIOLOGY

Wolcott and Powell · LABORATORY GUIDE IN ANIMAL BIOLOGY

There are also the related series of McGraw-Hill Publications in the Botanical Sciences, of which Edmund W. Sinnott is Consulting Editor, and in the Agricultural Sciences, of which R. A. Brink is Consulting Editor.

MANUAL OF
COMPARATIVE ANATOMY

OSMOND P. BRELAND, Ph.D.

Professor of Zoology
University of Texas

SECOND EDITION

New York   Toronto   London

McGRAW-HILL BOOK COMPANY. INC.

1953

MANUAL OF COMPARATIVE ANATOMY

Library of Congress Catalog Card Number: 52-10329

THE MAPLE PRESS COMPANY, YORK, PA.

PREFACE TO SECOND EDITION

The first edition of this manual has been given a very kind reception by numerous teachers and students. During the past few years many users have thoughtfully written the author and have made valuable suggestions for the modification of certain parts. As a result of these suggestions and recent studies, several major changes have been made in the revised edition. These include the use of boldface type rather than italics for the names of structures the first time the names are used, the addition of a section on the pigeon, and a revision in the system of classification that is followed A fourth major change concerns the drawing directions. These instructions were all grouped at the end of each chapter in the first edition. In the revision, the drawing directions have been inserted in the text at the places where the drawings are to be made.

The author wishes to express sincere appreciation to all who have contributed to this second edition of the manual. These include users who have suggested changes and several staff members at the University of Texas. He is especially indebted in this connection to Dr. Clark Hubbs, Dr. Frank Blair, and Homer Phillips.

The writer will greatly appreciate having possible errors or discrepancies called to his attention; he will also be pleased to receive suggestions for the further improvement of the manual.

O. P. BRELAND

AUSTIN, TEXAS
February, 1953

v

PREFACE TO FIRST EDITION

This manual has been written with two objectives in mind. First, the intention has been to make the directions so clear that anyone using the guide will be able to find the designated structures with a minimum of outside assistance. It is believed that this is of prime importance, since in large laboratory sections the amount of individual assistance given to the students by the instructors is necessarily limited. The manual is thus based on actual dissections, with the specimens before the author at the time of writing. Some of the directions included have been used in the laboratory as mimeographed sheets; when it has appeared necessary, the additional clarification of these instructions has been made.

The second objective has been to emphasize the comparative importance of the organs and structures that are studied. There is too often a tendency in a study of comparative anatomy for both student and instructor to overlook the comparative significance of the studies and, instead, to concentrate on certain animals or structures for their sake alone. While the latter method possesses certain aesthetic values, the comparative method appears to be much superior. Opportunity is thus frequently taken to compare certain structures with those found in previously dissected animals. In addition, short paragraphs are occasionally inserted to correlate the various systems as found in several forms. It is freely admitted that such discussions are necessarily limited, since this guide is not a textbook. It is felt, however, that the student will derive more of lasting value from his laboratory work if attention is called to the comparative importance of the study while he is actually making the dissections. By way of review and also to provide for the possibility that some of the animals may be omitted in certain courses, some of these brief comparisons are partly repeated under the discussions of the different forms.

In preparing this volume, the author has referred to many different sources. The names applied to the structures and many of the interpretations used have been accepted by comparative anatomists for many years. The author thus makes no claim to have contributed anything original regarding the data or interpretations contained in this manual. It is hoped, however, that the method of presentation may have a certain value. Within recent years, there has been a tendency among some writers to apply new terms to certain structures and, in some cases, to make slightly different interpretations of homologies from those previously accepted. While these innovations have something to recommend them, the author feels that the established practice should be followed in most cases until the new interpretations and terminology are more commonly accepted. It should not be inferred from the above statements that all homologies of the various structures are accepted without question by the majority of workers. In some instances there has been so much disagreement that the author has been at a loss to know which interpretation should be accepted. In some such instances, no correlations have been attempted; in others, an effort has been made to express the opinion of the majority.

It will be noted that certain animals and certain systems have been studied in considerably more detail than have others. This selection is based upon ease of study and upon the fact that there is a trend toward omission of minute details that do not help the student grasp the larger concepts of the subject as a whole.

More time for study has been allotted to the dogfish and to the cat than to any of the other forms. The dogfish is emphasized because it is believed that in work of this kind the student should have a thorough knowledge of fundamental vertebrate structure in a comparatively simplified form. It is felt that he will thus better understand the complexities of comparable systems in the higher animals. The cat is studied in detail because it represents the fundamental mammalian structure.

The skeletal system has probably been less emphasized in this guide than has any other system. This is because it is comparatively difficult to study and not because it is unimportant. A study of the skeletal system necessitates the preparation of skeletons by students or instructors or the purchase of prepared skeletons. The first method is frequently impracticable because of the time element, and the second is not feasible in many cases because of the expense involved. The cat skeleton is studied in considerable detail because it is quite similar to that of man, and for this reason is considered important for both the general and the premedical student.

The animals more or less accepted as standard in many laboratories are the dogfish, an amphibian—usually *Necturus*—and the cat. Although it is agreed that these animals are important, it is believed that certain evolutionary concepts are likely to be missed unless additional species are studied to a certain extent. In addition to the portions of the manual devoted to the above species, sections are also included on *Amphioxus*, the lamprey, the perch, and the turtle. *Amphioxus* is included because certain structures characteristic of vertebrates are present in this animal in a greatly simplified form. The lamprey is in many respects the most primitive of living vertebrates; yet, despite its primitiveness, certain definite specializations are present. These facts well illustrate the concept that extremes of both primitiveness and specialization may be present in the same animal. The turtle, as a representative of the class Reptilia, exhibits the beginnings of certain tendencies that are carried to completion in the higher animals. The section devoted to the perch is quite short and has been included because of the presence of certain ambiguities in bony fish as compared with other vertebrates. Any of these animals may, of course, be omitted at the discretion of the instructor.

The author has deemed it advisable to be definite with respect to the type of drawings to be made and to include in each case a list of labels that should be present. By this method more uniformity will be attained in the drawings presented by the students. Such a list of labels is helpful, for the student is frequently at a loss to know what labels should be placed on a given drawing. Moreover, if drawings are to be graded, the list of labels furnishes one definite criterion for both student and laboratory instructor. This is important in the interests of uniformity of grading when a large number of laboratory instructors are teaching the same course. Some laboratory instructors prefer to use prepared outline drawings, rather than to have the students make the drawings themselves. The drawings called for and the list of labels have been prepared with this possibility in mind, so that in most cases the required drawings will be essentially the same as those illustrated in the better series of outline drawings now on the market. A book of drawings such as "Outline Drawings for Laboratory Studies in Comparative Anatomy" by W. C. Senning, published by McGraw-Hill Book Company, Inc., New York, will prove helpful. Certain drawings may easily be omitted or modified to conform to different types of course.

The author wishes to express his appreciation to Doctors William Jackson Dobson, Griff Terry Ross, and Ardell Nichols Taylor, who have been of great assistance in the preparation of this manual. Several of the dissecting techniques that are used were developed by these men in their laboratory teaching. They also made helpful suggestions in the writing of the manual. In this connection, the author is especially indebted to Dr. Dobson, who read the entire manuscript and who made valuable contributions to its content and organization. Dr. Dobson also corrected the proofs of the manual and prepared the index.

In a manual of this kind, errors and omissions frequently occur despite all precautions. If such discrepancies are discovered, the author will appreciate having them called to his attention.

O. P. BRELAND

AUSTIN, TEXAS
August, 1943

CONTENTS

INTRODUCTION

Laboratory Materials. Certain laboratory and dissecting materials are essential for all courses in comparative anatomy. The requirements for different courses are variable, but the suggested list below is considered necessary for most of them. Unless otherwise directed, each student should obtain the following equipment:

1 metal-handled scalpel.
2 dissecting needles, or "teasers."
1 pair of heavy scissors with one point sharp and the other point blunt.
1 heavy probe.
1 light probe, sometimes called an "olive-pointed probe."
1 pair of straight-pointed forceps.
1 combination lock to be used on locker.
1 3H drawing pencil.
1 6-inch ruler.
1 Artgum eraser.
Drawing paper. The amount to be obtained will vary in the different courses.
1 piece of cheesecloth about 1 yard square to be used for wrapping about specimens.
2 small towels.
1 piece of good soap.

It will be noted that for most of the laboratory exercises specific drawings are called for, and a list of labels is given which are to be included in each case. Unless otherwise directed, these drawings should be made and completely labeled as indicated. The student should understand that the list of labels for each drawing does not necessarily include all the structures which should be learned for a particular exercise. While the majority of structures will in most cases be included in these lists, important structures may sometimes be omitted because of lack of space or because they cannot be well illustrated in a particular drawing. Each drawing should be completed before additional work is undertaken.

1

It is believed inadvisable to give specific drawing directions; many students have had some drawing experience, and instructors vary in their requirements. A few general suggestions, however, may prove helpful. In most instances, drawings should be placed in the center of the drawing plate, with the labels distributed equally along each side. A label should be at or near the same level on the page as the structure to which the lead line will pass. Lead lines from the label to the structures can thus be made parallel to the top and bottom of the drawing plate. If this cannot be done, keep the lead line from the label parallel to the top and bottom of the plate until near the structure, and then make a definite angle in the line so that it will pass directly to the structure to be labeled. When a large number of labels are to be placed in a small area, the student should first estimate the approximate positions of the labels before actually placing them on the page. In this way, unnecessary crowding of labels can be prevented. Do not cross lead lines. The left-hand margins of the labels should be kept straight. It is suggested that labels be made in the singular and that, when there are several identical structures, the lead line be drawn to only one of them. Labels should be printed. They should be begun with a capital letter, and the remainder of the word should be in small letters.

In describing the location of various structures, it is necessary to use certain orienting terms such as left, right, dorsal, or ventral. These terms as applied to the specimens are frequently confusing to the student who is beginning a study of anatomy, for he is usually dissecting from the animal's ventral side. This fact causes the animal's left to be to the student's right side, and vice versa. The student should therefore attempt to orient himself at once with this fact in mind. Unless otherwise indicated, all such terms refer to the body of the specimen. Thus, if the directions state that a blood vessel passes to the left, it means that the vessel passes to the *animal's* left side, rather than to the left side of the student. The principal terms that are used in referring to the various regions of the body are included in the list below. The student should study these terms and become thoroughly familiar with their meaning.

Anterior, or cranial.   Toward the head.

Posterior, or caudal.   Toward the tail.

Dorsal.   Toward the back, or top side, of the animal.

Ventral.   Toward the belly, or bottom side, of the animal.

Lateral. Toward the side. Sometimes used to indicate the outer surface of a structure, such as a limb.

Medial. Toward the mid-line of the body. Sometimes used to indicate the inner surface of a structure, such as a limb, as opposed to the outer, or lateral, surface.

Proximal. Near a point of attachment.

Distal. Distant from a point of attachment.

Peripheral. Toward the surface.

The student must realize that there is considerable individual variation in all animal structures; because of this, it is not possible to take into account in the directions all the exceptions to the general rule that are likely to be encountered. The student should thus not be unduly alarmed if certain structures in his specimen are not exactly as described in the manual. Anyone who doubts the existence of individual variation should examine the noses of all persons near him and notice whether any two are exactly alike.

CLASSIFICATION OF THE PHYLUM CHORDATA

The systems of classification of the phylum Chordata are somewhat more standardized than they were when the first edition of this book was published. However, there is still some disagreement relative to certain groups. The system used here is one that seems reasonably well accepted by many workers, and it follows closely the scheme advocated by Dr. Alfred S. Romer of Harvard University. Only living groups are included, and in some cases extra categories, such as subclasses and superorders have been omitted. Of the approximately twenty-five orders of living birds that are recognized, only five of the more common groups have been included.

PHYLUM CHORDATA

Subphylum 1. Hemichordata (Enteroptneusta)—the acorn-headed "worms": *Balanoglossus* and its allies.

Subphylum 2. Urochordata (Tunicata)—the sea squirts, or tunicates.

Subphylum 3. Cephalochordata—the lancelets: *Branchiostoma*, commonly called Amphioxus.

Subphylum 4. Vertebrata (Craniata)—animals with a backbone, or the beginnings of one.

Class 1. Agnatha—the lampreys and hagfishes.

Order 1. Cyclostomata—all living agnathans.

Suborder 1. Petromyzontia—the lampreys.

Suborder 2. Myxinoidea—the hagfishes.

Class 2. Chondrichthyes—fishes with cartilaginous skeletons.

Subclass 1. Elasmobranchii—sharks and similar forms.
Order 1. Selachii—sharks and dogfishes.
Order 2. Batoidei—skates and rays.
Subclass 2. Holocephali—the elephant fishes, *Chimaera* and allies.
Class 3. Osteichthyes—fishes with bony skeletons.
Subclass 1. Actinopterygii—fishes without internal nostrils.
Order 1. Chondrostei—*Polypterus*, sturgeons, and spoonbills.
Order 2. Holostei—gar pikes and bowfins.
Order 3. Teleostei—most of the common fishes. Includes perch, trout, bass, catfishes, etc.
   NOTE: Some authorities divide this group into many orders.
Subclass 2. Choanichthyes—fishes with internal nostrils.
Order 1. Crossopterygii—mostly extinct, one form, *Latimeria*, recently discovered off the African coast.
Order 2. Dipnoi—the lungfishes.
Class 4. Amphibia—frogs, toads, salamanders, etc.
Order 1. Apoda (Gymnophiona)—the caecilians.
Order 2. Urodela (Caudata)—the salamanders.
Order 3. Anura (Salientia)—the frogs and toads.
Class 5. Reptilia—the reptiles.
Order 1. Chelonia (Testudinata)—the turtles.
Order 2. Rhynchocephalia—*Sphenodon* of New Zealand.
Order 3. Crocodilia—the alligators, crocodiles, etc.
Order 4. Squamata—the lizards, snakes, chameleons.
Class 6. Aves—the birds.
Subclass 1. Archaeornithes—*Archaeopteryx* and a few other extinct forms.
Subclass 2. Neornithes—all living birds and a few extinct species.
Superorder 1. Palaeognathae—ostriches and their relatives.
Superorder 2. Neognathae—all other living birds.
Order 1. Anseriformes—ducks, geese, etc.
Order 2. Falconiformes—hawks, eagles, vultures.
Order 3. Galliformes—pheasants, jungle fowls, domestic chickens, and turkeys.
Order 4. Columbiformes—pigeons and doves.
Order 5. Passeriformes—the songbirds, including sparrows, thrashers, warblers, etc.
   NOTE: Eighteen additional orders of the superorder Neognathae are often recognized.
Class 7. Mammalia—the mammals.
Subclass 1. Prototheria—the egg-laying mammals.
Order 1. Monotremata—the duckbill and spiny anteater.
Subclass 2. Metatheria—the pouched mammals.
Order 1. Marsupialia—opossums, kangaroos, etc.
Subclass 3. Eutheria—the placental mammals.
Order 1. Insectivora—shrews, moles, hedgehogs.
Order 2. Dermoptera—the flying lemurs.
Order 3. Chiroptera—the bats.
Order 4. Carnivora—the flesh-eating mammals: cats, dogs, seals, bears, raccoons, etc.

Order 5. Hyracoidea—the conies.
Order 6. Proboscidea—the elephants.
Order 7. Sirenia—the manatees and dugongs.
Order 8. Primates—monkeys, apes, man.
Order 9. Edentata—the armadillos, sloths, anteaters.
Order 10. Pholidota—the scaly anteaters.
Order 11. Tubulidentata—aardvarks.
Order 12. Lagomorpha—rabbits and hares.
Order 13. Perissodactyla—hoofed mammals with an uneven number
of toes: horses, rhinoceroses, tapirs, etc.
Order 14. Artiodactyla—hoofed mammals with an even number of
toes: cows, pigs, camels, giraffes, etc.
Order 15. Rodentia—the rodents: rats, mice, guinea pigs, squirrels,
beavers, etc.
Order 16. Cetacea—the whales.

The student should learn the complete classification of all
animals that are studied. The classification of each species is
given at the beginning of the section devoted to the particular
animal.

CHAPTER I

AMPHIOXUS, OR BRANCHIOSTOMA

Phylum—Chordata
Subphylum—Cephalochordata

In a study of vertebrate zoology or comparative anatomy, Amphioxus is important from several standpoints. It has the three diagnostic features of the phylum Chordata (dorsal hollow nerve cord, notochord, pharyngeal clefts) in easily recognizable form and retains these throughout life. Many of the organ systems found in higher vertebrate animals are represented in Amphioxus in a highly simplified condition, and this helps one to understand better the complex additions and changes found in the more highly developed animals. Because of the similarities in fundamental structure between this animal and vertebrates, it is thought probable that Amphioxus is similar to the unknown ancestor of vertebrate animals. Unfortunately it is not possible to examine here all the systems of Amphioxus, but some of those which cannot be seen by means of the microscope will be briefly mentioned.

Within recent years it has been found that the name *Branchiostoma* was applied to this group of animals before the term Amphioxus was used. The true scientific name is thus *Branchiostoma;* but Amphioxus will be used here as the common name.

In the present study, each student will be given a preserved specimen and slides of stained and cleared whole specimens and sections. Do not at any time press on the cover slip or wipe the slides vigorously. If the cover slip is moved, the slides will be ruined. If the slides apparently need cleaning, ask the instructor to show you the correct method. Use only the *low power* of the microscope. The slides are too thick for high power, and the magnification would be too great for a study of this kind.

External and Internal Anatomy. For this work, use the whole preserved specimen, which is mature, and the stained cleared slide of an immature specimen. The clearing of the specimen on the slide has caused the animal to be semitransparent, so that much of its internal anatomy can be seen. For the external

6

structures examine both the preserved specimen and the slide. The preserved animal should be examined with the unaided eye or with a hand lens if one is available. The slide should be studied with the low power of the microscope.

Identify first the external structures. Locate the anterior end by finding the fingerlike **buccal cirri** (singular, cirrus) that occur in that region. These cirri are probably sense organs. Just dorsal and anterior to the cirri, the anterior end of the body forms a projection, the **rostrum.** The anterior funnel-shaped portion of the body to which the cirri are attached is the **oral hood.** The cavity within the oral hood is the **vestibule.** This cavity is not comparable with a mouth cavity. The mouth will be identified later.

Along the dorsal side of the body locate a semitransparent strip of tissue, the **dorsal fin,** which is strengthened by cube-shaped **fin rays.** Trace the dorsal fin posteriorly until an area is found toward the tail in which no fin rays occur. This rayless fin is the **caudal fin,** which surrounds the posterior end of the body on both the dorsal and ventral sides. Trace the caudal fin anteriorly on the ventral surface, and observe that it is continuous with the anterior fin that has fin rays. This is the **ventral fin.** Note, therefore, that the caudal fin is best identified by the absence of fin rays posteriorly, although there may be a few short rays in its anterior regions. It is sometimes slightly more expanded than are the dorsal or ventral fins. Find the **anus,** the posterior opening of the digestive tract, which opens near the posterior end of the ventral fin. The anus is sometimes difficult to identify as a definite opening, but in most slides the posterior end of the intestine will protrude somewhat ventrally as a darker stained projection. The anus occurs at the end of this projection. Anterior to the ventral fin are the **metapleural folds,** two folds of tissue that do not have definite fin rays. The structure of these folds can probably best be observed in the preserved specimen, since on the slide only the side of one of the folds can be seen. Their relationships with other parts of the body will also be better understood after a study of the cross sections. On the slide, at the region where the ventral fin ends and the metapleural fold begins will be seen a slight indentation, which represents an opening. This is the **atriopore,** through which water passes to the outside after it has circulated through the body.

Look on the side of the body posterior to the atriopore, and find a series of V-shaped markings; these occur all along the body but can best be seen posteriorly. They represent the muscle segments, or myotomes, which will probably be more evident on the preserved specimen. The small V-shaped marks themselves are **myocommata** (singular, myocomma), or connective tissue, which help to bind the muscles together. The material between two myocommata is a **myotome.**

For a study of the internal anatomy, use only the cleared slide, except that the **gonads,** or reproductive organs, should be located in the preserved specimen. No gonads are present in the specimen on the slide, since it is immature; but the preserved animal is a mature individual, and the gonads appear as little whitish rounded structures along the lateral and ventral surfaces of the body.

Just below the fin rays that support the dorsal fin is the **neural tube,** or nerve cord. This structure can be distinguished from the surrounding material by the presence of a series of darkly stained **pigment spots** along its ventral surface. It is thought that these pigment spots are sensitive to light. Trace the neural tube anteriorly, and locate at its extreme end the **eyespot,** which is darkly stained and somewhat resembles a large pigment spot. It was once thought that the eyespot was sensitive to light, hence the name; but recent evidence indicates that it probably does not function in this capacity.

Ventral to the neural tube is the **notochord,** a cartilage-like structure that runs the length of the body. It is easiest to identify in the rostrum. Examine this region, and observe the elongate projection that is ventral to the eyespot and extends anterior to it. From this point, trace the notochord posteriorly. It is usually stained somewhat differently from the nerve cord. The notochord functions as a support for the body, and its presence is characteristic of all animals belonging to the phylum Chordata. In most of the higher vertebrate animals, the notochord is a complete structure only in the embryo and is later replaced by the vertebrae of the backbone. In some lower vertebrates, as will be seen, the notochord partly persists, even in the adult. The extension of the notochord in Amphioxus anterior to the end of the nerve cord is unusual, since in vertebrate animals the anterior end of the notochord is some distance posterior to the end of the brain. This peculiar relationship between the nerve cord and notochord is responsible for the name *Cephalochordata* (head cord) being applied to the subphylum in which Amphioxus is classified.

There is no definite enlargement in Amphioxus that could be called a brain, but the anterior end of the neural tube is sometimes called the **brain region.** Two pairs of nerves, called **cerebral nerves,** originate from the brain region, but they cannot be seen in the slides.

Turn now to the anterior end and locate again the **vestibule,** the cavity within the oral hood. Some of the details of this region are difficult to see unless the slides are well stained. Within the vestibule, just posterior to the attachment of the cirri to the oral hood, are to be seen several darkly stained fingerlike projections that are directed anteriorly. These projections are connected at their base, or posterior end, to form a structure called the **wheel organ.** The projections, or lobes, bear cilia, the beating of which helps to create a current of water from the outside through the vestibule and on posteriorly.

Posterior to the base of the wheel organ is a membrane, the **velum,** containing an opening, the **mouth.** In the slide, you are looking at the edge of the velum, since it extends across the posterior part of the vestibule, so that it will appear as a line, which is usually stained slightly differently from the wheel organ. The mouth occurs in the center of the velum and thus cannot be seen from this view. The position of the mouth, however, may be designated as being near the center of the velum. Attached to the velum and surrounding the mouth are several **velar tentacles,** which may not appear on the slide or which may show up as small threadlike structures stained about the same color as the velum. The function of these tentacles is probably to prevent undesirable material from entering the mouth.

The mouth opens into the **pharynx,** the large latticed structure just posterior to the velum. Along the side of the pharynx, note the numerous **pharyngeal slits** (openings) and, on each side of these, the solid **pharyngeal bars.**

The pharynx leads posteriorly into the **intestine,** which is a much smaller tube without the latticed walls. Near the region where the pharynx opens into the intestine there occurs a blind outpouching, which extends anteriorly and which may be partly covered by the pharynx. This is the **liver diverticulum,** or hepatic caecum, which is considered to be homologous to the liver of a vertebrate animal. On some slides, the anterior end of the liver diverticulum either will be covered by the pharynx or will itself partly cover the pharynx, depending upon which side of the specimen is being examined. The anterior end of this structure, therefore, is not inside the pharynx, as might appear at first glance.

Surrounding the intestine and extending anteriorly around the pharynx is a cavity, the **atrium,** into which water passes from the pharynx through the gill slits. In the whole specimen, the cavity is best indicated ventral to the intestine, where the presence of the cavity causes the slide to be somewhat lightly stained in this region. The relationship of this cavity to the other parts of the body can be best seen in the cross-sectional studies. Locate again the atriopore, the opening through which water passes to the outside from the atrium.

It should be observed that no definite paired fins occur in Amphioxus, although median fins are present. There are no definite gills, but the respiratory function of gills is performed by the thin-walled pharyngeal bars, which contain blood vessels.

Drawing 1. External and Internal Anatomy—Lateral View. Make the drawing lengthwise of the drawing plate. Place anterior end of drawing at the top of the page with the ventral surface to your left. Label parallel to the true top and bottom of the sheet. Make drawing about 6 inches long. **Labels:** oral hood, vestibule (cavity), buccal cirrus, rostrum, eyespot, velum, wheel organ, mouth region, dorsal fin, fin ray, pharynx, liver diverticulum, gonad, notochord, neural tube, pigment spot, atriopore, intestine, ventral fin, anus, caudal fin, myotome, myocomma, pharyngeal bar, pharyngeal slit, velar tentacle (if seen).

Cross Sections. This study should include at least two transverse, or cross, sections made through the body at different levels. The sections will be of mature specimens, and therefore the gonads will appear in some slides. It should be kept in mind that the slides will not be exactly alike since they have of necessity been made at slightly different levels. It is therefore suggested that the student look at several different slides.

Section through Pharynx and Liver. The dorsal surface of this section can be distinguished by the fact that on this side there is a single central projection; on the ventral surface, there are two projections, one on each side. The dorsal protuberance is the **dorsal fin;** the ventral projections are sections of the **metapleural folds.** Within the dorsal fin the **fin ray** occupies most of the space and serves as its support. Just below the dorsal fin there occurs some connective tissue, below which is the somewhat rounded **neural tube,** or nerve cord, containing a small hole, the **neurocoel.** It has been indicated previously that all chordate animals have a hollow nerve cord, as illustrated in Amphioxus. Spinal nerves arise from the nerve cord but are difficult to identify with certainty in these slides. Below the neural tube is the **notochord,** a large rounded structure, considerably larger than the nerve cord.

On each side of the structures just mentioned and extending ventrally are large masses of muscle tissue. These are sections of the muscle segments that were identified externally as V-shaped structures. Each muscle mass is divided into smaller parts by connective tissue that appears as lines on the slides. Each muscle division is a **myotome;** the dividing sheets of connective tissue are the **myocommata.**

Beneath the notochord will be seen a large cavity, the **atrium,** in which are to be found several structures. Near the center of this cavity will be seen two rows of stained structures that occupy a dorsoventral plane. These represent a cross section through the pharynx, and each of the small stained structures is a **pharyngeal bar.** The clear unstained spaces between the bars are the **pharyngeal slits.** On the inner ventral surface of the pharynx is a definite groove in which may sometimes be seen little hairlike projections, or **cilia.** The groove is the **endostyle,** or hypobranchial groove, which functions in the obtaining of food. This groove was formerly considered to be homologous to the thyroid gland, a gland of internal secretion in vertebrate animals. Now, however, there appears to be some question regarding the validity of this conclusion. On the inner dorsal surface of the pharynx is a similar groove, the **epibranchial** (hyperbranchial) **groove.**

Note that the atrium, which surrounds the pharynx, is a specialized cavity and is not at all comparable with a coelom, or true body cavity. The atrium has almost obliterated the true coelom in this region.

Within the atrium will be seen a cross section of the **liver diverticulum.** This outpouching occurs on the right side of Amphioxus, but it might appear on either side in the slides, depending upon how the sections were mounted. There is a cavity in the liver diverticulum, but it may be collapsed on the slide. The gonads appear as stained rounded bodies in the lower lateral portion of the atrium; their size will vary in the different slides. Note that the gonads are not actually in the atrium but occur in its walls and simply protrude from them. On satisfactory slides, if one looks closely, around the inner surfaces of the gonads can be seen a very thin membrane, which separates them from the atrial cavity.   In some cases this membrane may have been lost when the section was made.   When the sex cells become mature within the gonads, they break through the walls into the atrium and are carried out through the atriopore, with the water current.   Fertilization and development occur in the water. There may be two gonads on the slides or only one, since only a single one may have been cut when the sections were made.

The **coelom,** or body cavity, of Amphioxus is peculiar, since the development of the atrium has nearly obliterated it in this region.   Around the pharynx there are several places where definite portions of the coelom may be seen.   The two spaces, one on each side of the atrium at the level of the epibranchial groove, are portions of the coelom, although these do not show up well in some slides.   Perhaps the best place definitely to locate a portion of the coelom is around one of the gonads.   Examine the edge of one of the gonads, and try to find a small space in this region that is definitely separated from the atrium.   These small spaces, which usually appear even in otherwise inferior slides, are parts of the coelom, or body cavity.

Drawing 2.   Section through Pharynx and Liver.   Place at top of drawing plate, and save bottom portion for drawing 3.   Make large enough to show all structures that are required.   **Labels:** dorsal fin, fin ray, neurocoel, neural tube, notochord, myotome, myocomma, pharyngeal bar, pharyngeal slit, gonad, liver diverticulum (if present), metapleural fold, endostyle, pharynx, atrium, epibranchial groove, coelom.

Section Posterior to the Pharynx.   This section will vary somewhat, depending upon the level at which it is made.   If cut just posterior to the pharynx, it will greatly resemble the section just described, except that the **intestine** will be present in the center of the section, rather than the pharynx.   Locate again the structures called for in the preceding study, except those which are associated with the pharynx.   The intestine is surrounded by a thin membrane, the **dorsal mesentery,** which helps to hold it in position.   The intestine is a tube, but in some slides it is partly collapsed, so the chances are that it will not be round.   It is usually an irregular-shaped structure near the center of the section.   The dorsal mesentery appears as a delicate strand around the intestine.   It is attached dorsally just beneath the notochord. The liver diverticulum will not be present if the section has been made posterior to its origin from the intestine.   If present, it will appear very much as it did in the pharyngeal section.   If the section happens to pass through the actual origin of the liver from the intestine, the intestine will show an outpouching on one side or will appear much larger than usual because of the addition of the liver cavity to the intestinal lumen. The liver is larger toward its origin than toward its end; sections in this region may thus appear even larger than the intestine, especially if the intestine is collapsed. Unless the instructor states otherwise, all sections will be anterior to the atriopore; the large cavity surrounding the intestine and liver (if present) is therefore the atrium.

Drawing 3. Section through Intestine. Indicate whether anterior or posterior to liver. Place at the bottom of the plate with drawing 2. **Labels:** all structures named above that can be found; dorsal mesentery, intestine.

The Circulatory System. The circulatory system of Amphioxus cannot be studied without the use of special techniques. However, this system should be mentioned briefly. The general plan of circulation is strikingly similar to that of the vertebrate system, although the system as a whole is comparatively simple and primitive. There is no definite heart, but the circulation is caused by the pulsation of a ventral vessel called the **ventral aorta.** From the ventral aorta, blood passes dorsally through the pharynx by way of **afferent** and **efferent branchial arteries.** These vessels join two dorsal aortas (radices aortae), which in turn combine posteriorly to form the **dorsal aorta.** From the dorsal aorta the blood continues posteriorly. Some passes into capillaries of the intestine and is then collected by a ventral vessel, the **subintestinal vein.** The blood in the subintestinal vein runs anteriorly into the **hepatic portal vein,** which breaks up into capillaries in the liver diverticulum. The **hepatic vein** carries the blood from the liver capillaries to the ventral aorta. The capillaries in the intestine, the hepatic portal vein, and the capillaries in the liver diverticulum form a system of veins called the **hepatic portal system.** This system of veins is characteristic of all vertebrate animals, although in these animals it becomes more complex than the system in Amphioxus. Amphioxus is the most primitive of the chordates in which this system occurs. From the ventral aorta, the circulatory route outlined above is repeated. Other circulatory routes also occur in the head, tail, and peripheral regions.

CHAPTER II

THE LAMPREY

Phylum—Chordata
Subphylum—Vertebrata
Class—Agnatha
Order—Cyclostomata
Suborder—Petromyzontia
Genus—Petromyzon

Lampreys occur in both fresh and salt water. The species to be studied here is a marine form. To the same group also belong the hagfish; these as well as many of the lampreys are parasitic on other fish when adult. Although the common name *lamprey eel* is sometimes used for these animals, this is really a misnomer, since they are very different from the true eel, which belongs to the class Osteichthyes.

In many respects the animals in this group are quite primitive, but several specialized features are present that are probably correlated with their parasitic habits. It should be kept in mind that these animals are true vertebrates, despite the peculiarities which occur in the members of the group. Our study of the lamprey will be somewhat limited, inasmuch as the fundamental vertebrate structures are not so well represented in this animal as in some of the other forms.

External Anatomy. At the anterior end of the body, locate the **buccal funnel,** the hoodlike structure inside of which are small **horny teeth.** These teeth are not homologous to the teeth of other vertebrates and so are called "horny teeth" to distinguish them. Peer into the buccal funnel and locate the **tongue** as a slight projection near the posterior side. Small **lingual teeth** are present on the tongue. The **mouth** occurs as an opening just above the tongue. The lamprey attaches to a fish by means of the buccal funnel and, by vigorous movements of the tongue, rasps away the flesh of the fish, which serves it for food. Around the edge of the buccal funnel is a series of small leaflike **buccal lamellae.**

On each side of the head is an **eye,** functional, but not very

14

large; in preserved specimens, the eyes usually have a cloudy appearance. In the middorsal line between the eyes is a single **nasal aperture,** or nostril. Just posterior to the eyes will be found seven pairs of **external gill slits.** Since the gills themselves are contained within saclike pouches, they cannot be seen from the outside. Locate the **anterior** and **posterior dorsal fins** in the middorsal line. The **caudal fin** surrounds the tail region. All the fins are supported by noticeable **fin rays.**

Note that the lamprey does not possess scales and that there are no lateral fins.

On the ventral surface, beneath the posterior dorsal fin, locate a small opening, the **cloaca.** The term anal pit is frequently applied to this opening; but since both digestive and urogenital systems open in this region, the term cloaca seems more appropriate. Protruding from the cloaca is a small **urogenital papilla,** although in some specimens it may be withdrawn. Both the urinary and reproductive products are discharged from this papilla out by way of the **urogenital aperture,** a small opening at the tip. Just anterior to the papilla, find the **anus** within the cloaca, the posterior opening of the digestive tract. Along the sides of the body, especially near the posterior end, observe the muscle segments, or **myotomes.** The myotomes are separated by the **myocommata,** or connective-tissue partitions.

Drawing 1. External Anatomy—Lateral View. Make full-page drawing of the lamprey from the side. Place head at top of page and ventral surface of the drawing to your left on the plate. Make labels parallel to regular top and bottom of drawing plate. **Labels:** buccal funnel, horny tooth, buccal lamella, eye, nasal aperture, external gill slit, anterior dorsal fin, posterior dorsal fin, caudal fin, fin ray, region of cloaca, myotome, myocomma, urogenital papilla.

Internal Anatomy. Make a mid-ventral incision through the body wall, beginning about 1 inch posterior to the last gill slit and continuing this incision posteriorly until it reaches ½ inch anterior to the cloaca. Lateral incisions should now be made, one at each end of the ventral incision, and should be extended dorsally about halfway to the middorsal line on one side. The flap of skin thus formed should then be carefully removed. This will leave a window in the cavity that contains the internal organs. The cavity thus exposed is the **pleuroperitoneal,** or abdominal, **cavity.** It is the posterior portion of the coelom, or body cavity, and is lined by a shiny membrane, the **peritoneum.**

The anterior portion of the coelom is the pericardial cavity, which will be studied later.

Digestive System. The large, partly exposed, somewhat pointed organ at the anterior end of the abdominal cavity is the **liver.** It is frequently greenish or gray in color. It is a single-lobed structure, and neither gall bladder nor bile duct is present. Lift up the end of the liver, and locate the small tubelike **intestine.** Then trace this posteriorly, and note that it is not differentiated into definite regions. The intestine opens to the outside by the **anus,** previously identified in the cloaca just anterior to the urogenital papilla. The anterior end of this tube is the esophagus, which will be studied later. Make a longitudinal slit in the intestine, and observe a rather definite ridge on one side. This ridge is the **typhlosole,** the function of which is to increase the digestive and absorptive surface of the intestine. In extending from the anterior to the posterior end of the intestine, the typhlosole takes a spiral course and is thus sometimes called the "spiral valve." Although small strands of mesentery may be found attached in places to the intestine, there is no continuous membrane such as is found in higher vertebrates. The lamprey does not have a definite pancreas, but groups of cells that may correspond to a pancreas have been found in the liver and the wall of the intestine. These cells cannot be seen in a study of this kind. A definite spleen is also absent. As will be noted later, the spleen is not a portion of the digestive system but is considered to be a part of the circulatory system.

Urogenital System. In all vertebrate animals, the reproductive and excretory systems are intimately connected. For this reason, the two systems are usually studied as a unit, which is spoken of as the **urogenital system.** The reproductive organ, or gonad, which is a single unpaired structure in the lamprey, may occupy a large portion of the abdominal cavity. The appearance of this organ varies with the season and with the sex. In any event, the gonad extends most of the length of the abdominal cavity and is attached to the dorsal wall by a mesentery. This structure has typically a number of secondary divisions. The **testis** of the male is frequently rather smaller than the **ovary** of the female, with the secondary divisions somewhat flattened and leaflike. The ovary of the female is sometimes of the same general appearance; but if well-developed eggs are present, it appears granular, and frequently the secondary divisions are more or less obscured. Examine the gonad of both sexes.

There are no ducts associated with the reproductive organ of either sex, a condition unusual in vertebrate animals. When the eggs and the sperm mature, they are simply discharged into the body cavity, and from here pass posteriorly into the urogenital papilla and to the outside by way of the urogenital aperture. Although the lamprey studied here is a marine form, it returns to fresh water to breed. Fertilization takes place in the water at the time of spawning, and the egg eventually hatches into a peculiar larval lamprey called *Ammocoetes*. This larva resembles Amphioxus in many respects and is thus important from an evolutionary standpoint. It passes through a distinct metamorphosis before attaining the adult form.

Next find the **kidneys,** which are ribbonlike bodies attached by one edge to the dorsal body wall. Examine the free edge of one of these organs, and on it locate a small duct that is somewhat thinner than the other portions of the kidney. Adult lampreys have a type of kidney known as the **mesonephric kidney,** or mesonephros. The duct just examined is therefore the **mesonephric duct,** sometimes called the Wolffian duct. This duct carries excretory products from the kidney to the urogenital papilla, whence they pass to the outside by way of the urogenital aperture.

The relationships of the structures in the region of the cloaca should now be examined. Extend the mid-ventral incision previously made to the anterior edge of the cloaca. Then very carefully remove the muscles from the posterior end of the abdominal cavity on the same side as the previous dissection. Remove the muscles as far posteriorly as the cloaca, but do not as yet break through the cloacal wall. With forceps carefully expose the full length of the **urogenital papilla** by picking away the tissue that surrounds it, including the cloacal wall on the side of the dissection. Note that the mesonephric duct bends sharply ventrally at the level of the cloaca and opens into the base of the urogenital papilla. Reproductive cells enter the papilla by way of **genital pores** that likewise occur at the base of the papilla. These pores occur lateral to the region at which the mesonephric ducts open into the base of the papilla. Take a small blunt probe, and attempt to locate these pores. Then push the probe through one of the pores, and note that the probe emerges from the papilla by way of the **urogenital aperture** near the tip of the papilla. The common cavity into which open both the mesonephric ducts and the genital pores is called the **urogenital sinus.**

Locate again the anus just anterior to the base of the urogenital papilla, and pass a probe through it into the intestine.

Drawing 2. Internal Organs—Lateral View. *A.* Make full-page drawing, and show only that portion of body in which lie the internal organs. Orient drawing and labels as above. **Labels:** liver, intestine, testis (in male), ovary (in female), kidney, mesonephric duct, urogenital papilla, cloaca.

B. Diagram of Cloacal Region—Ventral View. At one side of drawing plate, make an enlarged diagram of the region of the cloaca, showing relationships of all structures. **Labels:** kidney, mesonephric duct, cloaca, anus, urogenital sinus, urogenital papilla, urogenital aperture, genital pore.

Sagittal Section of Anterior End. A section of the anterior end that has been cut sagittally will be supplied for this study. An endeavor has been made to cut these sections directly through the middorsal and mid-ventral lines, but of course there will be some slight variations. The student should thus examine several sections. The sections may be quite short, or they may extend as far posteriorly as the heart; the following directions can be applied to either type. The instructor will announce which kind of section is to be used.

Anterior End of Alimentary Tract. Identify again the **buccal funnel,** the **horny teeth,** and the **tongue.** The **mouth** is the opening represented in the section by the space just dorsal to the protruding portion of the tongue. Posterior to the mouth opening is a space, the **buccal cavity,** or mouth cavity. If the buccal cavity is followed posteriorly, it will be noted that it leads into a tube, the walls of which are covered by little folds or ridges. This is the **esophagus.** Because of the way in which some of the sections have been cut, it may not always be possible to connect the buccal cavity directly with the esophagus. If the section is a long one, trace the esophagus posteriorly until it leads into the **intestine,** keeping in mind that in some sections the structures may not appear as complete tubes for their entire length.

Turn again to the tongue. This structure is worked by a complex system of muscles, spoken of collectively as **lingual muscles.** Identify these muscles posterior to the tongue. The tongue is strengthened by a **lingual cartilage,** which occurs within the body of the tongue, ventral and posterior to the tip. This cartilage is sometimes covered by lingual muscles and in some sections may be absent if the cut was made too far to one side. Probe the material in the body of the tongue. The cartilage is considerably harder than the tongue muscles that may be present.

Respiratory System. Locate again the anterior end of the esophagus. Below this structure there is another tube, the **pharynx,** or respiratory tube, the walls of which are perforated by **internal gill slits.** If the section is a long one, there will be seven of these; if it is short, only a few will appear. At the anterior end of the pharynx is a small fold of tissue, the **velum,** which separates the pharyngeal opening from the esophagus. The velum prevents food material from getting into the pharynx. The **gill pouches** into which open the internal and external gill slits almost completely surround the body in this region. Thus some sections may be cut so that the ventral portions of the pouches will appear ventral to the pharynx. This is especially true near the posterior end of a long section. These pouches may not show, if the section is a short one. Examine several specimens, and try to find one of the pouches. Each gill pouch contains two leaflike **gill lamellae,** which are the respiratory portions of the respiratory system. More details will be seen when the cross sections are examined.

Nervous System and Associated Structures. The **notochord** is not a part of this system, but since it is quite conspicuous and is near the nervous system, it will be considered at this point. This structure is the broad sheet of tissue, pointed at the anterior end, that is just dorsal to the esophagus. Note that it is well developed and that it is not partly obliterated by encroaching vertebrae. The latter condition will appear in the dogfish. Although the beginnings of vertebrae are present in the lamprey, they are undeveloped and are difficult to find in a study of this kind.

Above the notochord, locate the **neural tube,** or nerve cord, the anterior end of which is somewhat enlarged to form a **brain.** It is only feebly developed. The portion of the neural tube posterior to the brain is the **spinal cord.** Because of the small size of the brain, neither the divisions nor the cranial nerves that arise from the brain will be studied. It should be noted that the anterior end of the notochord does not extend anterior to the brain, as in Amphioxus, but ends somewhat posterior to the front end of the brain. This relationship between the two structures is characteristic of all vertebrates.

Olfactory Structures. Locate the **nasal aperture** in the middorsal region of the head. The cut forming the section should have been made through this opening. The nasal aperture opens into the **nasal canal,** a short tube that leads into a somewhat larger cavity, the **olfactory sac,** or capsule. The olfactory sac probably functions as an organ of smell. Below and somewhat posterior to the olfactory sac is a somewhat larger opening known as the **pituitary pouch.** The pituitary pouch is connected to the olfactory sac by a short tube; but unless the section is well made, this connection may not be seen. This cavity is possibly homologous to the anterior lobe of the pituitary gland as found in higher vertebrates, although, in these animals, there is no connection between the gland and the olfactory capsule. The pituitary gland in higher vertebrates is a gland of internal secretion.

The single olfactory opening and sac are considered by some to be a secondary development and to have resulted from a fusion of paired structures.

Other Structures. In the anterior region are several cartilaginous supports. The most anterior of these is the **annular cartilage** that supports the buccal funnel. This structure forms a ring around the basal portion of the buccal funnel; in the section, the ring has of course been cut through. Locate the cut edges of the ring, one at the posterior dorsal region of the buccal funnel just above the innermost row of teeth, and the other on the funnel just under the anterior end of the tongue.

The other cartilages that are present probably represent the beginnings of a very primitive skull. Each of these cartilages is sometimes given a separate name, but they are also collectively known as **cranial cartilages.** One of these occurs just dorsal to the tongue and buccal cavity; another is posterior and dorsal to the first cartilage. The posterior end of this second cartilage (really a third cartilage continuous with the second) extends ventral to the olfactory sac.

On the ventral side of the section, just dorsal to the muscles in that region, a series of small pinkish dots or streaks will appear. (If specimens are preserved in a colored solution, these will probably not be pink.) These dots or streaks represent portions of the **branchial basket.** This structure is a very complicated framework of cartilage that occurs within the body wall in the region of the gill pouches. It functions in respiration and support. It is not homologous to the cartilaginous or bony supports of the gills in other fish but is apparently a structure without homologies in other groups.

The following structures associated with the heart may of

course be omitted if the section does not extend that far posteriorly. Locate the **pericardial cavity** containing the **heart,** which is just posterior to the end of the pharynx. The cavity is lined by a membrane, the **pericardium.** The pericardial cavity is the anterior division of the coelom, while the pericardium is continuous with the peritoneum, the membrane that lines the pleuroperitoneal cavity. A large blood vessel, the **ventral aorta,** passes anteriorly from the heart ventrally to the pharynx. If the section is sufficiently long, the anterior end of the **liver** may be seen just posterior to the heart.

Drawing 3. Sagittal Section of Anterior End. Make full-page drawing, being sure to leave enough space for labels. Orient drawing and labels as above. **Labels:** buccal funnel, horny tooth, annular cartilage, cranial cartilage, lingual cartilage (or position if absent), mouth, buccal cavity, tongue, nasal aperture, nasal canal, olfactory sac, pituitary pouch, esophagus, lingual muscle, pharynx, internal gill slit, velum, gill lamella (if seen), notochord, spinal cord, branchial-basket cartilage. If section extends to heart, add pericardial cavity, heart, ventral aorta, pericardium, liver (if present), intestine (if present).

Cross Sections. Certain structures are best studied through the use of cross, or transverse, sections made at various levels of the body. This is especially true of some of the respiratory structures and blood vessels. Since the blood vessels of most specimens are not injected, they would be rather difficult to work out in detail.

In this study, only the major blood vessels will be considered. Before the work begins, the laboratory instructor will discuss the main circulatory routes and will illustrate them by the use of sketches. The cross sections will include the following and should be studied in this order: (1) section posterior to the second gill slit, (2) section posterior to fifth gill slit, (3) section through the heart (made just posterior to the last gill slit), (4) section anterior to the cloaca, and (5) section posterior to the cloaca.

The sections will have been made with razors by the laboratory instructors. In some sections, there will probably be a large amount of coagulated blood, which may be gently removed with a blunt probe. If some openings are difficult to identify, pass a small blunt probe through the opening from one side of the section to the other. This should aid in identification.

Some sections will be made so that the anterior side will represent one exercise, while the posterior face will be for another.

When this is true, it will be so stated in the discussion. The sections will be grouped so that when a student is given a section he will know which he is obtaining.

Section Posterior to Second Gill Slit. This section will occur on the anterior side of a rather large piece; the posterior side will be used for the next study. In the mid-line near the ventral surface on both anterior and posterior sides of this piece is a small mass of **lingual muscles** that appears lighter in color than most of the surrounding material. The muscle mass is larger on the **anterior** face, which should be used for this study.

The most noticeable structures in this section are the respiratory organs, which occupy a large portion of the lateral regions. These consist of leaflike **gill lamellae,** which occur on the walls of a cavity, the **gill pouch.** These pouches are connected with the outside by the external gill slits and with the pharynx by the internal gill slits.

Turn now to the dorsal portion of the section. The dorsal side can be identified by the presence in this region of the **notochord,** a large, round, cartilage-like structure. Just dorsal to the notochord is the smaller **spinal cord,** above which in some sections may be a **neural arch,** which probably represents a very primitive vertebra. These will not appear in some sections. On each side of the notochord is a section of an **anterior cardinal vein,** vessels that return blood to the heart from the anterior region of the body. These vessels are rather small in this region but become larger as they approach the heart. Just ventral to the notochord is the **dorsal aorta,** a relatively small vessel, which has heavy muscular walls. This vessel is formed by a combination of the **aortic arches** that pass from the ventral aorta through the gills. It is to be recalled from the discussion of the circulatory system of Amphioxus that the arches are broken up by gill capillaries into afferent and efferent branchial arteries. This same condition occurs in the lamprey, but these vessels cannot be seen in a study of this kind. The dorsal aorta carries blood to the posterior parts of the body.

Locate again the **lingual muscles** in the mid-line. Between the dorsal aorta and the lingual muscles there occur three rather definite openings. From dorsal to ventral, these are the **esophagus,** the **pharynx,** and the **ventral aorta.** The esophagus and the pharynx may be somewhat collapsed. The ventral aorta is much smaller than the other openings and may be filled with blood. This vessel carries all the blood directly from the ventricle of the heart and, as indicated above, is connected to the dorsal aorta by the aortic arches that pass through the gills. In some specimens, two ventral aortas may occur as an abnormality.

Ventral to the ventral aorta there occur two openings side by side. These are the **inferior jugular veins,** which return the blood to the heart from the ventral anterior part of the body. In the muscles of the body wall, especially ventrally, may be seen sections of the **branchial basket.** In addition to the structures mentioned, lymph spaces and other openings and structures difficult to identify may appear in some sections. It should be kept in mind that this section and the one following are made *anterior* to the heart and that veins in these regions are being traced *toward* the heart.

Drawing 4. Section Posterior to Second Gill Slit. Make drawing on upper half of page; use lower half for drawing 5. **Labels:** Gill pouch, gill lamella, notochord, spinal cord, anterior cardinal vein, dorsal aorta, ventral aorta, lingual muscle, inferior jugular vein, branchial-basket cartilage (if seen).

Section Posterior to Fifth Gill Slit. This section will occur on the posterior end of the piece used for the preceding study and can be distinguished from the former by the fact that here the lingual muscles are smaller and the jugular veins have now combined to form a *single* vessel. Identify these structures and those called for in the preceding study.

Drawing 5. Section Posterior to Fifth Gill Slit. Put drawing on lower half of page with drawing 4. Except for the smaller size of the lingual muscles and the combination of the two inferior jugular veins into a single vessel, this section is essentially the same as the previous section. Label only the lingual muscle and the inferior jugular vein.

Section through the Heart—Posterior to the Last Gill Slit. Identify the spinal cord and notochord as in the previous studies. Then find again the **dorsal aorta** just under the notochord. On each side of the dorsal aorta will be seen a projection of a rather irregular blood sinus. These projections may at times partly surround the dorsal aorta. They are the regions where the anterior cardinal veins (returning blood from the anterior region) and the posterior cardinal veins (returning blood from the posterior part of the body) join before entering the heart.

Just ventral to the dorsal aorta and continuous with these projections is the single **common cardinal vein,** formed by a combination of the anterior and posterior cardinal veins. Still farther ventrally, the common cardinal becomes the **sinus venosus,** which is usually represented by a somewhat larger space, although in the section no definite line of demarcation can be distinguished between the two. In most vertebrate animals that have common cardinal veins, there are two present, but in the lamprey a fusion has occurred to form a single vessel.

The sinus venosus opens into the **auricle** of the heart, which may be distinguished from the sinus venosus by the fact that it is much larger and lies ventral to it. The **ventricle** of the heart is quite muscular and normally lies to the right of the auricle. The two chambers are often colored somewhat differently. The auricle opens into the ventricle, but the point of entrance will probably not be seen. The heart is in the **pericardial cavity,** which is lined with the **pericardium.**

At about the level of the common cardinal vein, usually on the left side, locate the **esophagus,** which in this region curves to pass around the heart. In some sections, portions of the **liver** may occur lateral to the pericardial cavity. The position of the **inferior jugular vein** will perhaps vary more in this section than any other one structure. It enters the sinus venosus in this region and, in so doing, passes from the ventral region somewhat dorsally. In some sections, it will be found ventrally between the sections of the liver; in others, it will occur between the lower portions of the auricle and the ventricle. If the vein is not easily located, take a small blunt probe, insert it in the vein on the anterior face of the section, and gently push it through the vessel until it emerges on the side containing the heart.

Drawing 6. Section through the Heart. Make this drawing and drawings 7 and 8 on the same page. Place this drawing at the top of the page. **Labels:** dorsal aorta, union of cardinal veins, common cardinal vein, sinus venosus, auricle, ventricle, pericardial cavity, pericardium, liver (if present), esophagus, inferior jugular vein.

Section Anterior to Cloaca. This study and the following will be made on one piece, this being the anterior face of the section. This surface may be distinguished by the fact that there are two large openings side by side below the notochord on each side of and slightly below the dorsal aorta; on the posterior surface, only a single such opening occurs, and this below the artery. The appearance of these sections may vary slightly, depending upon the level at which they have been cut. Most of them will be near the cloaca, but anterior to it.

Identify again the spinal cord, the notochord, and the small dorsal aorta just under the notochord. On each side of the dorsal aorta and slightly below it is one of the two openings mentioned above. These are the **posterior cardinal veins,** which return blood to the heart from the posterior parts of the body. Below the posterior cardinal veins is a space, the **coelom,** or body cavity. Identify the **kidneys, gonads,** and **intestine.** The kidneys hang into the coelom as small projections, just ventral to the posterior cardinal veins. The intestine occurs as a tube near the mid-line. The gonads, if present, will be between the intestine and the kidneys.

Drawing 7. Section Anterior to Cloaca. Make drawing in center of sheet with drawing 6. **Labels:** dorsal aorta, posterior cardinal vein, kidney, gonad (if present), intestine, coelom.

Section Posterior to the Cloaca. This study should be made on the posterior face of the piece used for the above exercise. Since this section occurs posterior to the cloaca, there is, of course, no coelom present. The principal structures to note are the two blood vessels ventral to the notochord. The most dorsal is the **caudal artery,** which is simply the posterior extension of the dorsal aorta. The dorsal aorta becomes the caudal artery after it passes the cloaca. The single vein under the caudal artery is the **caudal vein.** Near the level of the cloaca, the caudal vein divides into the two posterior cardinal veins that were identified in the previous study. The caudal vein and caudal artery are connected by capillaries in the tail region. A portion of the **posterior dorsal fin** will occur on the dorsal side of the section.

Drawing 8. Section Posterior to Cloaca. Place drawing at the bottom of sheet with drawings 6 and 7. **Labels:** posterior dorsal fin, caudal artery, caudal vein.

Discussion. Although the above studies are all that will be undertaken for this animal, there are a few additional points of interest that should be mentioned. In addition to the main blood vessels that were identified, arteries and veins pass to and from the digestive tract. Aside from the items previously mentioned, perhaps the most outstanding feature of the cyclostome circulatory system is the absence of a system of veins called the **renal portal system.** These are vessels associated with the kidneys, and their presence is characteristic of all lower vertebrates except the cyclostomes. More details regarding this system of veins will be mentioned in future studies.

CHAPTER III

THE DOGFISH

Phylum—Chordata
Subphylum—Vertebrata
Class—Chondrichthyes
Subclass—Elasmobranchii
Order—Selachii
Genus—Squalus

Dogfish are marine forms that occur in rather large numbers on both the east and west coasts of the United States. They are frequently pests to fishermen. They are sometimes accidentally caught in fish nets, which they chew up with their sharp teeth. Two principal species are used in laboratory work, the spiny dogfish, *Squalus*, and the smooth dogfish, *Mustelus*. Although this discussion applies to the spiny species, the smooth form is quite similar. In certain parts of the United States, the dogfish is canned and sold to the public under the more appetizing name of grayfish.

The dogfish is considered to be one of the most important of laboratory animals in a study of comparative anatomy. Therefore, comparatively detailed dissections will be made. This animal presents several distinct advantages over most other comparable laboratory animals and, compared with higher vertebrates, is to be considered important from several standpoints. Many of the fundamental vertebrate features are present in the dogfish in a simple form; thus, a study of this animal enables one more nearly to understand the complex systems of higher vertebrates. More structures in the dogfish can be homologized with those of higher groups than is the case with respect to many other similar forms. Another distinct advantage in using the dogfish is to be found in the ease of dissection. All skeletal structures in this animal are composed of cartilage, which is much easier to cut than are skeletons that are formed of bone. This allows the student to observe with comparative ease such complicated structures as the brain and cranial nerves, the inner ear, and the eye muscles.

In most laboratories two specimens are used for the work on the dogfish. One is used for most of the systems except the circulatory, for which a separate injected specimen is obtained. The use of one or two specimens should somewhat determine the sequence in which the different systems are studied. If only one specimen is to be used for the complete study, the circulatory system should be examined relatively early, since the blood vessels are easy to destroy. Perhaps the best place for the circulatory study, if only one specimen is to be used, is after the exercise on the gross internal anatomy. This is so indicated in the text.

Most laboratories use immature, rather than mature, dogfish. When mature, they are 2½ to 3 feet in length, which makes them awkward to handle. Except for the urogenital system, immature fish are about as satisfactory for general laboratory study as are mature specimens.

EXTERNAL ANATOMY

The body of the dogfish is divided into **head, trunk,** and **tail,** although there are no definite lines of demarcation between the regions. Observe the spindle shape of the body, and note that the widest part of the body is about one-third of the distance from the head to the tail. This widest point may be difficult to determine if the specimen has been distorted by tight packing in the shipping barrel. It has been observed that this spindle shape is a very efficient type of streamlining.

When dogfish are being prepared for laboratory study, a portion of the skull is frequently removed, which exposes part of the brain and thus allows the preserving fluid to come in contact with it. Care should be taken not to injure the exposed portions. Holes are also sometimes made through the body wall, which allows the fluid to reach the internal organs.

Passing one's hand over the surface of the body from the tail toward the head produces the impression that the hand is being rubbed over sandpaper. This is caused by the presence in the skin of a special type of scale, called **placoid scales,** or dermal denticles. The scale consists of a basal plate buried in the skin and a very sharp point protruding from the skin and pointing toward the tail. The skin is thus not so rough when the hand is passed over it toward the tail. From a comparative stand-point, placoid scales are important because they are of the same general structure as teeth, and the two are considered to be homologous. It is thought probable that the teeth of higher vertebrates have been derived from placoid scales.

There are seven fins present in the dogfish, including the tail, or caudal fin. Nearest the anterior end of the body are the paired **pectoral fins.** These fins are attached to an internal cartilaginous portion of the skeleton called the **pectoral girdle.** Identify the ventral part of this structure by drawing the fingers across the ventral part of the body just in front of the anterior edge of each pectoral fin. Farther posteriorly on the ventral surface are the paired **pelvic fins.** If the specimen is a male, there will be two fingerlike projections called **claspers** attached to the medial surface of each pelvic fin. The claspers are used to transfer sperm cells to the female for reproduction. Fertilization in the dogfish is internal. The young develop within the body of the female and are born alive. Look at the pelvic fins of both sexes. The pelvic fins are attached to the **pelvic girdle,** but externally this girdle is not so easy to identify as is the pectoral girdle. On the back in the mid-line are two unpaired fins, the **anterior** and **posterior dorsal fins.** In the spiny dogfish, there is a **spine** in front of each dorsal fin, from which the common name "spiny dogfish" is derived. At the posterior end of the body is the **caudal fin,** or tail. The shape of this fin is asymmetrical; thus, the dorsal and ventral portions of the tail are not equal in size or shape. This type of tail is a *heterocercal tail.* Other types of tails found in fish are the diphycercal and homocercal types.

It should be noted that the dogfish is the first animal to be studied in this manual that has paired appendages—in this case, the pectoral and pelvic fins.

Along the sides of the body near the middle, identify the **lateral line,** a rather definite raised line, often slightly different in color from the surrounding surface, and extending lengthwise of the body. Within this lateral line are a series of very small sense organs known as the lateral-line organs. These structures are innervated by branches of a nerve from the brain (tenth cranial nerve). They are in communication with the outside by means of very small pores that occur along the lateral line. The exact function of these organs is a matter of controversy. It is thought probable, however, that one function is to aid the fish in sensing vibrations in the water, which indicate the presence of food or perhaps of danger. The lateral line is continuous with several canals on the head, but they are not so easily seen externally as is the lateral line. On the head are a large number of small holes, which sometimes occur in groups. These holes open to sense organs under the skin, and some of them are connected to the lateral-line system. Others, however, belong to a separate system, of uncertain function, the **ampullae of Lorenzini.** These ampullae are innervated by branches from some of the nerves from the brain (especially cranial nerves V and VII). Scattered over the body are a number of whitish spots thought by some to be a type of sensory spot.

Return now to the head. The anterior end of the head in front of the eyes is the **rostrum.** Note that the **eyes** do not have movable eyelids and thus cannot be closed. Just posterior and somewhat dorsal to the eyes are the somewhat triangular-shaped **spiracles,** openings that represent degenerate gill slits. The spiracles are considered by some to be partly homologous to the tympanic cavity (middle ear) and the Eustachian tube of higher vertebrate animals. In the dogfish, a few gill filaments are in the spiracles, but the structures are probably not of much importance in respiration. Between the two spiracles on the dorsal surface of the head are two small openings that may be difficult to locate in some specimens. These are the openings to canals that lead to the inner ear. The canals are the **endolymphatic ducts.** Neither an outer nor a middle ear occurs in the dogfish, although the spiracle is probably partly homologous to the middle ear in higher forms.

Just in front of the pectoral fins are five pairs of **gill slits.** Water enters the mouth, flows over the gills, and passes to the outside through the gill slits. Look into one of the gill slits, and see the filamentous parts of the **gills,** or respiratory organs. The cavity containing a pair of gills is a **gill pouch.** These structures will be studied in more detail later.

On the ventral surface of the head just posterior to the level of the eyes is the **mouth.** Be careful never to insert the finger in the dogfish's mouth. The teeth are surprisingly sharp and may easily inflict deep lacerations. Pull the mouth slightly open, and observe the several rows of **teeth** on the cartilaginous **jaws.** The teeth are quickly replaced if they are lost. The jaws, although composed of cartilage, are true jaws and not comparable with the buccal funnel of the lamprey. They have been derived from a portion of the visceral skeleton, to be mentioned later.

Anterior to the mouth on the ventral surface are two **nares,** or nostrils.   Each naris is partly divided into two portions by a fold of skin.   Stick a probe into one of the nares, and observe that the opening ends blindly and is not connected to the mouth cavity, as in some of the higher forms.   In this animal, the nares are concerned only with the olfactory function; when they connect to the mouth or pharyngeal cavity, as in some higher groups, they function also in respiration.

Between the pelvic fins is a large chamber that opens to the outside.   It has probably been noticed previously.   This is the **cloaca,** and the opening to the outside is the **cloacal opening.**   In some specimens, the intestine may protrude from this opening. If so, it should not be pushed inside but should be left as it is until a study is made of the internal anatomy, when it may more easily be pulled back into the body without injury.   If the intestine protrudes, study the cloaca with another student, and do not include the intestine in the drawing of the external anatomy.

By definition, a cloaca is a common chamber or region into which open the digestive, reproductive, and urinary systems.   In some groups, these systems do not open to the outside through a common opening, and a cloaca thus does not occur.   Look into the cloaca, and observe the flaplike **papilla** that projects into it. In the female, only the products from the kidneys pass through this structure, and it is therefore called the **urinary papilla.**   The ducts of the reproductive system open on each side of the papilla, and the eggs are discharged directly into the cloaca.   In the male, both urinary and reproductive products are discharged directly from the papilla, which is called the **urogenital papilla.** Anterior to the papilla within the cloaca is the **anus,** the posterior opening of the intestine.   This opening can probably best be identified at the time the digestive tract is studied.

Drawing 1.   External Anatomy—Lateral View.   Make a full-page drawing of the dogfish from the side.   Place it the full length of the drawing plate with the head at the top of the page and the ventral surface to your left.   Make labels parallel to the true top and bottom of the plate.   Be sure not to make drawing too large. **Labels:** pectoral fin, pelvic fin, anterior and posterior dorsal fins, spine, lateral line, eye, spiracle, position of endolymphatic duct opening, external gill slit, position of mouth, position of naris, position of cloacal opening, clasper (if male).

INTERNAL ORGANS

Make an incision through the ventral body wall about 1 inch in front of the cloaca and slightly to one side of the mid-ventral line. Extend the cut anteriorly to the pectoral girdle, being careful not to injure the internal organs. Do not cut through the pectoral girdle. On one side, make a lateral cut posterior to the base of the pectoral fin. Extend the cut dorsally, so that the body wall may be turned back. On the same side, make a similar lateral cut anterior to the pelvic girdle, and extend it dorsally as before. On the opposite side of the mid-ventral incision, cut through the body wall laterally and dorsally halfway between the pectoral and pelvic fins. These incisions will leave flaps of skin and muscle, which may be turned back for identification of the internal organs. Do not remove the flaps; they will protect the internal organs of your specimens in the preserving jars. At the end of the laboratory period, a string or piece of cheesecloth should be tied around the specimen to help hold the flaps of skin in place.

If the same specimen is to be used for a study of the circulatory system, great care should be taken not to injure the blood vessels. Two blood vessels, which of necessity had to be cut, should be noted at this time. These are the **lateral abdominal veins,** one on each side of the inner body wall.

The cavity that is now exposed and that contains the internal organs is the posterior division of the **coelom,** the **pleuroperitoneal cavity.** The anterior division of the coelom is the pericardial cavity, containing the heart. The general term *body cavity* is sometimes applied to the coelom, though in some cases it is used only for the posterior division, or pleuroperitoneal portion. The pleuroperitoneal cavity is lined by a very thin membrane, the **peritoneum,** which gives the inner body wall a shiny surface.

The coelom, or body cavity, differs considerably in the various vertebrate groups. These differences may briefly be noted as follows: In the dogfish, as indicated, there are two divisions of the coelom, an anterior pericardial cavity and a posterior division, the pleuroperitoneal cavity containing the visceral organs. These two divisions are separated by the transverse septum, a partition that occurs just anterior to the liver and that will presently be observed. With the development of lungs in higher groups, additional divisions of the coelom occur. In Amphibia and most reptiles, there is not much change, and the large posterior division is still called the pleuroperitoneal cavity. The lungs in these animals occur either wholly or partly within this cavity. In mammals and birds new divisions develop. Each of the two lungs is in a separate cavity, and these two cavities have become separated from the pleuroperitoneal cavity.   Each cavity containing a lung is a **pleural cavity.**   The remainder of the original pleuroperitoneal cavity is now simply the **peritoneal cavity,** while the pericardial cavity occurs as before.

The general term *abdominal cavity* is sometimes used for either the pleuroperitoneal or the peritoneal cavity.   Strictly speaking, it should probably be applied only to true peritoneal cavities. More details concerning these cavities and associated structures will be given when they are studied in the different specimens.

Turn again to the specimen.   If the intestine is partly protruded from the cloacal opening, it should be gently pulled back into the body cavity.   The stomach may at times be partly within the mouth cavity, in which case the instructor should be consulted, since it is more difficult successfully to replace the stomach than the intestine.

Digestive System and Spleen.   At the anterior end of the pleuroperitoneal cavity is the three-lobed **liver.**   The two lateral lobes extend posteriorly for nearly the full length of the cavity and may sometimes be partly covered by other organs.   The middle lobe is relatively short and contains the **gall bladder,** a membranous structure usually somewhat greenish in color.   The gall bladder functions as a storage organ for bile, material that is secreted by the liver.   Extending posteriorly from the right anterior edge of the gall bladder is the **bile duct,** a tube that is somewhat thicker in structure than the associated membranes. This duct carries the bile from the liver to the anterior end of the intestine, where it functions in digestion.

Just dorsal to the liver is the elongate **stomach.**   This organ is a posterior continuation of the esophagus, but externally there is no sharp line of demarcation between the two.   Follow the stomach posteriorly until it makes a sharp bend to the right and anteriorly and terminates in a small constriction.   The anterior straight portion of the stomach is the **cardiac** division (nearest the heart), and the smaller posterior region past the bend is the **pyloric** region.   The small constriction at which the stomach ends is a ring of muscle, the **pyloric sphincter.**   In life, it regulates the passage of food from the stomach to the intestine.

The intestine begins just past the pyloric sphincter muscle. Note again that the bile duct opens in this region.   This anterior portion of the intestine is the **duodenum.**   Somewhat covering the duodenum as seen from the ventral side is the rounded **ventral lobe** of the **pancreas.**   The **dorsal lobe** of the **pancreas** is more fingerlike and may be seen by spreading apart the intestine and the pyloric part of the stomach. A **pancreatic duct** leads from the ventral lobe of the pancreas to the duodenum but is very difficult to locate. In badly preserved specimens, the pancreas may be partly disintegrated. Posterior to the duodenum, the intestine widens considerably, the size being somewhat dependent upon when the dogfish had its last meal before capture. There is no definite division between the duodenum and the posterior portion of the intestine. Along the ventral surface of the intestine, locate a vein that passes lengthwise and gives off lateral branches to the intestinal wall at regular intervals. These lateral branches mark the internal attachment of the **spiral valve** within the intestine, a structure the function of which is to increase the digestive and absorptive surfaces of the intestine. This structure will be seen later. Posteriorly the intestine narrows and opens into the cloaca through the **anus.** Attached near the posterior end of the intestine, and usually to the right or dorsally, is a small fingerlike projection, the **rectal gland.** Its function is not definitely known.

It is obvious that the divisions of the intestine are not well differentiated. Although not all workers are in agreement, the **small intestine** is often considered to be the duodenum and the portion of the intestine as far posteriorly as the rectal gland. The **large intestine** is thus the small region from the rectal gland to the anal opening.

Attached to the left side of the stomach is a triangular organ, the **spleen.** This organ is functionally a part of the circulatory system. Its exact action is somewhat in doubt; it probably varies with the different groups. In lower forms, it probably aids in the manufacture of blood cells.

The Mesenteries. Attaching the organs to the body wall and extending between some of the organs are several supporting membranes called **mesenteries.** These are continuous with the peritoneum, the lining of the pleuroperitoneal cavity. During embryonic development, two large mesenteries form, the **dorsal mesentery,** attaching the digestive tract to the dorsal body wall, and the **ventral mesentery,** attaching the digestive tract to the ventral body wall. Most of the mesenteries that are present in the fully developed animal are derived from either one or the other of these embryonic mesenteries. From the dorsal mesentery are derived the mesogaster, the gastrosplenic ligament, the mesointestine, and the mesorectum. The lesser omentum, the falciform ligament, and the coronary ligament are derived from the ventral mesentery. Identify the mesenteries, and then review the preceding statements regarding their origins.

Push the stomach over to the right, and observe the **mesogaster,** the mesentery that suspends the stomach from the dorsal body wall. Between the stomach and the spleen is the **gastrosplenic ligament,** which is a division of the mesogaster. The **mesointestine** (sometimes called the "mesentery proper") is attached to the intestine and may best be seen by pushing the intestine over to the left. The rectal gland is supported by the **mesorectum.**

Spread the right lobe of the liver and the stomach apart, and find the **lesser omentum,** also called the "gastro-hepato-duodenal ligament," extending from the liver to the duodenum. This mesentery, which has been observed previously as the membrane containing the bile duct, is somewhat secondarily divided into two parts, which, however, are not sharply delimited. Look on the ventral surface of the liver, and note the **falciform ligament** that attaches it to the ventral body wall. Press the liver dorsally until a transverse partition can be seen at the anterior end of the pleuroperitoneal cavity. This partition is the **transverse septum,** which separates the pleuroperitoneal and pericardial cavities. It is somewhat comparable with, but not entirely homologous to, the diaphragm as found in mammals. The liver is attached to the posterior face of the transverse septum by the **coronary ligament,** which is anterior to and partly continuous with the falciform ligament. Push the liver aside, and try to see this mesentery. It is somewhat difficult to see at the present stage of dissection.

Study of the circulatory system should be started at this time if only the one specimen is to be used, but if a different specimen is to be used for that study, proceed as follows on the one already in use: Make a longitudinal slit in the ventral wall of the stomach, and examine its inner walls. Frequently the remnants of the dogfish's last meal, consisting of anything from squids to small fish, will be found within the stomach. Remove any contents that are present, wash out the stomach, and examine the inner walls. Internally, the esophagus and the stomach can easily be separated. At the anterior end, note a large number of projections, or **papillae;** posteriorly, only folds, or **rugae,** occur. The esophagus is the portion with the papillae; the posterior part containing only rugae is the stomach. Cut a small window in the wall of the intestine, wash it out, and examine the spiral valve.

Drawing 2. Visceral Organs—Ventral View. Include only an outline of that portion of the body which surrounds the organs. Pull the liver lobes out somewhat, and slightly spread the other organs so that most of them can be seen. **Labels:** pleuroperitoneal cavity, liver, gall bladder, bile duct, cardiac stomach, pyloric stomach, pyloric sphincter, duodenum, pancreas, rectal gland, spleen. It is not necessary to draw in the mesenteries unless the instructor so directs.

The Urogenital System. In vertebrate animals, as indicated previously, the reproductive and urinary systems are so intimately connected that they are usually studied together as the **urogenital system.** The student should study both male and female systems, since there are major differences between the two sexes, especially in the reproductive parts of the systems.

The chances are that all specimens will be immature and hence some of the structures will not show up so well as in mature individuals. If possible, the instructor will have demonstration specimens of mature males and females, so that those parts not seen in the class specimens can be identified from the mature animals.

For a study of the anterior region, it will be helpful to cut away some of the ventral body wall posterior to the transverse septum. If this is done, be sure to preserve the portion of the body wall to which is attached the falciform ligament, since the ducts of the female open in this ligament.

The Male. The **testes** (singular, testis) lie at the anterior end of the pleuroperitoneal cavity dorsal to the liver. They are elongate bodies, usually somewhat gray. Each testis is attached to the dorsal body wall by a mesentery, the **mesorchium.** Push the visceral organs over to the left. The **kidneys** are ribbonlike bodies on the dorsal body wall, one on each side of the mid-line, that extend almost the entire length of the body cavity. Not at all like the proverbial kidney bean, this type of kidney is less compact and more primitive than that found in higher vertebrates and is called a **mesonephric kidney** or sometimes simply a "mesonephros." The ventral surfaces of the kidneys are covered by the peritoneum; thus, these organs are really outside the coelom, a condition called *retroperitoneal.* Along the inner border of the kidney is to be seen a small tube, which is coiled in mature specimens and in those approaching maturity but is straight in immature forms. This is the **mesonephric,** or Wolffian, **duct.** In the mid-line between the kidneys is a white shining ligament that passes posteriorly parallel to the mesonephric ducts. This ligament is frequently mistaken for the mesonephric ducts, since in immature specimens it is usually easier to see than are the ducts themselves.

Trace the mesonephric duct posteriorly. It will now be necessary to open the cloaca. Do this by taking scissors and cutting from the anterior edge of the cloaca to the mid-ventral incision that was previously made. Be careful not to injure the **urogenital papilla.** This incision will partly cut into the intestine and better expose the rectal gland. Identify the large intestine and the anus if this has not already been done.

The mesonephric duct in the male dogfish carries both urine from the kidneys and reproductive cells (sperm) from the testes. Because of its reproductive function, this duct is sometimes called the **vas deferens** (plural, vasa deferentia). Toward the posterior end, this duct in mature specimens becomes straight and enlarges somewhat. In immature forms, the enlargement is hardly noticeable. This large straight region is the **seminal vesicle.** Trace the ducts until they open into the papilla. Products from the papilla pass into the cloaca by a small pore and thence to the outside by the cloacal opening. Cut the edge of the cloaca loose from the body wall, so that the papilla can better be seen. Then dissect dorsal to the papilla until it is well exposed. The size of the structures to be seen will depend upon the size of the specimen. In immature dogfish, some will not be easy to identify; for the parts he cannot find, the student should then examine the mature specimens on demonstration.

In mature specimens, the anterior portion of the urogenital papilla is protruded forward on each side to form two **sperm sacs.** These sacs are hollow and connect to the cavity in the papilla, the **urogenital sinus.** The sperm sacs are not well developed in immature fish. Although urine passes down the mesonephric duct, there is present also a pair of **accessory mesonephric ducts** in the posterior part of the kidney, which likewise carry urine and also connect to the papilla. These are small and difficult to find. Look for them by cutting through the peritoneum covering the posterior outer margin of the kidney. Gradually dissect toward the mid-line, removing the kidney tissue. The ducts are usually close to the mid-line, only slightly buried in the kidney tissue.

Mesonephric tubules, the functional units of the kidney, connect to both sets of the above ducts, but they are so small that they probably cannot be seen. Some of the anterior mesonephric ducts are connected directly to the testes by minute tubules, the **vasa efferentia** (singular, vas efferens), that pass from the testes through the mesorchium and into the kidney, where they connect to some of the anterior mesonephric tubules. These tubules in turn connect to the mesonephric duct.

Look on one side of the falciform ligament of the liver, and note a thin-walled tubule passing anteriorly and dorsally. These tubes are **vestigial oviducts** that formed in the embryo but, since the animal developed into a male, did not grow larger (see drawing directions 3, page 38).

The Female. In the female, the reproductive and urinary systems are not so intimately connected as in the male. The **ovaries** occur at the anterior end of the pleuroperitoneal cavity dorsal to the liver. The mesentery attached to each ovary is a **mesovarium.** Locate the kidneys along the dorsal body wall as two ribbonlike bodies stretching almost the entire length of the body cavity. The **oviducts** (Müllerian ducts) vary considerably depending upon the maturity of the specimen. In immature fish they are small white straight tubes, without visible mesenteries, along the inner margin of each kidney. In mature specimens, the oviducts are much enlarged and are suspended from the kidneys by mesenteries, the **mesotubaria** (singular, mesotubarium). Dogfish bear their young alive; thus, there may be several "pups" within the posterior region of the oviducts if the specimen is mature. In mature specimens, the posterior portion of the oviduct is enlarged and is called the **uterus.** If there are embryos present within the uterus, examine one, and note that the egg is still attached to its ventral surface. Although the young are born alive, most of the nutrition is obtained from the egg itself.

Trace the oviducts anteriorly over the anterior face of the liver until they combine in the falciform ligament to form a common opening, the **ostium.** There is no direct connection to the ovaries, a condition that prevails in the female of most vertebrate animals. Eggs from the ovaries break out into the body cavity and are then attracted to the ostium, which they enter, and pass down the oviducts. As the eggs proceed posteriorly, a thin membrane is applied to them by the **shell glands,** slight enlargements of the oviducts near the anterior end of the kidneys. The shell glands are not apparent in immature animals. Posteriorly the oviducts open into the cloaca lateral to the **urinary papilla.** In the female, only urinary products are discharged from the papilla.   Open the cloaca by taking scissors and cutting from its anterior edge to the mid-ventral abdominal incision.   This will better expose the papilla and the oviductal openings.   Identify again the anus and the large intestine.

The **mesonephric duct** does not show up well in the female, since it is covered by the oviduct and is buried within the kidney tissue.   It is only excretory in the female and thus carries only urine.   Disconnect the oviduct on one side near the posterior end of the kidney (if the oviducts are enlarged, cut the mesotubarium), and look for the duct within the kidney tissue on the inner, or medial, side of the kidney.   In immature specimens these ducts are threadlike and difficult to see.   They join the urinary papilla, which in turn opens into the cloaca.   The **urinary sinus** is the cavity within the papilla.   As in the case of the male, **accessory mesonephric ducts** are attached to the papilla, but they are frequently not apparent.   **Mesonephric tubules,** the functional units of the kidneys, connect to the main excretory ducts and deposit the kidney wastes in them.

Drawing 3.   Urogenital System—Ventral View.   Indicate whether male or female.   Draw only the system of your specimen, but study the systems of both sexes.   Draw in an outline of the body wall and the base of the liver so that the relative position of parts may be seen.   **Labels:** Male—kidney, testis, mesorchium, mesonephric duct, urogenital papilla, seminal vesicle (if a distinction is present in the specimen), sperm sac (if present), vestigial oviduct, cloaca.   Female—kidney, ovary, mesotubarium, uterus (if differentiated), shell gland (if differentiated), ostium, mesonephric duct, urinary papilla, oviduct, cloaca.

THE SENSE ORGANS AND THE NERVOUS SYSTEM

The sense organs and the nervous system are intimately interconnected and should therefore be studied in sequence.   The sense organs will be studied first, since by this procedure the brain and cranial nerves can be more easily exposed.   The only sense organs of the dogfish that will be studied in detail are the eye and the inner ear.

The Eye.   Observe again that no movable eyelids are present, although the folds of skin above and below the eye are sometimes called **eyelids.**   Remove the skin from above and below the *left* eye.   This partly exposes the **orbit,** or socket, the cavity within which the eye occurs.   Then remove some of the cartilage above the eye, being careful not to go too far medially, since to do so would injure the brain. With forceps clean away the material from around the eye until the eye muscles that attach to the eyeball are exposed. Be careful not to injure the muscles or the threadlike nerves that pass to some of them. Some nerves attach to the eyeball and should also be preserved. There are two sets of muscles that control the movements of the eye, the oblique muscles attached to the anterior inner surface of the eyeball, and the rectus muscles, attached to the inner medial portion of the eyeball.

Identify first the **oblique muscles,** of which there are two. The **superior oblique muscle** is attached to the dorsal anterior surface of the eyeball and to the anterior surface of the orbit. Note a small nerve that connects to the medial portion of this muscle, and try to preserve it. It is a nerve from the brain that will be identified later. The **inferior oblique muscle** attaches as does the superior oblique muscle, except that it is ventral to the latter. Press the eyeball slightly dorsally, and peer under the superior oblique to identify the inferior oblique muscle.

There are four **rectus muscles.** These all originate as a group from the posterior side of the orbit, diverge, and attach to the posterior and median sides of the eyeball. The **superior rectus muscle** is dorsal, and its insertion on the eyeball is near that of the superior oblique. In front of and ventral to the superior rectus is the **medial** (internal) **rectus muscle,** while posteriorly at the same level as the medial rectus is the **lateral** (external) **rectus muscle.** The **inferior rectus muscle** can best be seen from the ventral side. Raise the eyeball, and identify this muscle; it attaches to the ventral surface of the eyeball, close to the insertion of the inferior oblique.

The nerve from the brain that innervates the eye, the **optic nerve** (cranial nerve II), can also best be seen from the ventral surface. Again lift the eyeball, and observe this large nerve passing into the eyeball dorsal to and between the insertions of the inferior oblique and inferior rectus muscles. Take a probe, and separate the origins of the rectus muscles in the posterior portion of the socket. A small cartilaginous structure occurs here, the **optic pedicel.** The eyeball partly rests upon this cartilaginous perch.

Main Nerves of the Orbit. The study of the main nerves of the orbit may be made now or omitted until later at the discretion of the instructor. Many instructors believe that to identify the nerves in the orbit at this time will help to introduce the student

to the relatively complex nervous system. This exercise will
also demonstrate how anatomy is studied when the regional
method of study is used. The nerves mentioned here are all
identified again in the later discussion of the nervous system.
Nerves that arise from the brain are called **cranial nerves,** and
each has been given a name and a number. Additional cranial
nerves will be studied later.

The **optic nerve** has already been mentioned as the large nerve
entering the eyeball from the median anterior part of the socket.
This is cranial nerve II. All other nerves that are present are
also either complete cranial nerves from the brain or branches
from them. Note again the small nerve supplying the superior
oblique muscle of the eye. This is the **trochlear nerve** (cranial
nerve IV). Among the rectus muscles, just dorsal to the optic
pedicel, is a small threadlike nerve that passes under the superior
rectus muscle, runs along the inner (or medial) surface of the
eyeball under the superior oblique, and then passes into the
cartilage at the anterior side of the orbit. This is the **deep
ophthalmic nerve,** a branch of the trigeminal nerve, or cranial
nerve V. Across the dorsal portion of the orbit is a large nerve,
the **superficial ophthalmic,** a compound nerve that contains fibers
of both cranial nerves V and VII (facial). This and the deep
ophthalmic nerve combine in the cartilage anterior to the socket,
although this combination will probably not be seen in the present
study.

Now turn to the ventral side of the orbit. A large nerve
passes diagonally across the inner surface of the orbit, from the
region of the origin of the rectus muscles toward the anterior and
ventral region. This is the **infraorbital nerve,** also a compound
nerve that contains fibers of both cranial nerves V and VII.
At the anterior ventral region of the socket the infraorbital
nerve divides into two parts, an inner **maxillary branch** and an
outer **buccal nerve.** The **mandibular nerve** is also in the socket.
It enters the socket somewhat posterior to the entrance of the
infraorbital and passes along the posterior face of the socket.
The mandibular is smaller than the infraorbital, and it is a branch
of cranial nerve V. Most of the eye muscles receive branches
from cranial nerve III, the **oculomotor.** A branch of this nerve
may best be seen on the ventral surface of the eyeball. Lift
the eyeball, and identify this branch as it passes along the inner
eyeball surface, from the region of the inferior rectus muscle,
toward the inferior oblique muscle, which it innervates. Other

branches of the oculomotor nerve occur in the orbit, but the branches are difficult to find without injuring parts of the eye or the eye muscles. The abducens, another cranial nerve, innervates the posterior rectus muscle; but it is a small nerve, and its identification should be left until later. Do not make a drawing unless so directed by the instructor.

Parts of the Eye. The parts of the eye of the dogfish are essentially the same as those of higher vertebrates as far as gross structure is concerned. The eyes of most of the higher animals, however, appear to be more efficient than those of the dogfish. Before removing the eye from the socket, identify the following parts. The **conjunctiva** is a rather thin layer that covers the outer portion of the eye and is connected to the inner surfaces of the eyelids. This membrane was cut when the eyeball was loosened from the socket and can best be identified as rather loose folds of tissue that are probably still attached to the eyeball at the region where it was attached to the eyelids. This layer extends over the front of the eye, where it is transparent; it is thus hard to identify in this region. Although the conjunctiva is associated with the eye, it is not considered to be a true layer of the eye itself. The outer true layer of the eye is the **sclerotic coat.** It is light in color and is somewhat difficult to differentiate from the conjunctiva where the latter joins the eyelids. Medial to this region, however, the sclerotic coat is the only light-colored layer present, since the conjunctiva does not extend medially over the eye past its connection to the eyelids. In the center of the outer surface of the eye is a hole covered by a transparent layer. The hole is the **pupil,** and the transparent membrane covering it and the outer surface of the eyeball is the **cornea.** The cornea is the anterior extension of the sclerotic coat. Surrounding the pupil is a dark-colored layer also covered by the cornea. This is the **iris,** which in the human being may be colored brown, blue, or green. In higher vertebrates at least, the pupil is opened and closed by the iris to regulate the amount of light that enters the eye. In the dogfish, however, this mechanism probably does not work very well, since in life the lens is partly protruded through the pupil.

With scissors clip the eye muscles, beginning with the superior oblique and the superior rectus. Leave a portion of the muscles attached to the eyeball so that they may be identified later. Disconnect the optic pedicel from the eyeball, and leave it in the socket. After the eye has been removed, the optic pedicel should be more closely examined. Examine the attachment of the eye muscles on the eyeball, and be able to identify them. One can always identify the muscles and recognize whether the right or the left eye is involved if the optic nerve and portions of the muscles are still attached to the eyeball. Note that the optic nerve enters the eyeball just *ventral* to the medial rectus muscle and that this muscle is nearest to the optic nerve. This nerve also enters the eyeball closest to its anterior edge. When one orients the eyeball so that the medial rectus muscle is dorsal to the optic nerve, the other muscles are relatively easy to identify. This is especially true if the stubs of the muscles are rather long, since the ends of the four rectus muscles then have a tendency to converge toward each other.

Drawing 4. Eye Muscles—Medial Surface of Eye. Indicate whether right or left eye, and make drawing by looking at the surface of the eye that was in the orbit. Place drawing on the top half of a drawing plate, and leave the bottom portion for the next drawing. **Labels:** all eye muscles, optic nerve, position of optic pedicel.

With scissors make a short cut through the wall of the eyeball between the pupil and the optic nerve so that the ends of the cut will point toward these two structures. Then extend this incision all around the eye so that it passes through the pupil and the optic nerve. Separate the two pieces. Within the large cavity thus exposed will be seen a hardened rounded body, the **crystalline lens.** The lens is softer and more transparent in living specimens. The lenses of the dogfish and other fish differ from the lenses of some of the higher vertebrates in that those of the latter are biconvex rather than round. Identify again the iris, the pupil, and the cornea. Internally the iris will be seen to be a black smooth layer surrounding the pupil. Some distance posterior to the pupil this layer becomes somewhat roughened by radiating lines. This roughened area is the beginning of another layer, the **chorioid coat,** which is continuous with the iris. Internal to the chorioid coat is a light-colored layer, which is frequently folded or somewhat disintegrated in preserved specimens. This is the **retina,** the sensitive layer of the eye, which is a direct extension of the optic nerve from the brain. Grasp the edges of the retina with forceps, and note its attachment to the optic nerve.

The inner cavity of the eyeball in life is divided into several specific chambers, but some of these are difficult to identify in preserved specimens. These chambers are formed by the iris, the cornea, the retina, and the lens, which in life is attached to the iris and the retina. Since this attachment is broken in preserved animals, the limits of some of these divisions are difficult to see. The **anterior chamber** occurs between the cornea and the iris and can be identified by raising the edge of the iris surrounding the pupil with a probe and noting the small space between it and the cornea. This cavity in life is filled with a somewhat watery fluid, the **aqueous humor.** The **cavity of the vitreous humor** is rather large and occurs between the lens and the retina. Since the lens in preserved specimens is not attached, it lies partly within this cavity. The cavity contains a thick jellylike transparent material, the **vitreous humor.** Some of this material may be still within the eye cavity or may be attached to the lens. The **posterior chamber** of the eye is a small cavity between the iris and the lens. It also is filled with aqueous humor. Since the lens is no longer attached in its normal position, this cavity cannot be definitely identified.

Drawing 5. Diagram of Section of Eye. Place drawing on the bottom of the plate used for drawing 4. This drawing will of necessity be somewhat diagrammatical, since some of the parts are out of their natural position. Make drawing showing section through pupil and optic nerve with the lens slightly projecting into the pupil. In life, the retina is closely applied to the chorioid coat and extends nearly as far anteriorly as the base of the iris. **Labels :** conjunctiva, cornea, iris, pupil, retina, lens, optic nerve, anterior chamber, cavity of vitreous humor, posterior chamber, sclerotic coat, chorioid coat.

The Inner Ear. It has been indicated previously that the dogfish has only an inner ear and has no outer or middle ear. The spiracle is probably partly homologous to the middle ear as found in higher vertebrates. Since the inner ear is a very delicate structure, its dissection, if successful, will constitute a real achievement. The student should endeavor to dissect the inner ear in its entirety, for this is excellent practice in difficult dissection.

Remove the skin from the surface of the head between the spiracle and the endolymphatic duct opening on the *left* side. Also, remove the skin and muscles on the same side posterior to this region so that the cartilage of the skull is fully exposed. If this is correctly done, a slight prominence of the skull will be noted, containing the inner ear. Very carefully start shaving away the cartilage from this convexity. Be careful to take off very thin slices, and do not dissect toward the mid-line any farther than the outer edge of the depression in which lie the openings of the endolymphatic ducts. The inner ear consists of a large chamber, the **vestibule,** from which extend the **semicircular ducts.** There are three of these ducts lying in canals in the cartilage, two vertical and one horizontal. As the dissection proceeds, the **anterior vertical semicircular duct** will be the first to appear. It looks much like the cartilage surrounding it, except that it is somewhat more transparent. The **posterior vertical semicircular duct,** as the name implies, is posterior to the anterior canal and is buried slightly deeper. It will appear shortly, as the dissection proceeds. Continue to shave and chip away the cartilage, taking care to shield the eyes from the flying pieces. If any of these enter the eye, immediately rinse it thoroughly with water.

As the dissection proceeds, a **horizontal semicircular duct** will be exposed lateral and ventral to the other ducts. The dissection will be easier if part of the spiracle and some additional material lateral to the ear are removed. Do not dissect medial to the vertical canals, since to do so would probably injure the brain. Broad pointed forceps will be of great assistance in picking away the bits of cartilage. Eventually the triangular-shaped vestibule from which the ducts originate should be exposed. To expose the vestibule, it will be necessary to remove the cartilage between the horizontal and vertical ducts. These ducts arise from the dorsal and small side of the triangle and attach again at the base. At the point of attachment of each duct to the base, there is a bulblike enlargement, the **ampulla.** The anterior vertical and the horizontal ducts attach to the anterior base of the vestibule in close proximity to each other. The posterior vertical duct attaches to the posterior basal portion of the chamber. The endolymphatic ducts open into the dorsal part of the vestibule but these will probably not be seen because of their small size.

The vestibule has several indefinite divisions that are somewhat difficult to identify with certainty. There seems to be little agreement among workers as to the names that should be applied to these divisions or the exact limits of the several parts. The identification is further complicated because part of the vestibule is usually destroyed in the dissection. Attempt to identify two divisions. The **utriculus** is the anterior slightly dorsal smaller region from which arise the anterior vertical and horizontal ducts. These two ducts connect to the ventral portion of the same division; some writers apply another term, recessus utriculi, to this point of attachment. The larger posterior region is the **sacculus.** The posterior vertical duct arises from the dorsal portion of the sacculus and connects to the ventral posterior region of the same part. If the dissection is well made, a slight ridge may be seen separating the sacculus and utriculus.

Two additional points should be noted. On the posterior ventral surface of the sacculus, anterior to the ampulla of the posterior duct, is a slight projection called the **lagena.** This structure is thought to be the beginning of the cochlea, the structure in higher forms that functions in sound perception. In a poor dissection it will be practically impossible to identify. At the bottom of the sacculus, which by this time is probably partly broken, is to be seen a grainy mass of material called the **otolith.** It is thought probable that the otolith aids in maintaining the animal's equilibrium. In life, the inner ear is filled with a fluid called **endolymph.** Surrounding the ear, between it and the cartilage, is another fluid, the **perilymph.**

The whole inner ear is known as the **membranous labyrinth.** The reason for this name can be appreciated after a successful dissection of the complete structure. Branches of the auditory nerve (cranial nerve VIII) are attached to various parts of the ear, including the ampullae. Some of these branches may have been seen in the dissection.

Drawing 6. Inner Ear—Lateral View. Indicate whether right or left ear, and place in center of drawing plate. Place the anterior end to your left. **Labels:** anterior vertical semicircular duct, posterior vertical semicircular duct, horizontal semicircular duct, ampulla, utriculus, sacculus, lagena (if not seen, sketch in).

The Brain and the Cranial Nerves. Remove the skin from the whole dorsal surface of the head. Then remove the muscles from the posterior region for about ½ inch posterior to the level of the spiracles. Most of this has already been done on the left side. The material should be removed only dorsally, not laterally, since at this stage some of the nerves are likely to be destroyed by a lateral dissection. In many preserved specimens, a hole has already been made in the skull to allow the preserving fluid access to the brain, which exposes part of the brain. Even if no such hole has been made, a portion of the brain can frequently be seen through the cartilage after the skin and muscles have been removed. The portion that is most dorsal and that usually appears clearest through the cartilage is the **cerebellum.** This structure is about medially situated with respect to the anterior and posterior portions of the brain. Carefully remove the cartilage from the dorsal surface of the brain by shaving away thin slices and picking off pieces with forceps. Do not dissect laterally as yet, since the first objective is to expose the brain completely before attempting to find any of the nerves. If any lateral dissection should be necessary, it should be made on the side from which the eye and the ear have been removed. Expose the extreme anterior end of the brain, and for about ½ inch posterior to the level of the spiracle. Throughout the dissection, be careful not to injure any of the threadlike nerves that are likely to be encountered, especially above the orbit. The trochlear nerve, which passes above the orbit from the dorsal side of the brain to the superior oblique muscle, is quite easily destroyed. This nerve, which may have been identified in the study of the nerves found associated with the orbit, has probably already been destroyed on the side from which the eye has been removed; but when it is encountered on the opposite side, leave a small bit of cartilage surrounding it so that it will not be broken. Care should also be taken to preserve another much larger nerve to be seen in this region above the socket.

At the anterior end of the brain two stalks project and connect to the nasal capsules in the nasal cavities. These stalks should be exposed for their entire length.

Divisions of the Brain. When the brain has been fully exposed, the various parts should be identified. The divisions of the brain are essentially the same in all vertebrate animals, the principal differences being in the size and development of regions in the various groups. The cavity in which the brain and the spinal cord lie is lined with, and the structures themselves are covered by, membranes called **meninges.** There are two parts to these membranes, the **dura mater** (outer layer partly lining the cavity) and the **pia mater** (applied to the surfaces of the brain and the cord), but they are difficult to differentiate. Some writers, therefore, prefer to use the general term **primitive meninx** for both membranes, without attempting to differentiate between them. The more general term will be used here. In higher forms, the primitive meninx becomes more distinctly differentiated into definite membranes.

In identifying the parts of the brain, begin at the anterior region, which consists of the two projecting stalks previously mentioned. These two stalks are in direct contact with the large rounded **olfactory sacs** in the nasal cavities. These sacs apparently constitute the anterior part of the brain but are, nevertheless, not considered to be a part of it. Just posterior to the olfactory sacs and in contact with them are the somewhat smaller **olfactory bulbs,** which form the true anterior end of the brain. Extending posteriorly from the olfactory bulbs are stalklike portions, the **olfactory tracts,** or stalks. These tracts are connected posteriorly to a rather large portion of the brain. The part of the brain to which the tracts are attached include two portions which in the dogfish are not easily differentiated, the **olfactory lobes** and the **cerebral hemispheres.** Although there is no definite division between the two, the olfactory lobes are that anterior and ventral portion to which the tracts are attached, while the cerebral hemispheres are the posterior and dorsal regions. There is sometimes a faint indentation between the two portions. The term **telencephalon** is ordinarily used to include the cerebral hemispheres and the olfactory lobes, tracts, and bulbs in lower vertebrate animals. In the lower forms, this region of the brain apparently functions primarily in olfactory perception; and the cerebral hemispheres, which form the most important part of the brain in the more intelligent mammals, are not distinct or well developed.

Posterior to the telencephalon is a depressed region containing a cavity. In some specimens this cavity may still be covered by a membrane. This brain division is the **diencephalon** (thalamencephalon). The thin membrane that covers the cavity and that may or may not be present at this stage of the dissection contains a **chorioid plexus,** which consists of a large mass of blood vessels. The cavity within the diencephalon and covered by the membrane, if it is present, is the **third ventricle** of the brain. (There are two cavities, or ventricles, anterior to the third ventricle, one in each cerebral hemisphere.) Attached to the roof of the diencephalon in life is a small stalklike structure that is practically never seen in dissections of this kind. This structure is the **epiphysis,** or pineal body, the function of which is uncertain. It was at one time thought to have an endocrine function in mammals, but this function is now doubted.

Posterior to the diencephalon are the two **optic lobes,** sometimes called "corpora bigemina." The dorsal optic lobes, plus the ventral portion of the brain in this region, make up the **mesencephalon,** or midbrain. The terms optic lobes and mesencephalon are sometimes used synonymously, although, strictly speaking, this is not correct, since the optic lobes form only the dorsal portion of the mesencephalon. In higher forms, the ventral portion of the mesencephalon is more differentiated. Partly overhanging the optic lobes and extending posteriorly is the most dorsal portion of the brain. This is the **cerebellum,** the dorsal portion of the **metencephalon.** The ventral portion of the metencephalon is not well differentiated in the dogfish. On each side of the cerebellum is an anterior projection of the most posterior division of the brain. These anterior extensions are called **auricles,** because of their earlike shape, and are parts of the **medulla oblongata** or the **myelencephalon.** Some writers consider that the auricles should be regarded as parts of the cerebellum. A **chorioid plexus** occurs in the roof of the medulla, and this covers a cavity, the **fourth ventricle.** Posterior to the medulla is the **spinal cord,** although there is no definite line of demarcation between the two.

Drawing 7. Brain and Cranial Nerves—Dorsal View. Before dissecting for the cranial nerves, make a full-page drawing of the dorsal surface of the brain, leaving room for the cranial nerves to be added later. Remove the chorioid plexuses from the third and fourth ventricles. When the cranial nerves have been identified, add them to the drawing on one side only. Label the nerves on this side and other structures on the opposite side. Place roman numerals after each nerve as a designation. Do not begin labeling until the drawing is complete, and then carefully estimate the position of the labels to avoid crowding. Show only the bases of the branches of the cranial nerves that are called for. **Labels:** olfactory sac, olfactory bulb, olfactory tract, olfactory lobe, cerebral hemisphere, diencephalon, third ventricle, optic lobe, cerebellum, medulla oblongata, position of olfactory nerve, optic nerve, oculomotor nerve, trochlear nerve, trifacial root (V and VII combined), superficial ophthalmic nerve, deep ophthalmic nerve, infraorbital branch, maxillary branch, buccal branch, mandibular nerve, hyomandibular nerve, abducens, glossopharyngeal nerve, petrosal ganglion, vagus.

The Cranial Nerves. There are a number of pairs of nerves arising from the brain and passing to various parts of the body.

Some of these have probably been identified previously. Since these nerves have their origin in the brain within the skull, or cranium, they are called the **cranial nerves.** In fish and Amphibia, there are ten pairs of cranial nerves. In reptiles, birds, and mammals, there are two additional pairs, making twelve. From fish to man, the name, number, and origin of the first ten pairs of nerves are essentially the same. The general distribution is also quite similar in the different groups, though as structures are added or become modified in higher forms, this has also changed somewhat.

The nerves are numbered with roman numerals, beginning at the anterior end of the brain. To comparative anatomists, the number of a certain nerve is as important as the name; in illustrations or discussions, the numbers of certain nerves are often used rather than the names.

Those nerves which transmit impressions from the various sense organs to the brain are called *sensory nerves.* Those which transmit impulses from the brain to muscles or glands, causing these structures to react, are called *motor nerves.* Some of the cranial nerves contain both motor and sensory fibers and so are called *mixed nerves.*

The student should learn the name, origin, number, and general distribution of all the cranial nerves and should be able to identify them in a specimen. He should also know which are sensory, which are motor, and which are mixed nerves.

Start at the anterior end of the brain and work posteriorly. Some of the anterior nerves may be seen without much additional dissection.

I. OLFACTORY NERVE. The olfactory nerve consists of a large number of small fibers extending between the olfactory bulb and the olfactory sac. It is difficult to identify this nerve as a definite structure since it is composed of such small fibers. Carefully dissect between the bulb and the sac, and see if you can pick up some of these fibers. The olfactory nerve is sensory.

II. OPTIC NERVE. The optic nerve was identified during the study of the eye. It arises from the ventral lateral surface of the diencephalon, passes into the eye socket and on into the eyeball. The origin may be seen by pushing the brain slightly to one side, care being taken not to injure the brain. This nerve is sensory.

III. OCULOMOTOR NERVE. The origin of the oculomotor nerve should not be identified until later, since it arises from the ventral surface of the mesencephalon. Loosen one of the eyeballs from its socket by removing the tissue around it so that the muscles can be seen. In so doing, be sure not to cut any of the nerves in the orbit. Raise the eyeball, and observe one branch of the oculomotor nerve passing along the ventral surface of the inferior rectus muscle, across the eyeball, and to the inferior oblique muscle. Some of the branches of this nerve may have been identified in the previous study of the eye. Branches from it also supply the superior, medial, and inferior rectus muscles, and it sends small branches to some of the muscles within the eye itself. In higher vertebrates at least, the branches of this nerve which pass into the eye send impulses to the muscles which help in adjusting the size of the pupil to different light concentrations and to those which change the shape of the lens in accommodating for near and distant vision. These actions are probably not well developed in fish. Directions will be given later for finding the origin of the oculomotor nerve from the brain. It is a motor nerve.

IV. Trochlear Nerve. The trochlear nerve arises from the dorsal posterior surface of the mesencephalon; it is the small nerve previously mentioned as passing through the cartilage above the eye. It may have been identified in the previous study of the nerves of the socket. Look on the side of the specimen having the intact eye, and carefully push the brain away from the cartilage. The trochlear nerve is small and appears to originate between the optic lobes and the ventral part of the cerebellum. It passes anteriorly and supplies the superior oblique muscle of the eye. The trochlear is a motor nerve.

To identify the additional nerves, more dissection will be necessary.

V, VII. Trigeminal and Facial Nerves. In the adult, the roots of the trigeminal and facial nerves are found in the brain as a common root, sometimes called the **trifacial root**. The fibers of these two nerves are so intimately associated that it is not possible to separate them in a study of this kind. Many of the branches that come from the common root contain fibers from both nerves. Special methods of study are necessary to determine this fact.

Take off the cartilage above the intact eye socket if this has not already been done, being careful as usual not to destroy any nerves in this region. Try also to preserve the trochlear nerve in its entirety; but if this is not possible, cut it, and leave a recognizable stub attached to the brain. Passing through the dorsal part of the eye socket and into the cartilage above it is the **superficial ophthalmic nerve,** containing fibers from both cranial nerves V and VII. This branch was probably previously identified in the study of the eye. Do not destroy this nerve. This branch passes anteriorly into the region of the rostrum, where it innervates some of the ampullae of Lorenzini. Leave the eyeball in the socket for the present. In many cases, most of the branches of the trifacial root except those associated with the socket can be identified on the side from which the eye and the ear have been removed. It is suggested that the student first expose the root of the two nerves on the side where the eye and the ear have been removed; then, if all the branches cannot be found, the opposite side may be used. As the dissection progresses, the trifacial root will appear as a large trunk arising from the medulla at about the level of the posterior end of the cerebellum and passing somewhat ventrally. During the dissection, the **auditory nerve** (VIII) will probably be seen. This nerve passes to the inner ear. It occurs just posterior to the trifacial root and is a stout short nerve with many branches that should be seen in the depression into which fitted the inner ear. Preserve this nerve.

When sufficient cartilage and tissue have been removed, identify the branches of the trifacial root. Most of these branches occur partly within the orbit of the eye and may have been identified when the eye muscles were studied. If so, these should be identified again for review. Turn back to the intact eye, and clean away the tissue and cartilage until the muscles can be seen. Look between the external rectus and the superior rectus muscles, and observe a small nerve that passes between them to the eyeball and then runs anteriorly along the eyeball to the anterior edge of the socket, where it then passes into the cartilage. This is the **deep ophthalmic nerve,** which contains only fibers of the trigeminal nerve (V). After passing into the cartilage, it continues anteriorly and joins the superficial ophthalmic nerve. This nerve is also distributed to the snout along with the superficial ophthalmic. Raise the eyeball, and identify the **infraorbital branch** passing across the inner edge and floor of the orbit. At the anterior edge of the socket, it branches into an inner **maxillary branch** [composed of trigeminal (V) fibers] and an outer **buccal branch** containing only fibers from the facial nerve (VII). Branches of these nerves are distributed to the anterior sides of the rostrum, where they supply the skin, ampullae of Lorenzini, and anterior end of the lateral line. The **mandibular nerve** is the most posterior branch within the orbit and contains only fibers of the trigeminal nerve. It can be located on the posterior face of the socket. This branch supplies some of the muscles of the lower jaw, some of the gill muscles, and the skin along the lower jaw.

The other branches of the trifacial root do not occur in the socket and, if present, should be identified on the side opposite the intact eye. The **hyomandibular nerve** is composed entirely of fibers from the facial nerve. Its connection with the trifacial root lies partly under the anterior fibers of the auditory nerve. It passes diagonally across the cavity that contained the inner ear and can best be located by picking away the cartilage and other material in this region. Near the anterior edge of the cavity of the inner ear, the hyomandibular nerve has an enlargement, or ganglion, that shows up much better from the ventral side of the nerve. A small nerve, the **palatine,** arises from this ganglion and passes ventrally and anteriorly into the mouth, the lining of which it innervates. Follow the main hyomandibular branch posteriorly and laterally. It proceeds posterior to the spiracle and then laterally to the posterior side of the head, where it divides into several branches. This nerve sends fibers to the lateral line, muscles of the hyoid arch (support of the tongue), and portions of the mouth and tongue. The trigeminal and facial nerves are mixed nerves since they contain both motor and sensory fibers.

VI. ABDUCENS. The abducens (abducent nerve) innervates the lateral rectus muscle of the eye. It is a small nerve sometimes difficult to see. To locate the abducent nerve, look on the ventral surface of the lateral rectus muscle near its origin. The nerve is closely applied to the muscle surface, and it may be necessary somewhat to separate the lateral rectus muscle and the infraorbital nerve, which occurs in this region, in order to see the abducent nerve. This nerve arises from the ventral surface of the medulla; thus, its origin will not be seen until later. Embryologically, the abducens arises at a level that is between the trigeminal and facial nerves; hence its designation as number VI. The abducens is a motor nerve.

VIII. AUDITORY NERVE. The auditory nerve has been mentioned previously as the short branched nerve passing to the inner ear. It has probably been seen already; if not, look just posterior to the trifacial root. The auditory nerve arises laterally from the medulla, but somewhat more ventrally than the dorsal part of the trifacial root. One branch partly overlaps the proximal portion of cranial nerve IX, which is just posterior to the auditory nerve. The auditory nerve is sensory.

IX. GLOSSOPHARYNGEAL NERVE. The glossopharyngeal nerve arises from the side of the medulla, posterior to the previously discussed group of nerves. It may sometimes be seen through the cartilage along the floor of the cavity of the inner ear. It passes laterally and posteriorly parallel to the hyomandibular branch of the trifacial. As mentioned before, the basal portion is partly covered by a branch of the auditory nerve. Pick away the cartilage so as to expose fully the glossopharyngeal nerve, and follow it posteriorly and laterally. Some distance from its origin from the brain, this nerve enlarges to form a spindle-shaped ganglion, the **petrosal ganglion.** Even though it is not possible to see all the nerve, it can often be identified by this ganglion. Near the level of the first gill pouch the glossopharyngeal nerve divides into three branches. The first branch is given off from the anterior surface of the nerve and is easy to find. It passes into the anterior surface of the first complete gill pouch. (Some writers consider the spiracle as being the first gill pouch; in that case, this branch passes to the *second* pouch.) This nerve is the **pretrematic branch** of the glossopharyngeal nerve. The second branch arises from the posterior surface of the main trunk just posterior to the pretrematic branch and is somewhat difficult to find. This is the **pharyngeal nerve,** which passes to the mouth. The **posttrematic branch** appears to be a direct continuation of the glossopharyngeal nerve. It is relatively large and passes to the posterior surface of the first complete gill pouch. The glossopharyngeal nerve is a mixed nerve.

X. VAGUS (PNEUMOGASTRIC). The vagus is the largest and most posterior of the cranial nerves. It arises from the side of the medulla on a level with the posterior end of the fourth ventricle. Uncover the basal portion of the nerve, and follow it posteriorly and laterally. Posteriorly about ½ inch or slightly more, the vagus passes through the floor of a large cavity that is frequently filled with coagulated blood. This is a large blood sinus, the anterior cardinal sinus, the position of which should be noted for future work on the circulatory system. Within this sinus, the nerve divides into two branches, an inner nerve, the **lateral branch,** which passes to the lateral line; and an outer branch, the **visceral nerve.** The visceral nerve sends twigs to the posterior gill pouches and, as its name implies, continues posteriorly, where it supplies branches to the heart and parts of the digestive tract. It should be noted that the lateral branch does not arise lateral to the visceral branch; the name is derived from the lateral line that it supplies, rather than from its position of origin. It will not be necessary to trace out the branches unless the instructor so directs. The vagus is mixed.

The student should remember that, if he cannot find the nerves on one side, he should dissect for them on the opposite side.

One additional nerve associated with the brain should be noted. Look on the inner surface of one of the olfactory tracts, and try to find a small threadlike nerve passing from the anterior region of the telencephalon, along the olfactory tracts, and on anteriorly into the olfactory sacs. It is sometimes closely applied to the surface of the tract, and careful examination may be necessary to locate it. Also, it is easily destroyed. There is considerable controversy regarding the status of this nerve, which is called the **terminal nerve**. It was discovered some time after the other cranial nerves were known. Some workers regard it as a true cranial nerve and assign it the number 0 to prevent breaking up the established sequence of the numbers of the other nerves. Others maintain that it should not be considered a true cranial nerve. Its true function has not been definitely established.

Various schemes have been proposed to help the student remember the names of the cranial nerves. Among these the best is a rhyme which the author has never seen in print and for which, if published, he is therefore able to give no specific acknowledgment. The first letter of each of the words of the rhyme is the same as the first letter of a cranial nerve, beginning with cranial nerve I and going through XII. (The last two words of the rhyme are not applicable to the dogfish but can be applied to those animals with 12 cranial nerves.) The number of the cranial nerve that each word represents is placed above the first letter of the word in question. The lines have been changed slightly from the original version.

I   II   III   IV   V   VI VII VIII IX   X   XI   XII
On old Olympus' towering tops, a fop and glutton vended some hops

Despite the absurdity of this jingle, it has been found to serve as an aid to students by fixing in their minds the names and order of the cranial nerves (see drawing directions 7, page 48).

The Ventral Surface of the Brain. Some instructors prefer to give a test or to hear recitations on the dorsal brain surface and the cranial nerves before beginning this study, since most of the nerves will be destroyed when the brain is removed from the body. Therefore, do not begin this work until directed to do so by the instructor.

Before starting to remove the brain from the skull, find the origins of some of the cranial nerves that have not been previously located. Push the brain slightly to one side, and note a small nerve passing from the ventral part of the mesencephalon into the eye socket. This is the root of the oculomotor nerve (III), which innervates some of the eye muscles. Some of the branches of this nerve were identified in the orbit.

Carefully cut through the trifacial root and the origin of the auditory nerve on one side. Then push the brain slightly over to the opposite side. The abducent nerve (VI) will be seen to arise from the ventral part of the medulla just under the roots of the nerves previously cut. It passes anteriorly into the eye socket, where it innervates the lateral rectus muscle.

Cut the nerve cord just posterior to the origin of the vagus. Then cut the vagus nerves near their origins on both sides, but try to leave recognizable stubs attached to the brain. Carefully lift the posterior part of the brain, and disconnect any points of attachment between it and the skull. Gradually work anteriorly, clipping nerves and points of attachment until the whole brain has been removed. Be especially careful between the eyes; there is a portion of the brain in this region that fits into a ventral cavity, and unless care is exercised this portion might be broken off. Observe again the origins of the oculomotor, abducent, and optic nerves.

If the brain is well preserved when removed, a blood vessel should be observed on its ventral surface. This blood vessel will vary in appearance, depending upon whether or not the specimen is injected. If injected, the blood vessel should be red or yellow in color (depending upon the color of the injecting material); if not, the chances are that blood will not be present, and the vessel is therefore likely to be light in color, about the same color as the brain. This vessel, sending branches to various brain regions, is the internal carotid artery.

Locate the ventral surface of the telencephalon. Just posterior to this region are several structures associated with the diencephalon. The most anterior of these is the **optic chiasma,** the region where the optic nerves cross as they attach to the ventral surface of the diencephalon. Fibers from the optic chiasma pass into the diencephalon and eventually into the optic lobes. Although the optic nerves themselves arise externally from the diencephalon, in lower vertebrate animals the optic lobes contain the sight centers. In higher forms, the cerebral hemispheres, which become greatly developed, contain the most important sight centers. Posterior to the optic chiasma is a two-lobed structure, the **infundibulum.** Posterior to the infundibulum, there occurs an extension, the **hypophysis,** or pituitary body. In mammals, at least, this structure is one of the endocrine glands that secretes important substances into the blood. It is not known whether or not such a function occurs in the dogfish. Do not make a drawing unless directed to do so by the instructor.

Two additional parts of the nervous system of the dogfish should be mentioned briefly. These are the **spinal nerves** and the **autonomic nervous system.** Neither of these will be studied, but the student should know that these two groups of nerves occur in the dogfish. The spinal nerves arise from the spinal cord and pass laterally to various parts of the body, especially to muscles and the skin. Some of these nerves combine opposite each of the paired fins, to form a mass of interconnected nerves called a **plexus.** The autonomic nervous system is represented by a pair of longitudinal ganglionated fibers embedded in the dorsal body wall and lying somewhat parallel to the vertebral column. This system is not well developed in the dogfish, and the fibers are difficult to find. In higher vertebrates, at least, the autonomic system is of importance in transmitting nervous impulses which help to regulate the actions of many organs of the body.

THE MOUTH, PHARYNX, AND RESPIRATORY SYSTEM

The study of the mouth, pharynx, and respiratory system should not be attempted until there is essentially no future use for the specimen, since this work will more or less completely ruin it. However, if an additional specimen is available for a study of the circulatory system, the work may be done now, since there are only a few additional minor studies to be made on the specimen. The work on the muscular system, if it is to be performed on this specimen, should be done before the present exercise. Otherwise, the injected specimen may be used for the muscular system.

If the circulatory system has already been studied in this specimen, the following dissection has probably been made. If not, proceed according to the following directions. With scissors, cut from one corner of the mouth posteriorly under the gill slits, and continue through the pectoral girdle. This will expose the anterior end of the esophagus and the liver, which should be disconnected from the anterior region so that a flap is formed by the ventral portion that can be turned to one side. The **buccal cavity,** or mouth cavity, is the anterior portion of the cavity thus exposed. Examine again the upper and lower jaws and the several rows of teeth that occur on each. Look at the section that has been made through the lower jaw. Posterior to this there is another rather large bar of cartilage, which has likewise been cut. This is the **hyoid arch,** an element of the visceral skeleton. More details regarding these skeletal elements will be given presently. Trace the hyoid arch across the floor of the mouth. On its anterior surface within the mouth cavity is a fold of tissue that represents the beginning of a **tongue,** although it is not well developed.

The **pharynx** is the posterior continuation of the mouth cavity. Within the walls of the pharynx open five pairs of **internal gill slits** and the **spiracle,** which is a degenerate gill slit. Observe again the **external gill slits,** and pass a probe from the external slit into the pharynx by way of the internal slit. The probe will pass through a cavity that contains a gill. This cavity is the **gill pouch,** sometimes called the **visceral pouch.** Although the term gill pouch is used for the gill cavity in the dogfish as well as in the lamprey, the pouch is not nearly so saclike as in the latter species. These pouches form in the embryo of higher vertebrates; but since no gills occur in these groups, the term visceral pouch is ordinarily used. Cut into two of the adjacent gill pouches by extending the external gill slits dorsally and ventrally. Between the two gill slits that have been cut there occurs a strip of tissue, on each side of which there is a filamentous gill-like structure. This strip of tissue, which extends to the outer body wall, is the **interbranchial septum.** Each gill-like structure on each side of the septum is a **demibranch,** or half a gill. The two demibranchs within a gill pouch constitute a complete gill, or **holobranch.** (Some writers consider that the two demibranchs on each side of a septum constitute a holobranch, but we shall use the above interpretation.) Examine one of the demibranchs. It consists of outer filaments, attached to an inner supporting arch.   On the inner edge of the supporting arch is a series of fingerlike projections, the **gill rakers.** Look at the cut end of one of the supporting arches, and locate a small cartilaginous bar within it.   This cartilaginous bar is the **gill arch,** the skeletal element that supports the gill.   Small holes will probably be seen in the section around the gill arch.   These holes represent the blood vessels that pass through the gills. With forceps pick away the filaments of one of the demibranchs and some of the tissue from the adjacent interbranchial septum until one or more of the **gill rays** are found.   These are fine cartilaginous projections attached to the gill arch that aid in support.   A drawing is not required.

THE GILL ARCHES, OR VISCERAL SKELETON

There are seven gill arches in the dogfish, some of which have become modified into other structures in the adult.   These arches collectively constitute the **visceral skeleton,** which is sometimes called the splanchnocranium.

In vertebrate anatomy, the terms gill arch, visceral arch, branchial arch, and pharyngeal arch are used somewhat loosely. Some writers use the terms synonymously, while others employ them with slightly different meanings.   Gill arches or their homologues occur in higher vertebrates; but since no gills are present in most of these animals, the terms visceral, branchial, or pharyngeal are probably more applicable than the term gill arch. In fish and amphibians with gills, the reverse is true, and the term gill arch is more appropriate.   The terms will be used more or less synonymously, but the student should keep these points in mind.   In those vertebrates without gills, visceral or gill arches form in the embryo after which they either degenerate or become partly modified into other structures.

The arches are numbered from anterior to posterior.   Special names are applied to some of them.   The first arch is the **mandibular.**   Even in the dogfish, this structure has become modified. In the specimen, locate the cartilages that form the upper and lower jaws.   The lower jaw has been cut through on one side. Both upper and lower jaws in the dogfish have been derived from the mandibular arch.   Each half of the upper jaw is called the **pterygoquadrate.**   Each half of the lower jaw is **Meckel's cartilage.**   Arch 2 is the **hyoid arch,** which was located in the study of the mouth and pharyngeal cavities.   It occurs just posterior to the lower jaw.   The lower part of this arch supports the tongue. The upper portion of the arch has become modified into a skeletal element known as the **hyomandibular,** to which the lower jaw is attached. Arches 3 to 7 have no special names, are not modified in the dogfish, and are thus simply called **gill arches.** They serve as support for the gills. The gill arches were also identified in the previous study. Find them again as the cartilaginous arches in the bases of the demibranchs. They can also be felt with the fingers as they pass across the floor of the pharynx between the gills on each side. Each gill arch consists of several parts, each part receiving a special name. The details, however, are difficult to work out unless one has a skeleton especially prepared for study. Identify all the gill arches.

The skull of the dogfish is difficult to study without prepared specimens. It should be kept in mind, however, that all the skeleton, including the skull, is composed entirely of cartilage. The skull is a very simplified structure called the **chondrocranium,** to which a roof of cartilage has been added. In the embryonic development of the skull of higher vertebrates, the first step is the formation of a cartilage chondrocranium very much like that of the dogfish. To this original chondrocranium, bones are added, which almost completely enclose it. In addition, some parts of the chondrocranium are replaced by other bones. The skull of higher vertebrates is thus a composite structure; but although it is considerably more complicated than the skull of the dogfish, the beginning of the structure is essentially the same. A drawing of the gill arches is not required.

THE NOTOCHORD, VERTEBRAE, AND ASSOCIATED STRUCTURES

It was pointed out in the studies of Amphioxus and the lamprey that one characteristic of chordate animals is the presence of a cartilage-like structure along the dorsal side of the body, the **notochord.** This structure forms in the embryo of all chordate animals and may persist in the adult or may degenerate. If the vertebrae of the adult are well developed, the notochord is either absent or partially so. If the vertebrae are not well formed, the notochord usually persists in the adult and aids in supporting the body.

The dogfish represents an intermediate stage in the history of the notochord. The vertebrae have started to replace it, but it is still fairly well formed in the adult. In the adult of higher vertebrates, the replacement of the notochord by the vertebrae is carried to completion.

Cut off the tail about 1 inch posterior to the cloaca.   In the center of the section, with its long axis directed dorsoventrally, is a cartilaginous **vertebra** containing several structures.   In the ventral portion of the vertebra are two blood vessels represented by holes, one dorsal to the other, and separated by a thin membrane.   The dorsal vessel is the **caudal artery,** a posterior continuation of the dorsal aorta, and the ventral vessel is the **caudal vein.**   The caudal vein divides into two parts at the level of the cloacal opening to form the two renal portal veins, which will be seen during the study of the circulatory system.   That portion of the vertebra which contains these blood vessels is known as the **hemal arch.**   Dorsal to these vessels and occupying the approximate center of the vertebra is the rounded **notochord.** This is a circular structure; and if one looks closely, he can see that the tissue on the outside of the notochord is more compact than the material in the center.   This shell on the outside is the **notochordal sheath.**   If the section has been made correctly, there will be portions of the vertebra on each side of the notochord.   This is the **centrum** of the vertebra.   If the notochord fills all the central portion of the vertebra, the section has been made toward the end of the vertebra rather than near the center, and no centrum is thus present.   In such a case, make other thin sections until a centrum appears.   Dorsal to the notochord is the whitish **spinal cord.**   See if you can find a minute hole in the spinal cord.   It is to be recalled that one feature of chordate animals is the presence of a dorsal hollow nerve cord, although in the adult this hollow canal is sometimes difficult to find.   The canal within the vertebra and in which the spinal cord lies is the **neural canal.**   The portion of the vertebra surrounding the spinal cord and neural canal is the **neural arch.**

Drawing 8.   Cross Section of Tail.   Place in center of page, and make drawing about 2 inches in diameter.   **Labels:** vertebra, caudal artery, caudal vein, notochord, hemal arch, neural arch, notochord, centrum, spinal cord.

The relationship between the notochord and the vertebrae can probably be best appreciated by a study of a median sagittal section of the portion of the tail used for the cross-sectional study. Make the sagittal section by cutting so that the scalpel passes through the middorsal and mid-ventral lines of the section. Locate the notochord near the center of the section.   If the dissection has been made correctly, it will be noted that the notochord is a complete structure, but that a narrow portion alternates with a much wider region. The narrow part of the notochord is within the centrum of the vertebra, which has thus replaced parts of the notochord in these regions. The wider parts of the notochord occur at the ends of the vertebrae and between them. The centrum of each vertebra has concave ends, a condition known as *amphicoelous*. The presence of this partially persistent notochord is characteristic of many members of the Chondrichthyes, the class to which the dogfish belongs. Locate the blood vessels and spinal cord in the section. A drawing need not be made unless the instructor considers it desirable.

THE MUSCULAR SYSTEM

If two specimens are available for the study of the dogfish, the muscular system should be the first study made on the injected animal. A study of the circulatory system will be the only other work to be done on this specimen.

The dogfish has a comparatively simple muscular system as compared with higher vertebrates. In this work, there will be made a study of only a few of the more important muscles and muscle groups, as a basis for a more detailed study in higher forms.

Remove a strip of skin, about 2 inches in length, from one side of the body between the posterior dorsal fin and the pelvic fins. Start the skinning ventrally and remove the strip carefully so that no muscles will stick to it. The exposed portions should include both the middorsal and mid-ventral lines of the body. The muscles along the sides of the body are **parietal,** or somatic, **muscles.** In the dogfish, these muscles are quite clearly divided into divisions, or segments, which illustrates the fundamental segmentation that is characteristic of vertebrate animals. In a majority of vertebrates, the muscle segments form in the embryo, but most species are not so obviously segmented as adults. As in the case of Amphioxus, each of these segments is a **myotome,** and the strips of connective tissue that separate the myotomes are the **myocommata.** Observe that these myotomes are somewhat more complex than those of Amphioxus, being shaped more like a W than a simple V.

A longitudinal strip of tissue, called the **lateral septum,** divides the myotomes into dorsal **epaxial** and ventral **hypaxial** muscles. This division into epaxial and hypaxial muscles does not occur in Amphioxus or the lamprey but persists in higher vertebrates.

Look at the middorsal and mid-ventral lines, and observe that the muscles of each side of the body are sharply separated at these points.   The whitish connective tissue in the mid-ventral line that separates the muscles on each side is the **linea alba.** This sharp separation of the muscles of each side also occurs in other vertebrates.   The sheets of connective tissue that occur in the middorsal and mid-ventral lines separating the muscle groups are called **raphes.**

Muscles of the Jaws and Gills.   Take off the skin from one side of the head from the middorsal to the mid-ventral lines. This should include an area from just posterior to the eye to the last gill slit.   There are a large number of muscles in this region, but only a few of the more important ones will be identified.

Somewhat above the base of the pectoral fin, locate a piece of cartilage that lies diagonally across the body.   This is a portion of the pectoral girdle, the **scapular process.**   Just anterior to the scapular process and partly touching it is a relatively large muscle the fibers of which pass diagonally across the body almost at right angles to the scapular process.   This is the **trapezius,** which is considered by some authorities to be partly homologous to the trapezius in higher vertebrates.

There are two groups of **constrictors,** the function of which is to help expel water from the gill pouches.   The **dorsal constrictors** occur just above the gill slits, anterior and somewhat ventral to the trapezius.   There are a series of these muscle fibers passing obliquely across the body.   The **ventral constrictors** occur on the ventral surface of the head.   They greatly resemble the dorsal constrictors in general appearance.   Just posterior to the angle of the jaw is the **adductor mandibularis,** a thick muscle mass, the function of which is to help close the mouth.

Somewhat specialized muscles have become attached to the pelvic and pectoral fins for the movements of these parts.   They will not be studied in detail, but the student should skin the base of the pectoral fin and observe the muscles in this region.

THE CIRCULATORY SYSTEM

The circulatory system is composed of the arteries, the veins, the capillaries that connect the arteries and veins, the heart, and the blood that circulates within the blood vessels.   In addition, there is a rather indefinite system of vessels and sinuses that is connected to the blood vessels called the *lymphatic system.*   Some writers divide the circulatory system into the blood system and the lymphatic system. Within the vessels and spaces of the lymphatic system, there slowly circulates a more or less colorless fluid, the *lymph*. This material is formed from part of the blood that passes through the capillary walls and differs from blood primarily in that it does not contain any red blood cells. Although the lymphatic system is very important from a physiological standpoint, no attempt will be made to study it, since the vessels and sinuses are so indefinite.

The blood system in vertebrates is a closed system, in contrast to an open-type system of many invertebrate animals. The blood thus always remains within definite vessels in vertebrates, although, as indicated above, some of the liquid portion of the blood forms lymph by passing through the walls of the capillaries.

There are two types of blood—that which contains a relatively large supply of oxygen, usually called *aerated*, and the *unaerated* blood in which there is only a small amount of oxygen and a large amount of carbon dioxide. The term *pure* is sometimes applied to the aerated blood, and the term *impure* to the unaerated type. These two terms are definite misnomers, but they are frequently used.

A **vein** is a blood vessel that carries blood *toward* the heart. It may contain aerated or unaerated blood, but in most instances unaerated blood is carried. If the vein is a rather large indefinite space, it is sometimes called a **sinus**. It is not possible to make definite distinctions between veins and sinuses, and thus the two terms are used somewhat interchangeably. Many of the veins of the dogfish are large and indefinite, and therefore the term sinus is quite appropriate for them. An **artery** is a vessel that carries blood *away from* the heart. Again, arteries may carry either aerated or unaerated blood, but most artereis contain aerated blood. In addition to this functional difference, other differences occur between these two types of blood vessels. Arteries are more definite than veins, and the walls of arteries are more muscular and much more elastic than are those of veins. The arteries and veins are connected by minute vessels called **capillaries**. Thus an artery will carry blood to an organ and break up into capillaries. These capillaries eventually combine to form larger and larger vessels until a larger vein is formed that carries the blood back toward the heart and away from the organ. In many instances the arteries supplying blood to an organ are closely paralleled by the veins carrying blood away from the same organ.

In studying the circulatory system, the student should constantly keep in mind the functions of the various vessels and learn to trace blood from one part of the body to another.

Unless a separate specimen is used for this study, this work should be done just after the study of the internal anatomy. If a fresh animal is available, open the abdominal cavity as was done for the study of the internal organs; do not as yet break through the transverse septum. Most specimens will have been injected through an artery in the tail region, so that the tail will be partly cut off. A plug is usually inserted in the injected vessel to prevent the injection fluid from running out. In most instances only the arteries will have been injected; but if double-injected specimens are used, the instructor will state that this is so. The arterial injection will cause the arteries to appear red or yellow, depending upon the color of the injection fluid that was used. The injection of this material into the arteries causes the blood to be pushed into the veins, so that the veins will appear black or bluish in color. Unfortunately, the veins sometimes break, allowing the blood to escape. In this event, some of the veins are likely to be colorless, which adds considerably to the difficulties of the study.

After opening the abdominal cavity, note a dark vein along the inner surface of each lateral body wall. These are the **lateral abdominal veins,** which will be mentioned again later. Spread the organs somewhat, and observe the differences in appearance between the arteries and the veins.

The Veins of the Pleuroperitoneal Cavity. The veins will be studied first, since they are more easily destroyed than are the arteries.

The Hepatic Portal System. A portal system is a system of veins that begins in capillaries in some portion of the body and ends as such in capillaries in another region. In the dogfish, there are two such portal systems, the **hepatic portal** and the **renal portal,** which will be studied later.

The hepatic portal system begins in capillaries in the organs of the digestive tract. These capillaries uniting form larger vessels, and these larger veins in turn combine to form the hepatic portal vein which passes into the liver where it breaks up into capillaries. The hepatic portal system thus ends as such in the liver capillaries, but other vessels pick up the blood from this system and carry it anteriorly into the heart.

Locate the **hepatic portal vein** in the lesser omentum as a bluish duct alongside and somewhat dorsal to the bile duct. If only a small amount of blood is present in this vessel, it will appear whitish; but movement of liquid within it can usually be seen if one squeezes the membrane and holds it between himself and the light. The branches that combine to make up the hepatic portal vein can best be located on the organs that they drain. After the branches have been located, they should be traced toward their junction in the lesser omentum, where the hepatic portal is formed. The actual points of combination are sometimes difficult to find with certainty. The **gastric vein** is the most anterior vessel; branches of it may be seen on the walls of the ventral portion of the stomach. The gastric vein passes toward the hepatic portal vein somewhat parallel but posterior to an artery (the gastric), which will probably show up better than the vein. Look on the intestine to locate the other two branches that help to make up the hepatic portal vein. On the right side of the intestine is the **anterior intestinal vein.** It passes forward dorsal to the ventral lobe of the pancreas. At the posterior edge of this pancreatic lobe, the anterior intestinal vein receives a small **anterior splenic vein** from the right and anterior lobe of the spleen. This vein is sometimes difficult to find. It can usually be located as a small vein passing from the tip of the right end of the spleen and along a small bit of mesentery between the pyloric end of the stomach and the ventral lobe of the pancreas. Locate the **posterior intestinal vein** on the left side of the intestine. Posteriorly it receives small branches from the rectal gland. Near the middle of the intestine, it passes to the left across the body cavity to the posterior end of the dorsal lobe of the pancreas. At this region, it receives the short **posterior splenic vein** from the spleen. The posterior intestinal vein after receiving the posterior splenic vein then passes anteriorly along the elongate dorsal lobe of the pancreas and joins the hepatic portal vein just anterior to the tip of this pancreatic lobe. Trace the hepatic portal vein anteriorly where it passes into the right lobe of the liver. In the liver, this vein breaks up into capillaries, which in turn join other veins, the hepatic veins, that open into one of the divisions of the heart. The entrances of these hepatic veins into the heart will be seen later. It should be remembered that a hepatic portal system is present in simplified form in Amphioxus.

Branches from the hepatic portal system carry digested food from the digestive tract.

Drawing 9. Hepatic Portal System—Ventral View. Make a full-page drawing, and sketch in the visceral organs to show relationships. **Labels:** Veins—hepatic portal, anterior intestinal, anterior splenic, posterior intestinal, posterior splenic, gastric.

The Renal Portal System. This system of veins, as the name implies, is associated with the kidneys. It begins with capillaries in the tail and passes into the kidneys, where capillaries are formed, ending the system as such. Other vessels, to be located later, carry the blood from the kidneys toward the heart.

Remove the wooden plug from the end of the body. The injection fluid is now hardened and therefore will not run out. Then make a thin cross section across the tail region so as to form a fresh surface for examination. This cut will reveal two blood vessels in the ventral portion of the section. The **caudal vein** is the ventral vessel. The dorsal vessel is the caudal artery, the posterior continuation of the dorsal aorta, which will be studied presently. The arteries were injected through this vessel. The caudal vein has not been injected, but frequently injection material will occur there because the two vessels are so close together. Now make rather thin *dorsal* cross sections anterior to the original section, leaving the ventral portions of the sections attached to the body. Continue to make sections until the caudal vein divides into two branches at about the level of the cloacal opening. Each of these veins is a **renal portal vein.** Pass a small probe into one of them, leave it there, and turn to the posterior end of the kidney within the body cavity. Loosen the posterior end of the kidney from the body wall, and locate the probe lying in a rather indefinite space, which is the continuation of the renal portal vein. The term **renal portal sinus** is sometimes applied to these vessels in this region, since they are rather indefinite spaces. Small **renal veins,** too small to see in a study of this kind, pass from the renal portal sinuses into the kidney. The renal portal system ends with the renal veins, but the renal veins then join branches from the **posterior cardinal veins,** which carry the blood toward the heart. Find the posterior cardinal veins by pushing the visceral organs to one side and looking between the kidneys. In the mid-line is an artery (the dorsal aorta) yellow or red in color, while on each side of the artery and parallel to it is a vein that is black or blue in color. These are the posterior cardinal veins. Trace them anteriorly, and note that they become larger toward the anterior end of the pleuroperitoneal cavity. Just posterior to the transverse septum and dorsal to the gonads, the veins expand tremendously into the **posterior cardinal sinuses.** Blood from the gonads passes into these sinuses, but the connections are difficult to see. The entrance of the posterior cardinal sinuses into the heart will be seen later.

A brief statement concerning the embryonic development of the posterior cardinal and renal portal veins is necessary at this point because of comparisons to be made later with higher forms. In the embryonic development of these vessels, two groups of veins are developed, the posterior cardinal veins and other embryonic vessels, the **subcardinal veins.** The posterior cardinal veins occur, one on each side, for almost the entire length of the pleuroperitoneal cavity and connect with the caudal vein from the tail. The embryonic subcardinal veins form between the posterior ends of the former vessels and are connected with them by capillaries and sinuses. During the course of development, the anterior portions of the posterior cardinal veins become disconnected from the posterior portions and then become continuous with the subcardinal veins. The anterior portions of the posterior cardinal veins as found in the adult dogfish are thus formed from the embryonic posterior cardinal veins, while the posterior portions are derived from the embryonic subcardinal veins. The new connection between the anterior ends of the posterior cardinal veins and the subcardinal veins leaves the posterior portions of the embryonic posterior cardinal veins unconnected anteriorly with the former vessels except by capillaries. The posterior ends of the embryonic posterior cardinal veins thus remain in the adult dogfish as the renal portal veins, with capillary connections to the posterior ends of the adult posterior cardinal veins.

Drawing 10. Renal Portal System—Ventral View. Include also the lateral abdominal veins, and sketch in the kidneys. Make a full-page drawing. **Labels:** caudal vein, renal portal vein, renal vein (sketch in), posterior cardinal vein, lateral abdominal vein, iliac vein (to be added after it is identified).

The Arteries of the Pleuroperitoneal Cavity. Push the visceral organs over to the right, and locate again the **dorsal aorta** in the middorsal line, between the posterior cardinal veins. If the injection has been done correctly, this artery will be red or yellow in color.

The first branch of the dorsal aorta to be located is the **coeliac artery.** This vessel arises from the anterior end of the aorta and passes posteriorly between the stomach and the *right* lobe of the liver. Spread these two organs apart, and locate the artery. The actual origin from the aorta should not be located until later, since to find it now might result in destroying other structures. This vessel passes into the posterior part of the lesser omentum and divides into branches that go to the various visceral organs. The larger branches are connected by capillaries to the veins of the hepatic portal system. The point of division of the coeliac artery is somewhat obscured by mesentery. Pick away this material, and identify the branches. Three branches are evident, the **gastric artery,** passing to the stomach, the **hepatic artery,** which runs anteriorly into the liver parallel to the bile duct and hepatic portal vein, and the **anterior intestinal artery.** It should be noted that the gastric and hepatic arteries really arise from a very short common trunk, rather than directly from the coeliac artery itself. This short trunk is sometimes called the **gastrohepatic artery.** The anterior intestinal artery passes posteriorly parallel to the anterior intestinal vein, dorsal to the pyloric sphincter muscle and the ventral lobe of the pancreas. It gives off small branches to the duodenum and the pancreas and continues posteriorly along the right side of the intestine next to the anterior intestinal vein, supplying branches to the intestine.

At the posterior edge of the dorsal mesentery, the dorsal aorta gives rise to two arteries, which occasionally may branch from a single trunk. These vessels are the **gastrosplenic** and the **superior mesenteric** (posterior intestinal) **arteries.** The gastrosplenic artery goes to the spleen, and small branches pass from it to the lower end of the stomach. The superior mesenteric artery passes to the intestine, where it runs posteriorly along the left side parallel to the posterior intestinal vein. Branches from the superior mesenteric artery supply this portion of the intestine. Somewhat posterior to the above two, the **inferior mesenteric artery** passes from the dorsal aorta to the rectal gland. Two inferior mesenteric arteries sometimes occur as an abnormality. At about the level where the gastrosplenic and superior mesenteric arteries are given off, the dorsal aorta runs dorsally into the tissue, so that it cannot be seen in the abdominal cavity posterior to this region. Near the level of the pelvic fins, the dorsal aorta gives rise on each side to an **iliac artery.** These vessels may be seen as they pass across the dorsal body wall toward the pelvic fins, although their actual origin from the aorta cannot be seen, since the latter is covered with tissue at

these points. Trace one of the iliac arteries. It passes posteriorly and laterally toward the base of the pelvic fin, gives off
a small posterior branch to the fin and the rectal region, and then
turns sharply anteriorly. The branch to the fin is called the
femoral artery. It is small and sometimes hard to find. After
giving off the branch to the pelvic fin and the rectum, the iliac
artery is called the **posterior epigastric artery.** It passes anteriorly along the ventral body wall and eventually combines with
the anterior epigastric artery from the anterior region of the body,
which will presently be identified. All the above details are
somewhat difficult to work out except in well-injected specimens.
The dorsal aorta continues posteriorly and, posterior to the
cloacal region, is called the **caudal artery,** which has probably
been identified previously. This is the artery through which
the specimen was injected and in which was inserted a wooden
plug. Identify again the caudal artery in the cross section of
the tail above the caudal vein.

Drawing 11. Visceral Arteries—Ventral View. Make a full-
page drawing, and sketch in the visceral organs as was done for
the hepatic portal system. **Labels:** Arteries—dorsal aorta,
coeliac, gastric, hepatic, anterior intestinal, gastrosplenic,
superior mesenteric, inferior mesenteric, iliac, posterior epigastric (if seen).

Circulatory Structures Anterior to the Transverse Septum.
Locate the pectoral girdle externally, and just anterior to it
remove a triangular-shaped piece of skin that measures about 1
inch on each side. Have one side of this triangle on the anterior
edge of the girdle, but do not as yet break through the girdle, since
to do so would destroy important blood vessels in this region.
With scalpel and forceps, carefully remove the muscles within the
triangle from which the skin has been removed. Do this carefully until, about 1/4 inch dorsally, a thin membrane is encountered that covers a cavity. This membrane is the **pericardium,**
which lines the **pericardial cavity.** The pericardium is comparable to the peritoneum that lines the pleuroperitoneal cavity;
the pericardial cavity is the anterior division of the coelom.
Carefully break through the pericardium, and observe the **heart**
within the pericardial cavity. Enlarge the opening until all
parts of the heart can be seen. The anterior edge of the pectoral
girdle may be cut away, but do not as yet completely break
through it.

Parts of the Heart. The heart of the dogfish consists of two divisions that are comparable to the chambers found in higher vertebrates. These divisions, or chambers, are the auricle and the ventricle. In addition, there are structures associated with the heart that are not found as such in the higher groups. The most ventral portion is the single bulblike **ventricle,** from which a tube passes anteriorly, the **conus arteriosus.** Dorsal to the ventricle and opening into it is the **auricle.** From the ventral view, the sides of the auricle are somewhat dorsal and lateral to the ventricle, so that one sometimes gets the impression that there are two auricles, though there is only one. Raise the ventricle with forceps, and dorsal to it identify the **sinus venosus,** a triangular-shaped, thin-walled sac that opens into the auricle. Note again that there are only a single auricle and a single ventricle in the dogfish. As one studies forms above the dogfish, it is seen that the conus arteriosus and sinus venosus become less important, so that in birds and mammals neither of these structures as such is present. The sinus venosus forms in the embryo of these animals, but in the adult it has become incorporated into the right auricle as the *sinuauricular node,* a small bit of tissue that cannot be definitely identified in gross dissection. Nerves that help to control the rate of heartbeat pass to this node, and from here the impulses spread to the auricles and ventricles. The conus arteriosus persists through the amphibians. It forms in the embryos of reptiles, birds, and mammals, but the complete structure is not present in the adult because of the modification of the arteries leaving the heart. These changes are correlated with the appearance of septa, which divide the auricle and ventricle into two chambers each. More details of these changes will be mentioned later. The auricle and the ventricle are thus the only chambers of the heart that are easily comparable to the divisions of the heart in higher animals; but, as indicated, these two portions become divided by septa, so that two auricles and two ventricles eventually occur.

The Aortic Arches. In the embryonic development of all vertebrate animals, two main arteries are directly concerned with the blood that leaves the ventricle of the heart. These are the **ventral aorta,** which carries the blood anteriorly directly from the ventricle, and the **dorsal aorta,** which carries the blood posteriorly and from which the main arteries branch that pass to the organs of the body. These two vessels are connected by a series of arterial loops called the **aortic arches.** In those vertebrates which possess gills, the aortic arches break up into capillaries as they pass through the gills. The capillaries thus divide the aortic arches into the **afferent branchial arteries** passing from the ventral aorta to the gill capillaries and the **efferent branchial arteries** (sometimes called epibranchial arteries) passing from the gill capillaries and combining to form the dorsal aorta. Six pairs of aortic arches can be homologized throughout the vertebrate series. These six arches form in the embryo, and in most groups some either are dropped out during development or become modified to form other arteries in the adult. The aortic arches are numbered 1 to 6, beginning at the anterior end of the body. These facts should be kept in mind during the next studies.

The Afferent Branchial Arteries and the Ventral Aorta. As soon as the pericardial cavity and regions of the heart have been studied, additional skin and muscles should be removed from the ventral surface to facilitate the dissection. Continue to pick away the muscles and trace the conus arteriosus anteriorly. Just anterior to the pericardial cavity, the conus arteriosus is continued forward by the **ventral aorta,** which is somewhat smaller than the former. Expose the ventral aorta for its full length, but in so doing do not injure the arteries that arise from its sides. The ventral aorta, conus arteriosus, and branches from the ventral aorta are usually not injected, because it is difficult to get the injection fluid to pass through the gill capillaries when the injection is made through the caudal artery. Because of this lack of injection, the branches from the ventral aorta are sometimes hard to see. On the conus arteriosus and the ventricle will be observed small arteries that are usually injected. These are the **coronary arteries,** which supply blood to the pericardial cavity and parts of the heart. They usually arise from the loop formed by the second efferent branchial artery, although there is some variation in their point of origin. They will be observed again when the efferent branchial arteries are studied.

The main arteries associated with the ventral aorta are the **afferent branchial arteries,** of which there are five pairs. The most proximal branches arise at the base of the ventral aorta very close to the junction of the conus arteriosus. These vessels are somewhat dorsal, so that it will be necessary to remove more material than for the anterior branches. The material may be picked away with forceps. On each side a large artery arises, which almost immediately divides into two parts passing to the gills. Anterior to these two pairs of arteries, another

afferent branchial artery occurs on each side and passes undivided
into the gills.   The most anterior vessels are given off from the
ventral aorta about $\frac{1}{2}$ inch anterior to the middle branches.
There is a single branch on each side, which passes toward the
gills and divides into two parts just before it reaches them.   The
latter branches then run into the gills; in locating the branches
it will probably help somewhat to open the first gill pouch by
splitting it through the first gill slit.

Drawing 12.   Heart and Associated Vessels—Ventral View.
Place drawing in center of the page, and show only the bases of
the larger vessels.   Draw parts of the heart and the associated
arteries before dissecting for the veins.   When the study of the
veins is completed, add them to the drawing.   The drawing
must necessarily be somewhat diagrammatical, since the vessels
occur at several levels and since some of them will not be fully
dissected.   **Labels:** ventricle, conus arteriosus, sinus venosus,
auricle, ventral aorta, coronary artery, afferent branchial
artery, hepatic sinus, common cardinal vein, posterior cardinal
vein, lateral abdominal vein, subclavian vein.

Veins of the Heart.   All the large veins that return blood from
the body to the heart open into the sinus venosus.   The blood
then passes into the auricle, from here to the ventricle, and
thence out through the conus arteriosus and into the ventral
aorta.   Some of the veins that open into the sinus venosus have
already been identified in the posterior part of the body.   Others
will now be identified, and the point at which those previously
identified enter the sinus venosus will be located.

Gradually cut away the anterior edge of the pectoral girdle
in the mid-line until the posterior part of the heart is exposed.
If most of the girdle is removed, be careful not to injure the
sinus venosus or the transverse septum.   Raise the ventricle
and cut transversely across the middle of the sinus venosus,
being sure to leave a sizable posterior portion for study.   Wash
out this posterior part.   After rinsing this structure, be careful
not to press on the liver, since to do so will cause blood and other
material to enter the sinus venosus.   On the posterior inner
surface of the sinus venosus may be seen two rather large openings, one on each side of the mid-line.   These are the openings of
the **hepatic sinuses.**   Insert a probe in one of these openings,
and note that the probe passes into the liver.   The hepatic
sinuses are formed from a large number of **hepatic veins** within
the liver.   Blood brought to the liver by the hepatic portal sys-

tem is carried into the sinus venosus by the hepatic sinuses. Do not as yet attempt to locate the hepatic veins, since to do so would destroy other important vessels.

Remove the anterior margin of the pectoral girdle on one side, as was done medially. Then remove the material that covers the posterior lateral ends of the sinus venosus on that same side. It will be noted that the posterior lateral ends of the sinus venosus are somewhat drawn out into rather definite veins. Each of these ends of the sinus venosus is a **common cardinal vein,** or Cuvierian duct. Most of the larger veins on each side open into this portion of the sinus venosus. Slit the common cardinal vein on the exposed side, so that the openings of these veins may be observed. On the anterior wall is a rather large opening usually in association with several smaller ones. The large opening is the entrance of the **inferior jugular vein,** and the smaller holes probably represent branches of this vein. Lateral to the opening of the inferior jugular vein, the common cardinal vein is formed from a combination of the **anterior cardinal** and **posterior cardinal sinuses.** The actual point of combination of the two sinuses is somewhat difficult to identify. Push a probe posteriorly from the ends of the common cardinal veins, and note that the probe enters one of the posterior cardinal sinuses in the abdominal cavity. These sinuses have been identified previously. The anterior cardinal sinuses have also been previously seen in tracing out the branches of the vagus nerve. Make a longitudinal incision above the gill slits, parallel to and slightly ventral to the lateral line. Continue deepening the incision until a rather large cavity is encountered. This is the anterior cardinal sinus. It has a rather thin floor, which may be cut through unless special care is used. Stick a probe posteriorly into the sinus, and observe that the probe passes into the end of the common cardinal vein. If pushed farther posteriorly, the probe will enter the posterior cardinal sinus, indicating that there is a connection between it and the anterior cardinal sinus. The anterior cardinal sinus returns blood from the anterior region of the head, including the area around the eye.

The common cardinal veins receive the **lateral abdominal veins** from along each side of the abdominal wall, in addition to those veins already mentioned. These vessels were seen during the study of the veins in the pleuroperitoneal cavity. The lateral abdominal veins enter the common cardinal veins at their ends, but their exact points of entrance are somewhat difficult to find.

If the specimen is to be used for a study of other systems, the entrances of the veins into the common cardinal veins should not be looked for at present. If the specimen will not be needed later, however, remove the material from the posterior side of the pectoral girdle, push the organs to one side, and trace the lateral abdominal veins anteriorly until they open into the common cardinal veins just anterior to the posterior cardinal sinuses. The lateral abdominal vein receives blood from the body wall and anteriorly is joined by branches from the pectoral girdle and a **subclavian vein** from the pectoral fin. The joining point of the lateral abdominal and the subclavian veins is difficult to see. Trace the lateral abdominal veins posteriorly in the abdominal cavity. They continue posterior to the cloaca, where the two vessels combine. From the pelvic fins, each lateral abdominal vein receives an **iliac vein,** while branches from the region of the cloaca join these veins in this region. The veins near the posterior region usually contain little blood, but at least the iliac vein on one side or the other can usually be found.

The Efferent Branchial Arteries and Associated Vessels. Recent work on the circulatory system of the dogfish has led to changes in the names of several arteries associated with the efferent branchial arteries. There is still some disagreement relative to the homologies of some of these arteries as compared with higher groups, but the interpretations used in this manual are those which seem to be most generally accepted.

It should be kept in mind that blood from the afferent branchial arteries, which have already been observed, passes into the capillaries of the gills, where the blood is aerated. This aerated blood is then picked up by the efferent branchial arteries that lie in the roof of the mouth and the pharynx. With scissors cut from the right corner of the mouth posteriorly, and ventral to the external gill slits, to the level of the pectoral girdle. If the girdle has not been previously cut and if the specimen is not to be used for additional work, break the girdle at this time. If additional studies are to be made of this specimen, follow the dissection directions that the instructor will give. Loosen the liver and esophagus so that these organs and the flap of tissue below the mouth can be laid over to one side. On the roof of the mouth is the membranous lining of the mouth cavity; this membrane covers the blood vessels to be studied. With the point of the scissors, make a slight incision in the anterior region of the membrane, and then with forceps strip it from the roof of the mouth and the pharynx.   Some additional material will probably have to be picked away before all the arteries will appear.

Pull away the membrane as far posteriorly as the anterior end of the esophagus, and identify the **efferent branchial arteries** as four pairs of large arteries passing posteriorly and combining in the middorsal line to form the **dorsal aorta.**   The dorsal aorta continues posteriorly into the pleuroperitoneal cavity.   Turn now to the anterior region in front of the first efferent branchial artery.   Carefully expose the first efferent artery and the roof of the mouth anterior to it.   On the roof of the mouth and the pharynx are several arteries that are connected to the efferent branchials.

The **hyoidean epibranchial** is the most lateral artery on each side.   It arises from the anterior edge of the first efferent artery just posterior to the inner opening of the spiracle.   This artery was formerly called the common carotid.   From its point of origin, the hyoidean epibranchial artery passes toward the mid-line and then runs anteriorly, close to the inner edge of the spiracular opening.   As it passes forward, it is joined on its inner surface by a small artery that arises from the first efferent branchial artery just before it joins the dorsal aorta.   These small arteries, one on each side, represent the anterior extensions of the two embryonic dorsal aortas that fuse to form the dorsal aorta of the adult.   These vessels were formerly called vertebral arteries.   The hyoidean epibranchial artery continues anteriorly and then turns sharply medially toward the middorsal line. At the angle that is formed when the hyoidean epibranchial artery turns medially, an artery is given off from its outer surface that passes laterally and anteriorly.   This is the **stapedial artery.**   This branch is usually covered by tissue; before it can be located, some of the material on the outer surface of the hyoidean epibranchial artery must be removed.

After the stapedial artery is given off, the vessel passing to the mid-line is called the **internal carotid.**   This artery passes to the mid-line, where it combines with the internal carotid from the opposite side.   Shortly after they combine, the internal carotids separate.   Carefully scrape away the cartilage anterior to the union of these arteries until their point of separation can be seen. Follow one of these branches laterally, and observe that the internal carotid is joined by another artery, which comes from the spiracle.   This is the **spiracular epibranchial artery,** which is the anterior continuation of an artery that passes to the spiracle and breaks up into capillaries. This artery will be identified presently. After receiving the spiracular epibranchial artery, the internal carotid continues anteriorly and dorsally, where it helps to supply the brain with blood. Some of its branches were probably observed in the study of the ventral surface of the brain.

Turn again to the first efferent branchial artery. Fully expose this vessel as it passes into the gills, until it is apparent that the single artery is formed by a combination of two arteries from the gill pouch. These two arteries are connected to each other at the ventral side of the gill pouch and thus form a complete loop around the pouch. This arterial loop is an **efferent collector loop.** An efferent collector loop also occurs in the other gill pouches, except in the last pouch, where there is only a partial loop. These vessels have been cut through on the side where the dissection was made, but the above facts may be determined by dissection on the opposite side. Locate again the origin of the hyoidean epibranchial artery, and observe that in reality it arises from the anterior portion of the first collector loop. Follow this part of the collector loop laterally. Perhaps ½ inch lateral to the origin of the hyoidean epibranchial artery and just posterior to the hyoid arch, the collector loop gives rise to the **afferent spiracular artery,** which passes medially to the spiracle. The afferent spiracular artery is quite near the surface on the dorsal side of the body and can best be traced on this side. Turn the dogfish on its ventral surface, remove the skin posterior and lateral to the spiracle, and look for the artery. It can sometimes be seen without much dissection. Gently pull away the tissue lateral and ventral to the spiracle until the artery is found. Then trace it to the spiracle, and observe the capillaries from the vessel that pass to the spiracular wall. These capillaries will probably not appear if the artery is not well injected. The afferent spiracular artery is continued anteriorly from the capillary network in the spiracle by the spiracular epibranchial artery noted above. Expose the front edge of the spiracle, and observe this artery as it passes almost straight ventrally and anteriorly. It is to be recalled that the spiracular epibranchial artery passes on anteriorly and joins the internal carotid. This combination has already been seen.

Turn back to the ventral surface of the specimen. The **external carotid** is sometimes difficult to find if the specimen is not well injected. Locate the first efferent branchial artery on the side opposite the one where the gills were cut through. Then trace this to the first internal gill slit. The external carotid arises from the ventral side of the first efferent collector loop and passes forward. Locate the *ventral* edge of the first internal gill slit. This occurs in the floor of the mouth just posterior to a portion of the hyoid arch. With forceps pull away the membrane from the floor of the mouth near this edge of the internal gill slit, and locate the efferent arterial loop. The external carotid is a small vessel that arises from the ventral, or anterior, edge of this arterial loop and passes forward along the lower jaw. This vessel is called the mandibular by some writers. Because of its small size, it is not studied in some courses.

In some specimens an **esophageal artery** will be seen to arise from the second or third efferent artery near the gills and pass posteriorly along the ventral surfaces of the posterior efferent arteries. This vessel sends small branches to the esophagus. It does not show up well in some specimens. Locate the ventral edge of the second gill slit in the floor of the pharynx, and pull away the tissue so that the loop of the second efferent branchial artery will be exposed. From the end of this loop (usually) there arises one of the coronary arteries that have been previously seen in the pericardial cavity and on the wall of the heart. Other loops sometimes contribute to the formation of these arteries.

Clean away the tissue from the anterior end of the dorsal aorta, being careful not to injure any vessels that are present. The first branch from the dorsal aorta normally occurs just anterior to the most posterior pair of efferent arteries. A **subclavian artery,** one from each side, passes from this region laterally toward the pectoral fin. Trace one of the subclavians. It passes somewhat posteriorly and laterally across the dorsal wall of the posterior cardinal sinus, then turns ventrally along the posterior edge of a cartilage of the pectoral girdle. The artery sends off the **brachial artery** into the pectoral fin, while the main vessel then continues toward the mid-line. This continuation of the subclavian artery is the **anterior epigastric artery.** Just before attaining the mid-ventral line, the main vessel turns sharply posteriorly and continues along the body wall, somewhat parallel, but ventral, to the lateral abdominal vein. The anterior epigastric artery eventually anastomoses with the posterior epigastric artery from the iliac artery. This point of union probably cannot be seen in all specimens. The anterior epigastric artery is considered to be homologous to the internal mammary artery in mammals and to the anterior epigastric artery of other groups. In most groups, the anterior epigastric arteries are quite small and are therefore not usually studied except in the most detailed courses. As the subclavian passes across the body wall toward the front fin, it gives off several branches, but most of them usually do not show up well. Two sometimes appear. The **lateral artery** passes posteriorly along the dorsal body wall and is given off somewhat before the brachial passes into the fin. It is usually buried in tissue. Lateral to this point, a **ventrolateral artery** arises that passes posteriorly and supplies muscles in that region.

Observe along the course of the dorsal aorta the small **parietal arteries** that are distributed to the muscles of the back. In the region of the kidney, small **renal arteries** pass into the kidney from the dorsal aorta. The origin of the coeliac should now be located. It arises from the dorsal aorta from its ventral surface posterior to the subclavians and passes ventrally and posteriorly, giving off branches into the visceral organs. Most of these branches have already been identified. See if you can find small **genital arteries** passing into the gonads (ovaries or testes) from the coeliac near its origin. In immature specimens, these arteries are difficult to find unless they are well injected.

Let us now briefly consider the condition of the aortic arches and associated vessels in the dogfish as compared with the similar vessels in higher forms. In the early embryo of the dogfish, as well as of other vertebrates, the dorsal aorta forms as two longitudinal vessels that later fuse posteriorly into the dorsal aorta as found in the adult. In this animal six pairs of aortic arches also form in the embryo. These arches are broken up by gill capillaries into the afferent branchial and efferent branchial (epibranchial) arteries. In the adult dogfish, it is to be noted that four complete arches are retained in typical form, while the ventral part of a fifth is represented in the afferent branchial arteries. It has been determined that arch 1 is the arch which is not typically represented, while the ventral part of arch 2 occurs only in the afferent branchial arteries. This is the first afferent branchial artery. The hyoidean epibranchial artery is considered by some to represent the dorsal portion of aortic arch 2, while the afferent spiracular and the spiracular epibranchial represent, respectively, the ventral and dorsal parts of aortic arch 1. The carotid arteries of the dogfish are not so well developed as are those of higher forms, but the portions of this system that are present are considered to be homologous with the arteries of higher groups. In the higher forms, as will be seen, the internal and external carotid arise from a common vessel, the common carotid, but this latter vessel does not occur in the dogfish. In the dogfish, the external carotid on each side is derived from a forward extension of the ventral aorta (with a contribution from aortic arch 1), and the internal carotids arise from anterior extensions of the dorsal aorta. This is essentially the way in which these vessels are derived in the higher vertebrates, except that additional elements are added in some cases. In these animals, when aortic arches 1 and 2 are lost in the adult, a common carotid artery will appear that is derived from an anterior part of the ventral aorta and aortic arch 3. The internal carotid of these higher forms is thus composite: the distal portion arises from the anterior extension of the dorsal aorta, while the basal, or proximal, part is formed from aortic arch 3. The addition of aortic arch 3 to the basal part of the internal carotid of higher vertebrates results when aortic arch 3 loses its embryonic connection with the dorsal aorta. The composition of the external carotid remains essentially the same in all vertebrates. It arises as an anterior extension of the ventral aorta.

Drawing 13. Efferent Branchial and Associated Arteries— Ventral View. Make a full-page drawing showing all efferent arteries and their branches on both sides. Sketch in the spiracle. Start drawing toward the top of the page, so that the dorsal aorta, lateral arteries, and anterior epigastric arteries can be included. **Labels:** Arteries—efferent branchial, dorsal aorta, hyoidean epibranchial, stapedial, internal carotid, spiracular epibranchial, efferent collector loop, afferent spiracular, coronary, esophageal, subclavian, anterior epigastric, lateral (if seen), ventrolateral (if seen), parietal, renal, base of coeliac.

CHAPTER IV

THE PERCH

Phylum—Chordata
Subphylum—Vertebrata
Class—Osteichthyes
Subclass—Actinopterygii
Order—Teleostei
Genus—Perca

From a comparative standpoint, the work to be done on this animal is not of particular importance. From a biological standpoint, however, the perch and similar fish are quite interesting. Perhaps the greatest interest lies in the fact that these animals present many incongruities that cannot be homologized satisfactorily with other vertebrates. It seems probable that the members of this class are some distance removed from the direct line of evolution of most of the higher vertebrate animals.

The term bony fish is sometimes applied to this group (especially to the order Teleostei) because the skeleton is partly composed of bone, as opposed to the cartilaginous skeleton of the Chondrichthyes. The most highly developed of the bony fish are the Teleostei, the group that includes most of our common fish. A good example of this group is the perch, a common fresh-water fish in some parts of the country.

External Anatomy. The body of the perch is laterally compressed, in contrast to the depressed body of the dogfish. Despite this difference, however, observe that in the perch, as well as in the dogfish, the widest part of the body is about one-third of the distance from the head to the tail. As indicated previously, this formation makes the animals somewhat streamlined and allows them to swim swiftly through the water with a minimum of resistance. Most of the swifter fish are somewhat streamlined.

The body of the fish is indefinitely divided into **head, trunk, and tail.** Several fins are present. On the dorsal surface locate the **anterior dorsal fin** and the **posterior dorsal fin.** Unbranched **spines** support the anterior dorsal fin, while softer branched **fin**

80

rays occur in the posterior dorsal fin. The **caudal fin,** or tail, differs in shape from that of the dogfish in that the dorsal and ventral portions of the tail in the perch are essentially the same size and shape. This is a **homocercal** type of tail, as opposed to the heterocercal tail of the dogfish.

On the ventral surface in the mid-line, note the single **anal fin,** a structure that is not present in the dogfish. Still farther anteriorly are the paired **pelvic fins,** which are sometimes called the **ventral fins** because of their forward migration, compared with the primitive position which is farther posterior. In many teleosts the pelvic fins have migrated anteriorly, and in a few species they may even be anterior to the pectoral fins themselves. On the sides, just anterior to the pelvic fins, are the **pectoral fins,** which still retain their primitive positions. The principal support for the fins (other than the anterior dorsal fin) are the soft-branched **fin rays,** although a few of the fins sometimes have a spine or so on the anterior margin.

A **lateral line** occurs along the side of the body. The scales differ considerably from those of the dogfish. Take a probe or a scalpel, and remove several. Note that they are rounded and that they are overlapping when on the fish. They do not have a small point near the center, as does the placoid scale. It has been pointed out that the placoid scales as found in the dogfish are considered to be homologous to the true teeth of higher vertebrates. They are derived embryologically from both the ectoderm and the mesoderm and exhibit the essential structure of teeth. Most of the scales found in the perch are **ctenoid scales.** Scales of this type are wholly mesodermal in origin and therefore are not homologous to teeth. The buried edge of the ctenoid scale is somewhat toothed; from this fact the name ctenoid (comblike) is derived.

Turn next to the head. The **mouth** is *terminal* in contrast to the ventral mouth of the dogfish. Just anterior to each **eye** are a pair of **external nares,** or nostrils. The most posterior opening of each pair is rather large and is slightly dorsal to a line drawn across the center of the eye. The posterior openings are not covered. The anterior opening is about ⅛ inch anterior and is covered by a protecting flap. It is somewhat smaller than the posterior opening. The occurrence of two pairs of nares is probably a secondary division, since there is only a single nasal capsule for each pair of nares on each side. Probe into one of the openings, and note that the nares *do not* connect with the mouth cavity.   In most airbreathing vertebrates, a connection is established with the outside from the mouth or the pharynx, by way of the external nares.   In this group, however, the nares perform only an olfactory function.

On each side of the head is a flaplike structure, the **operculum,** which covers the gill slits and the gills.   All the gill slits thus actually open to the outside by a single opening between the operculum and the body wall, rather than individually as do those of the dogfish.   Lift up the operculum, and observe the **gills** and **gill slits** that are underneath.   As compared with the dogfish, the number of gills and gill slits have been reduced. There are only four of each present.   In the dogfish, it is to be recalled that the gill slits are widely separated by the interbranchial septa.   These septa are practically nonexistent in the perch; the gills and associated structures are all that occur between slits.   The gills are supported by bony **gill arches,** on the edges of which are fingerlike **gill rakers.**   On the posterior edge of the operculum is a complicated structure composed of a membrane supported by bony rays.   The membrane is the **branchiostegal membrane,** and the bony supports are the **branchiostegal rays.**   This structure aids in drawing the water through the mouth and the pharynx and out through the gill slits.

Just anterior to the anal fin is a comparatively large opening, the **anus,** and just posterior to the anus is a much smaller opening, the **urogenital pore,** which is sometimes hard to locate in preserved specimens.   Since the digestive and urogenital systems do not open into a common chamber, there is no cloaca in the perch.

Drawing 1.   External Anatomy—Lateral View.   Place drawing lengthwise of the drawing plate, with the head at the top and the ventral surface to your left.   Make labels parallel to the regular top and bottom of the page.   Make drawing about 6 or 7 inches in length.   **Labels:** anterior dorsal fin, posterior dorsal fin, caudal fin, anal fin, pelvic fin, pectoral fin, head, trunk, tail, ctenoid scale (draw in only a few), fin ray, spine, external naris, operculum, lateral line, position of anus, position of urogenital pore.

Internal Anatomy.   The internal organs can best be studied by removing one side of the body wall.   Make a mid-ventral incision from the anus anteriorly to about the level of the pectoral fins. Then extend the cut dorsally to just above the most posterior projection of the operculum.   Make a similar lateral and dorsal cut from the region of the anus to about this same level dorsally. Now lift this flap of tissue, and entirely remove it from the body. In some specimens, there will be a large quantity of white and yellow fatty tissue that covers the internal organs. This should be carefully removed with forceps. Dorsal to the visceral organs is the **swim bladder,** or air bladder, a large membranous structure that takes up about half the abdominal cavity. This structure is not present in the dogfish. Since the walls of the swim bladder are relatively thin, they may have been broken when the side of the body was removed. In this case, there will be a large empty space in place of the membranous swim bladder. The principal function of this structure in the perch is hydrostatic, since in the adult there is no connection between it and the pharynx.

The visceral organs are as usual contained within the **pleuro-peritoneal cavity,** or abdominal cavity, which is the posterior division of the coelom. The anterior portion of the coelom, the pericardial cavity, contains the heart and associated structures. The heart will not be studied in the perch, since it is quite similar to that of the dogfish. The walls of the pleuroperitoneal cavity are lined with the **peritoneum,** and **mesenteries** help to hold the organs in place.

Digestive System. Locate the **liver,** the large organ at the anterior end of the abdominal cavity. In life this structure is reddish, but in preserved specimens it is sometimes gray or whitish. The liver is somewhat lobed. A **gall bladder** and a **bile duct** are also present but are sometimes hard to locate. The bile duct opens into the duodenum, as in the dogfish.

With forceps, pull away most of the liver, in order to expose the organs underneath. Locate the **esophagus,** the very short tube covered by the liver. It is difficult to distinguish the line of demarcation between esophagus and **stomach.** The stomach is divided into two definite regions, a **cardiac** portion, which is a direct continuation of the esophagus and which posteriorly forms a blind pouch, and a smaller **pyloric** division, which protrudes somewhat ventrally from the cardiac region.

Between the pyloric portion of the stomach and the anterior end of the intestine (duodenum) is the **pyloric sphincter,** which forms the dividing line between the stomach and the intestine. The pyloric sphincter is somewhat difficult to identify in the perch, however, since in this region there occur three fingerlike blind pouches that open into the duodenum. These are the **pyloric caeca** (singular, caecum) the function of which is to increase the digestive and absorptive surfaces of the digestive tract. From the pyloric caeca, the intestine continues anteriorly for a short distance and then turns posteriorly. Two or three loops are usually made before the intestine opens to the outside at the **anus.** The coils of the intestine may be seen after the stomach has been raised.

The **spleen** is the small, rounded, usually reddish body within the coils of the intestine. It is not a part of the digestive system but probably functions in connection with the circulatory system. There is no definite pancreas, but scattered groups of cells have been discovered in the walls of the intestine that probably correspond to a pancreas.

The Urogenital System. Break into the swim bladder if it has not been previously broken into. The student should study both male and female systems. The **kidneys** and **mesonephric ducts** (Wolffian ducts) are similar in the two sexes. The former are not very definite structures but greatly resemble those found in the dogfish. They are mesonephric kidneys. These structures occur as two elongate bodies on the dorsal surface of the body wall above the swim bladder, one on each side of the vertebral column. The mesonephric ducts are quite small and are rather difficult to find in such small animals. They emerge from the posterior end of the kidneys, combine into a single duct, and enlarge to form a small **urinary bladder** just before the urogenital pore. The excretory material is discharged to the outside by way of the urogenital pore.

THE MALE. The reproductive organs, or gonads, vary considerably in size during the year; if the fish was captured during the reproductive season, the gonads may be quite large. Locate the **testes,** a pair of ribbonlike structures (unless enlarged for reproduction) just above the intestine. From the posterior end of each testis, a tube, called the **vas deferens,** leads to the urogenital pore and thence to the outside. In most other vertebrate animals with a mesonephric kidney the mesonephric duct performs the functions of both excretion and reproduction in the male. It thus seems probable that these extra tubes, the vasa deferentia, are not homologous with the vasa deferentia of other vertebrates having mesonephric kidneys.

THE FEMALE. There is a single ovary in the female, which possibly resulted from a fusion of two in the embryo. As in the male, the reproductive organ will vary in size with the season of collection. The ovary is usually more granular in appearance than are the testes. There are no oviducts, or Müllerian ducts, as such. The tube that extends posteriorly from the ovary is attached directly to it and is simply a posterior extension of the ovary itself. This duct, therefore, is not considered to be homologous to the oviduct of other vertebrates and will be called the **ovarian duct.** In most other vertebrate animals, the oviducts and the ovaries are not directly connected. The ovarian duct passes posteriorly and opens to the outside by way of the urogenital pore.

The circulatory system, sense organs, nervous system, and other structures are similar to those found in the dogfish and so will not be studied. Comparatively speaking, perhaps the greatest advance of the bony fish over the dogfish is the occurrence of true bone in the skeleton.

Drawing 2. Visceral Organs—Lateral View. Orient drawing on plate as in drawing 1, make about the same size, and label as previously. Have organs more or less in natural position, but draw in the liver with dotted lines, since it has been partly removed and since it covers many of the other organs. **Labels:** swim bladder, pleuroperitoneal cavity, liver, gall bladder, bile duct (sketch in, if not seen), esophagus, stomach, intestine, pyloric caecum, spleen, kidney, mesonephric duct (sketch in, if not seen), urogenital pore, ovary or testis, vas deferens, or ovarian duct.

CHAPTER V

NECTURUS

Phylum—Chordata
Subphylum—Vertebrata
Class—Amphibia
Order—Urodela (Caudata)
Genus—Necturus

Necturus, sometimes called the *mud puppy*, is a salamander that spends its whole life in the water. Some salamanders live for only a time in the water, shed their gills, and spend their adult lives on land. This animal, however, retains its gills throughout life.

The Amphibia, of which Necturus is a representative, are sometimes called "typical vertebrates" because they are intermediate in structure between the lower and higher forms. They retain certain primitive features that occur in fish and yet have certain characteristics that anticipate more complex conditions to be found in higher vertebrates. Some of these characteristics are doubtless correlated with the fact that the Amphibia are the first group of vertebrates partly to conquer the land habitat.

From many standpoints this animal is perhaps not so satisfactory for laboratory study as the bullfrog. Many students, however, have used either frogs or toads as specimens in their elementary biology courses, and the selection of the bullfrog would entail too much repetition. Also, Necturus exhibits certain features important from a comparative standpoint that are not found in frogs and toads.

The present directions are based upon the use of a single injected specimen per student or pair of laboratory partners.

EXTERNAL ANATOMY

The body of Necturus is indefinitely divided into **head, trunk, and tail.** Although there is no definite neck present, this animal (as well as other Amphibia) does have one cervical, or neck, vertebra, which somewhat anticipates the well-developed neck of higher forms. The body is scaleless and in life is quite shiny

86

from the secretions of skin glands. Anyone who has handled these animals in life will bear witness to their sliminess. Two pairs of legs are present and, although not well developed, have the same general divisions as the better developed legs of higher vertebrates. It is to be noted that this is the first group of animals to develop legs, in contrast with the fins of fish. It is maintained by some biologists that the development of legs that are capable of bearing the body is one of the most important reasons why the Amphibia were able partly to conquer the land. Many fish have a modified swim bladder that is as efficient as the lungs of some Amphibia, but the absence of well-developed legs seems to be one important reason why they cannot venture on land to any extent. The legs of frogs and toads are, of course, much more efficient than those of Necturus and the other salamanders, but even in the latter the basis for well-developed legs is present. Each limb has only four **digits,** although man and many other vertebrates have five digits for each limb. The number 5 is considered to be the typical digit number; it is thought probable that Necturus has lost digit 1, the structure that corresponds to our thumb and great toe.

Some of the intestines and the heart of the specimen may protrude from an incision in the ventral body wall. The creatures, if injected, are usually injected through the heart, and the smaller vessels to the intestine are often examined at this time to ensure a successful injection.

Locate the terminal **mouth** at the anterior end of the body. There is a pair of fairly well-developed **lips,** upper and lower. Just above the upper lip is a pair of minute openings, the **external nares,** or nostrils. Their internal connections with the mouth cavity will be seen later. Just dorsal to the corners of the mouth are the two small **eyes,** without any movable eyelids. Along each side of the body there are three **external gills,** which function in respiration. Between the first and second and the second and third gills are the **external gill slits.** In some specimens some of the gills may have been pushed into the gill slits. In such a case, pull the gills out with forceps. Simple lungs, to be seen later, are also present; these allow the animals to obtain some oxygen from the air, while a certain amount of respiration is carried on through the skin as well. The external gills are not homologous to the internal gills of fish. They are composed primarily of ectoderm and mesoderm, while the internal gills of fish are formed mainly from the endoderm and mesoderm.

Note the fold of skin on the ventral surface just anterior to the gills. This fold is usually considered to be the dividing line between head and trunk. In the mid-line posterior to the hind pair of legs is the **cloacal opening.** Both digestive and urogenital products pass through this aperture   The cloacal opening marks the posterior limit of the trunk. Do not make a drawing unless directed to do so by the instructor.

THE MUSCULAR SYSTEM

The muscles will not be studied in detail, but enough will be identified to indicate that this animal possesses a number of muscles comparable to those present in higher animals.

Skin the animal on one side from the middorsal to the mid-ventral lines, including the gill region and the fore and hind limbs. The skin is quite easy to remove. Start on the dorsal side, and make a longitudinal incision through the skin from the end of the nose past the hind limbs, being careful not to cut through the underlying muscles. The skin may then be pulled off with the fingers or forceps, but in taking it off be careful not to remove any of the muscles. As the skin is removed, note the **superficial fascia,** the whitish connective tissue that occurs between the muscles and the skin.

Muscles of the Head and the Gills. Just above and anterior to the base of the gills there usually occurs a large vein that sends branches anteriorly. This is the **jugular sinus,** from which blood passes posteriorly by way of the external jugular vein. Several of the muscles will be located by reference to this sinus and its branches.

Locate the **temporal muscle** just lateral to the middorsal line of the head. This is a rather wide muscle that extends anteriorly and above the eye. Lateral to the temporal muscle is a large muscle that covers much of the side of the head posterior to the eye. This is the **masseter.** The fibers of these two muscles extend in slightly different directions, and the two are separated by a slight depression along which passes an anterior branch of the jugular sinus. Both these muscles are attached to the lower jaw; when they contract, the lower jaw is raised, closing the mouth. Therefore, they are said to be *elevators* of the lower jaw. Posterior to the masseter is another depression, in which lies another branch of the jugular sinus. This depression separates the masseter from posterior muscles. There are really two muscles posterior to the depression, one covering the other.

The muscle on top is the **mylohyoid,** which passes anteriorly and ventrally and covers the outer surface of the floor of the mouth on one side. Trace this muscle around to the ventral surface of the lower jaw, and note that it is attached to a **raphe** in the mid-ventral line. Observe also that the posterior edge of this muscle is partly responsible for the fold seen externally that marks the dividing line between head and trunk. The mylohyoid is a relatively thin muscle. Carefully cut through the mid-ventral raphe under the lower jaw, and lift up this end of the mylohyoid. Just under this muscle, a small muscle occurs on each side of the mid-ventral line. These are the **geniohyoids.**

Lateral to the geniohyoid on each side, a rather large muscle is to be seen that passes posteriorly and dorsally under the mylohyoid. This is the **external ceratohyoid.** Peel the mylohyoid away from the surface of the external ceratohyoid, and follow both muscles dorsally. Toward the dorsal side, the mylohyoid becomes much thinner and is continued over the ceratohyoid as a thin semitransparent fascia that is attached to the bases of the gills. Note that the external ceratohyoid is also attached to the gills. The function of the latter muscle is to move the gills forward. Between the masseter and ceratohyoid at about the level of the corner of the mouth is the **digastric.** This muscle is comparatively small but is usually easily separable from the other two muscles. The digastric is attached to the lower jaw in such a way that its contraction causes the lower jaw to be lowered, thereby opening the mouth. It is thus a *depressor* muscle. Posterior to the masseter and dorsal to the external ceratohyoid is a muscle shaped somewhat like a fan and attached to the bases of the gills. This is the **levator branchiarum,** the function of which is to raise the gills. It is suggested that a sketch be made of these muscles, but do not hand in the drawing unless asked to do so by the instructor.

Muscles of the Shoulder and Forelimb. Raise the gills and look beneath and posterior to them. There is usually a certain amount of fascia in this region, which should be pulled away with forceps. On the upper portion of the lateral surface of the body posterior to the gills is a fan-shaped muscle, the fibers of which are divided into two ventrally converging groups. The fibers pass from the dorsal part of the body toward the base of the forelimb. This is the **trapezius.** It is attached to the shoulder blade just in front of the base of the forelimb. (Some recent workers have applied different names to the two parts of the trapezius and have omitted the name trapezius for animals below the reptiles. These writers use the term cucullaris for the posterior division of the trapezius. The name trapezius is retained in the present work, however, because the cucullaris division of this muscle seems to be at least partly homologous to the trapezius of higher forms.) Posterior to the trapezius and at about the same level is the **dorsalis scapulae,** which passes ventrally and attaches to the humerus, the large bone of the upper arm. The dorsalis scapulae probably represents the deltoid muscle of higher vertebrates. Still farther posteriorly is the **latissimus dorsi,** originating dorsally from several groups of fibers which converge ventrally and attach to the humerus.

On the dorsal surface of the upper arm, in close proximity to the ends of the latissimus dorsi and dorsalis scapulae, is the **triceps brachii,** which extends the length of the upper arm and covers most of the dorsal surface. There are two muscles on the ventral surface of the upper arm, and these are quite easily separable. The anterior muscle is the **biceps brachii**; the posterior is the **coracobrachialis.**

The muscles on the ventral side of the body associated with the pectoral girdle will not be studied, since in injected specimens some of the muscles have usually been injured. A sketch of the above muscles should be made for future study.

Muscles of the Trunk. Look along the sides of the body, and observe the muscle segments, or **myotomes,** separated by sheets of connective tissue, the **myocommata.** Along the sides of the body, find the longitudinal septum that separates these muscles into dorsal **epaxial** and ventral **hypaxial muscles.** The hypaxial muscles on the trunk have become differentiated into three layers that correspond to the same muscles in higher forms. The outer layer is the **external oblique muscle.** Make a short longitudinal incision through this muscle anterior to the hind limb. Just under the external oblique is the **internal oblique muscle,** the fibers of which extend at nearly right angles to those of the external oblique. The inner layer, the **transverse muscle,** should be located by cutting through the internal oblique muscle. It is quite thin, and care should be exerted not to break through it.

Look in the mid-ventral line and find the **linea alba,** the strip of connective tissue that separates the muscles on each side of the body. At the posterior end of the linea alba on each side is one of the **rectus abdominis muscles,** the fibers of which extend longitudinally. A drawing is not required.

THE MOUTH AND PHARYNGEAL CAVITIES

With scissors cut posteriorly from the angle of the mouth along the sides of the head to just in front of the first pair of gills. Do this on both sides so that the two jaws can be widely separated. The cavity thus exposed consists of an anterior **mouth cavity** and a posterior **pharynx.** Observe the two rows of poorly developed **teeth** on the upper jaw and the single row on the lower jaw.

Now look for the **internal nares,** the internal continuation of the external nares. Because of the small size of the external nares and the nasal passages, it is practically impossible to pass a probe from the external to the internal nares. Look on the roof of the mouth, and locate the ends of the two rows of teeth on one side. A small depression occurs between these two ends. The internal naris lies in this depression, covered by a fold of skin that usually adheres to the outer row of teeth. Probe gently just medial to the end of the outer row of teeth until the naris is located, covered by a fold of skin. It should be noted that the connection between the external nares and the mouth cavity is a distinct advance over the condition found in fish. This arrangement allows the animal to take air into the mouth cavity and thence into the lungs without opening the mouth. Higher vertebrates carry this condition even further by developing a hard palate, or secondary roof of the mouth (to be seen in the cat's skull), which causes air to pass directly into the pharynx without entering the mouth.

On the floor of the mouth note the fairly well developed **tongue.** As in the dogfish, this structure is supported by the **hyoid arch,** one of the visceral, or gill, arches. Observe the cut sections of this arch at the sides of the tongue, and feel the arch within the tongue itself.

On the walls of the pharynx on each side are two **internal gill slits.** The anterior slit is usually easier to find than is the posterior one. Pass a probe from the inside through to the outside of the slit, and note again that the external slits occur between the first and second and the second and third external gills. Observe the **gill arches,** or visceral arches, on each side of the gill slits. The sides of the gill slits correspond to the gill pouches that occur in the dogfish; but since the gills of Necturus are wholly external, no gills are present within the pouches.

On the floor of the pharynx, in the mid-line between the posterior pair of gill slits, is a tiny longitudinal slit that is difficult to find.   This is the **glottis,** the opening that allows air to pass through the larynx and into the lungs.   Look for this slit with a probe; when it is located, feel around it, and note that the area surrounding it is somewhat harder than the associated areas. This hardness is caused by the presence of supporting cartilages, which form a very primitive **larynx,** or voice box.   The Amphibia are the first group in which a larynx is found.   Some of the supporting cartilages are thought to have been derived from some of the gill arches that are present in fish.   A drawing is not required, but a sketch for future reference is suggested.

INTERNAL ANATOMY

Make two ventral incisions, one on each side of the mid-ventral line, so as to leave a strip of tissue about $\frac{1}{4}$ inch wide between the two cuts.   The incisions should extend from just in front of the pelvic girdle anteriorly to the pectoral girdle, but do not as yet break either of the girdles.   Do not cut through the strip of tissue.   This method of opening the pleuroperitoneal cavity, while seemingly cumbersome, is necessary to protect certain blood vessels and points of attachment in the mid-ventral line.   After the two longitudinal incisions have been made, make crosscuts dorsally on each side from the middle of the original incisions. This will allow the organs to be moved about somewhat.

The cavity that has been exposed is, as in previous animals studied, the posterior portion of the coelom, the **pleuroperitoneal,** or abdominal, **cavity.**   It is lined with the **peritoneum.**

Organs of the Pleuroperitoneal Cavity.   The **liver** occupies a large portion of the mid-ventral region of the abdominal cavity. Note the mesentery by which it is attached to the body wall in the mid-line.   This is the **falciform ligament.**   The sides of the liver are somewhat lobed or serrated, but the lobation is not so definite as in the dogfish.   Near the end of the liver, find the **gall bladder.**   Look on the animal's left side, dorsal to the liver, and identify the elongate **stomach.**   Attached to the stomach by the **gastrosplenic mesentery** is the **spleen.**   Dorsal to the stomach on each side is to be seen an elongate simple **lung.**   Note that the lungs are not separated from the other organs; hence the use of the term pleuroperitoneal cavity for this portion of the coelom. Follow the stomach posteriorly.   Unlike the stomachs of most vertebrates, this organ in Necturus does not curve anteriorly near its posterior end but is a straight tube.   The **pyloric sphincter** marks the end of the stomach and the beginning of the **intestine.**

The anterior end of the intestine is the **duodenum,** into which open the **bile** and **pancreatic ducts.** The duodenum continues posteriorly for a short distance and then turns forward and to the right. Just anterior to the bend of the duodenum and dorsal to the liver is the lobed **pancreas.** Posteriorly, the duodenum is continued by the remainder of the small intestine, which is sometimes called the **ileum.** Extend the longitudinal incisions through the body wall posteriorly on each side nearly to the cloaca, cutting through the pelvic girdle if desired. The posterior end of the intestine is somewhat larger than the remainder and is called the **large intestine.**

The organs of the urogenital system should now be identified, although they will be studied later in more detail. The **kidneys** lie one on each side of the middorsal line, covered by other organs. They are slightly more compact than the kidneys of the animals previously studied, but they are still mesonephric kidneys. In the female, the most noticeable parts of the urogenital system are the **ovaries** and **oviducts** (Müllerian ducts), which lie ventral to the kidneys. The mesenteries of the ovaries and oviducts are, as usual, the **mesovaria** and the **mesotubaria,** respectively. The ovaries are granular irregular-shaped bodies, the size of which will vary, depending upon the stage of sexual activity of the animal when it was captured. The oviducts lie somewhat lateral to the ovaries and are tightly coiled. They are attached by mesenteries (mesotubaria) to the kidneys. Locate the kidneys dorsal to the ovaries and oviducts if they have not been seen already. The **testes** of the male are attached to the ventral surfaces of the kidneys. The mesentery of the testis is the **mesorchium.** Find the kidneys dorsal to the testes. In both sexes, the **bladder** opens into the ventral side of the posterior end of the intestine. Its size will vary in different specimens, depending upon whether it is distended or collapsed. The posterior end of the intestine into which the bladder opens also receives the urogenital ducts. This region is, therefore, the **cloaca.**

Drawing 1. Visceral Organs—Ventral View. Make a diagram of the visceral organs as though the strip of tissue were not present in the mid-ventral line. Assume that the liver has been pulled over to the animal's right side and that the other organs are spread somewhat. Make an outline of the body to show relative positions. **Labels:** pleuroperitoneal cavity, liver, gall bladder, bile duct (sketch in, if not seen), stomach, pyloric sphincter, duodenum, pancreas, ileum, large intestine, kidney, testis (if male), ovary (if female).

THE CIRCULATORY SYSTEM

This system will be studied in detail before the other systems, since some of the vessels are relatively small and are easily destroyed. Necturus is unfortunately not a very satisfactory animal in which to study detailed circulatory structures, although certain important circulatory changes are represented in this animal compared with the condition in the dogfish. Those vessels will be emphasized which are of comparative value in illustrating these changes, as well as those which apparently anticipate conditions that exist in higher forms.

The Veins in the Pleuroperitoneal Cavity. Raise the strip of body wall in the mid-ventral line, and look on its inner surface just posterior to the tip of the liver. The vein applied to the body wall and receiving branches from it is the **ventral abdominal vein.** This vessel is considered to be homologous to the lateral abdominal veins, since it is thought to have been derived from a fusion of the latter. The ventral abdominal vein also receives an anterior branch along the ventral body wall to which the falciform ligament is attached. The ventral abdominal vein passes anteriorly and at the level of the posterior end of the liver enters this organ. After its entrance into the liver, the ventral abdominal vein joins the hepatic portal vein near the end of the liver; but the point of union is sometimes difficult to see, especially if the end of the liver was previously pulled from the body cavity when the specimen was injected.

The Hepatic Portal System. As is true of the dogfish, it is easier to find some of the branches of the hepatic portal system on or near the organs that they drain and then trace them to the hepatic portal vein. Locate the mesentery (**mesointestine**) that is attached to the small intestine. Stretch this mesentery somewhat, and observe the large vein that occurs in it passing parallel to the small intestine. This is the **mesenteric vein,** which receives smaller **intestinal veins** from the small intestine. Some posterior branches are also received from the large intestine. Trace the mesenteric vein anteriorly into the substance of the pancreas. It receives some small branches from this organ, passes anteriorly, and joins the hepatic portal vein. Locate that portion of the pancreas which occurs between the bend of the duodenum and the dorsal surface of the liver. One lobe of this organ extends anteriorly between the stomach and the dorsal side of the liver. Along the surface of this anterior pancreatic lobe, embedded in the tissue, is the **gastrosplenic vein.** Trace this branch anteriorly as it passes from the tip of the pancreatic lobe to the end of the spleen. A small vein from the spleen joins this vessel at this point. The gastrosplenic vein runs along the surface of the spleen for a short distance and then passes across the posterior part of the **gastrosplenic mesentery** to the stomach. Trace the gastrosplenic vein posteriorly and into the substance of the pancreas. With forceps gently pick away some of the pancreatic tissue and see if you can find the junction of the gastrosplenic and mesenteric veins to form the **hepatic portal vein.** This combination should appear in a few specimens, although it is sometimes hard to find. The hepatic portal vein proceeds immediately into the liver. Soon after its entrance into the liver, the hepatic portal vein receives the ventral abdominal vein. It then passes anteriorly along the dorsal surface of the liver in a groove, where it may be easily seen. Note the numerous branches that this vein gives off to the liver and the anterior **gastric veins** that it receives from the anterior end of the stomach. The hepatic portal vein breaks up into capillaries in the liver. Hepatic veins, to be seen later, pick up the blood from these capillaries and carry it anteriorly (see drawing directions 2, page 97).

The Postcaval Vein and Its Branches. Necturus is the first animal in which we have encountered a postcaval vein (also called the posterior vena cava). This vessel has probably been derived from the hepatic sinuses and the posterior portions of the posterior cardinal veins as found in the adult dogfish. (The posterior portions of the posterior cardinal veins of the adult dogfish are embryologically derived from a pair of embryonic veins that fuse with them, the subcardinal veins. It is from these subcardinal portions of the posterior cardinal veins that a part of the postcaval vein is derived.)

In higher vertebrates, most of the blood from the posterior part of the body enters the postcaval vein, since the posterior cardinal veins as such are absent in these forms. Even in Necturus, the postcaval is the most important vein in this region, although the posterior cardinal veins still persist. Locate the postcaval vein by looking on the right side of the liver in the middorsal line between the kidneys. The ovaries and testes,

since they lie ventral to the kidneys, should be separated.   Trace
this vein anteriorly.   Near the middle of the liver it passes ventrally into its substance.   It continues anteriorly within the
liver, is joined by hepatic veins from this organ, and then passes
into the sinus venosus of the heart as two hepatic sinuses, to be
found later.   Turn back to the region between the kidneys, and
locate the **renal veins** that arise from the kidneys and join the
postcaval vein.   Small **genital veins** are also received by this
vessel from the reproductive glands, but these are small and
difficult to find (see drawing directions 2, page 97).

The Renal Portal System and the Posterior Cardinal Veins.
Certain parts of this system are unfortunately quite difficult to
find.   The **renal portal vein** is easiest to find at the posterior
end of the kidney.   Extend the ventral incisions in the abdominal
wall posteriorly until all of the kidneys can be seen, if this has
not been done already.   Look just posterior to the end of the
kidney, and locate a vein that passes from the body wall to the
dorsal surface of the kidney.   This is the renal portal vein.
Trace this vein posteriorly across the body wall, and note that
it is joined by two veins at this point.   These are the **pelvic vein,**
which proceeds *ventrally* along the body wall toward the mid-
ventral line, and the **femoral,** which comes from the hind limb.
The two pelvic veins, one from each side, join ventrally to form
the ventral abdominal vein, previously identified.   The chances
are that this combination has now been destroyed.   Now look
on the dorsal surface of the kidney just posterior to the place
where the renal portal vein reaches its surface from the body wall.
See if you can find a small vein coming from the tail region, passing along the posterior dorsal surface of the kidney, and joining
the renal portal vein at this point.   This is a branch of the **caudal
vein,** which brings blood from the tail and which is in reality
the posterior end of the renal portal vein.   The renal portal
vein passes anteriorly along the kidney and sends off branches
into this organ that eventually connect with the renal veins,
which in turn join the postcaval.

It should be noted that blood from this posterior region may
thus be returned toward the heart by one of two routes, either
by way of the ventral abdominal vein and its connections, or by
the renal portal vein and its associated vessels.   Anteriorly, the
renal portal vein has a tendency to become obscure on the kidney
surface.   These vessels are continued anteriorly by two other
veins, the **posterior cardinal veins.**   Near the region where the

postcaval vein passes from the middorsal line to the liver, the posterior cardinal veins form a connection with the postcaval. Try to find this connection. The posterior cardinal veins, one on each side of the dorsal aorta (an injected vessel in the middorsal line), proceed anteriorly and are joined by the anterior ends of the renal portal veins previously mentioned. The latter connection is usually difficult to find. The posterior cardinal veins eventually join the sinus venosus. As they pass anteriorly, these vessels receive small **parietal veins** from the body wall; these are sometimes easier to see than are the posterior cardinal veins. Try to find the posterior cardinal veins and these branches from the body wall. In the male, lift up the thin anterior end of the kidney, and look in the mesentery that connects it to the body wall. In the female, the veins are in the mesentery that connects the oviduct to the body wall. Raise the oviducts, and look dorsal to them to find the vessels in the female.

It should be noted that the renal portal system of Necturus is not essentially different from that of the dogfish. In both cases, the caudal vein passes forward from the tail and divides into the renal portal veins that supply the kidneys. Associated vessels, however, are slightly different. In the dogfish, blood from the capillaries of the renal portal veins in the kidneys passes anteriorly by way of the posterior cardinal veins. In Necturus, the postcaval vein picks up this blood; but, as indicated previously, the postcaval vein is formed partly from the posterior ends of the posterior cardinal veins as found in the adult dogfish. One added complication in Necturus is that the femoral veins from the hind limbs have now connected with the renal portal veins, whereas in the dogfish the veins from the pelvic fins join the lateral abdominal veins.

Drawing 2. Veins of the Pleuroperitoneal Cavity—Ventral View. This drawing should be a composite of the hepatic portal system, the renal portal system, and other veins of the posterior region. After the hepatic portal system has been studied, the drawing should be started, but space should be left for the vessels to be added later. Sketch in the liver, intestine, and pancreas, and place these and the hepatic portal system to your left on the drawing plate, leaving the center of the page for the postcaval vein, the renal portal system, and associated vessels. Draw in a kidney to your right. As soon as one study is completed, these vessels should be added to the drawing. The instructor may prefer to have the heart and associated vessels added to the drawing later. If so, he will announce this; sufficient space should be left at the top of the page. If the heart and associated vessels are added to the drawing, the additional labels should be taken from drawing directions 4. **Labels:** Veins—ventral abdominal, mesenteric, intestinal, gastrosplenic, gastric, hepatic portal, postcaval, renal, genital (sketch in, if not seen), renal portal, femoral, posterior cardinal, parietal.

The Arteries of the Pleuroperitoneal Cavity. If the specimen is injected, the arteries will be considerably more conspicuous than are the veins. In such specimens, the arteries should be red or yellow in color. At the anterior end of the liver, make a mid-ventral incision anteriorly from the liver through the pectoral girdle, being careful not to injure the heart. This incision will allow the structures near the anterior end of the abdominal cavity to be more easily located. Locate the **dorsal aorta** in the middorsal line by looking on the right side of the stomach and by separating this organ from the liver. It may help somewhat to clip a part of the mesentery that connects the stomach and the liver at their ends, but leave enough mesentery to be recognizable. Near the anterior end of the stomach, a large **gastric artery** passes from the dorsal aorta to this organ and sends off branches to its walls. Follow the dorsal aorta posteriorly. Near the pyloric sphincter (anterior to it in some specimens) a **coeliacomesenteric artery** is given off that is usually somewhat surrounded by mesentery. This vessel passes posteriorly and ventrally and splits into several branches, which go to the various visceral organs. In most specimens, the origin of these branches from the coeliacomesenteric artery is somewhat obscured by the substance of the pancreas, in which case some of this material should be picked away. A **splenic artery,** the most anterior branch of the coeliacomesenteric artery, passes anteriorly along the same lobe of the pancreas that contains the gastrosplenic vein. In some cases a small branch may pass from this artery to the stomach. A **pancreatico-duodenal artery** runs through the substance of the pancreas, giving off small branches, and across to the duodenum. Posteriorly, an **intestinal** branch passes to the anterior end of the ileum. The **hepatic artery** to the liver is sometimes not well injected. It can usually best be located by looking between the lobes, or scallops, of the liver on the right side just anterior to the gall bladder. This vessel proceeds to the liver, gives off twigs to the gall bladder, and then runs anteriorly on the dorsal surface of the liver within the same groove that contains the hepatic portal vein.

After giving rise to the coeliacomesenteric artery, the dorsal aorta continues posteriorly and sends off a large number of **mesenteric,** or intestinal, **arteries** that pass to the intestine. At the level of the kidneys and the gonads, locate the **renal arteries** to the kidneys and the **genital arteries** to the gonads. Observe also the **parietal arteries** from the dorsal aorta to the body wall.

In the posterior end of the body cavity near the renal portal vein, an **iliac artery** arises on each side from the dorsal aorta. It gives off branches to the body wall and bladder and then proceeds into the hind leg, where it is then called the **femoral artery.** The dorsal aorta continues on into the tail as the **caudal artery.**

Drawing 3. Arteries of the Pleuroperitoneal Cavity—Ventral View. Sketch in the liver, stomach, pancreas, spleen, and intestine, as was done for the venous system, and place these organs to your left on the drawing plate. The dorsal aorta should be in the center of the page. If the instructor prefers to add the efferent arteries to this drawing, space should be left at the top, and the additional labels taken from drawing directions 5. **Labels:** Arteries—dorsal aorta, gastric, coeliaco-mesenteric, splenic, pancreatico-duodenal, mesenteric, hepatic, intestinal, renal, genital, parietal, iliac, caudal.

The Heart and Associated Vessels. If the specimen has been injected through the ventricle of the heart, the pericardial cavity will be partly opened and the ventricle will probably protrude from it. This injection through the ventricle usually partly destroys some of the divisions of the heart and makes more difficult the locating of some of the associated vessels. Remove a triangular-shaped piece of skin anterior to the ventricle. If the ventricle is not exposed, the piece of skin should be removed just anterior to the pectoral girdle. Then, with forceps, pick away the underlying muscle until the heart and its divisions are evident. As in the dogfish, the heart lies in the pericardial cavity, the anterior division of the coelom, which is lined with the **pericardium,** a thin membrane corresponding to the peritoneum that lines the pleuroperitoneal cavity. Do not injure the vessels leading from the ventricle.

Examine the heart, and identify as many of the parts as you can. If injection was made in this region, the chances are that several parts will have been distorted. With the structure of the dogfish's heart in mind, however, one should not have much difficulty in identifying the parts. The most important change that has occurred in the heart of Necturus, compared with the animals previously studied, is the appearance of a septum that forms two complete auricles. The occurrence of two auricles somewhat anticipates the appearance of a four-chambered heart in higher forms, where, in addition, two ventricles occur. Locate the bulbous **ventricle** and the **conus arteriosus** passing anteriorly from it. On each side of the conus arteriosus is an **auricle.** Look dorsal to the ventricle, and find the thin-walled **sinus venosus** that opens into the *right* auricle.

Note, therefore, that Necturus has a heart with three true chambers, two auricles and a single ventricle. These chambers are comparable to the two auricles and two ventricles found in higher vertebrates. As indicated previously, the conus arteriosus and sinus venosus are not considered to be true heart chambers in this manual, although some writers so consider them.

Just anterior to the conus arteriosus is a large bulblike enlargement, the **bulbus arteriosus,** which is the posterior portion of the **ventral aorta.** In front of the bulbus arteriosus, **afferent branchial arteries** arise from each side of the ventral aorta. These vessels should not be fully exposed as yet. The chances are that they are at least partly visible at present; if so, do not remove any additional tissue. They will be more fully dissected later.

Remove the tissue from the ventral and anterior end of the liver, and locate two large membranous vessels emerging from the liver and passing toward the sinus venosus. These are the **hepatic sinuses,** the anterior extensions of the postcaval vein. Note also in this region the **transverse septum,** the partition that separates the pericardial from the pleuroperitoneal cavity. **Hepatic veins** join the postcaval vein within the liver substance, and one of these may be seen on the ventral surface of the liver passing anteriorly and joining the postcaval at the anterior end of this organ. Trace the hepatic sinuses anteriorly, and note that they pass into the sinus venosus. In specimens with the heart somewhat mutilated, it is difficult to find the line of demarcation between the sinuses and the sinus venosus. With forceps gently pick away the material at the side of one of the hepatic sinuses. This vessel is joined in this region by a large vein, the **common cardinal vein.**

The common cardinal vein receives an **anterior cardinal vein** (sometimes called jugular vein) from the anterior region, a **subclavian vein** from the limb and associated regions, and a **posterior cardinal vein** from the abdominal cavity. This latter vessel was previously located in the posterior region. The anterior cardinal vein is the most anterior branch. With forceps, pick away the tissue covering the common cardinal vein, and note that this vessel passes laterally and somewhat dorsally. The anterior cardinal joins the common cardinal vein just under the skin, dorsal and anterior to the base of the forelimb. A large amount of muscle will thus have to be removed from the ventral side; proceed carefully, since the veins in this region usually do not show up well. If the point of entrance of the anterior cardinal vein cannot be discovered by the above method, pick away the muscle lateral to the bulbus arteriosus and posterior to the afferent branchial arteries. Two vessels combine in this region to form the anterior cardinal vein (see below) and they sometimes contain more blood than does the latter.

Opposite the bulbus arteriosus, an **external jugular vein** from the floor of the mouth and an **internal jugular** from the brain and the roof of the mouth combine to form the anterior cardinal vein. In this region, the internal jugular sometimes runs anteriorly along one of the gill arches that is usually exposed by this time, although there is some variation in this vessel. Trace the anterior cardinal posteriorly to the common cardinal vein. The **subclavian vein** joins the common cardinal vein very near the surface of the skin, somewhat anterior and dorsal to the base of the forelimb. Locate this vessel lateral and posterior to the point where the anterior cardinal joins the common cardinal vein. The subclavian vein passes posteriorly and laterally and above the level of the front limb is formed by a combination of a **brachial vein** from the limb and a **cutaneous vein** from the skin. The cutaneous vein functions in skin respiration. The posterior cardinal joins the common cardinal vein on its posterior edge, but the combination is often obscure. The left auricle receives a **pulmonary vein** from the lungs, but the point of entrance is not always evident. The pulmonary veins, one from each lung, combine into a common trunk before joining the right auricle. One of these veins will be located later along the lung surface when the pulmonary artery is studied. The aortic arches of Necturus that connect the ventral aorta with the dorsal aorta are divided by capillaries in the gills into afferent and efferent branchial arteries, the same situation that occurs in the dogfish.

Some of the afferent branchial arteries have already been seen as lateral branches from the ventral aorta. Pick away the tissue on one side, and fully expose these vessels. There are two main branches on each side from the ventral aorta; the posterior of these divides into two parts near the gills. There are thus three afferent branchial arteries. Just before the anterior afferent branchial artery passes into the gills, it gives rise to a small **external carotid artery** that proceeds medially and anteriorly to the floor of the mouth. Trace one of the afferent arteries into the gills, and observe the small capillaries that pass into the gill filaments. An exchange of gases takes place within the gills between the blood and the water, and thus respiration is accomplished. Necturus also respires to a certain extent through the skin and with the lungs.

Drawing 4. The Heart and Associated Vessels—Ventral View. The point of entrance of some of the posterior veins into the heart should be indicated so that their association with the heart will be better understood. Place the drawing in the center of the page unless it is to be added to drawing 2. **Labels:** ventricle, auricle, sinus venosus, conus arteriosus, ventral aorta, bulbus arteriosus, afferent branchial artery, hepatic sinus, hepatic vein, common cardinal vein, external carotid artery, anterior cardinal vein, subclavian vein, posterior cardinal vein.

The Efferent Branchial Arteries and Associated Vessels. Extend the incisions previously made at the corners of the mouth posteriorly to just in front of the gills, unless this has been done already. Then, *on one side only*, extend the incision farther posteriorly, ventral to the base of the gills and medial to the base of the front legs. Continue posteriorly until the lower jaw and the posterior ventral region can be pulled over to one side, exposing the roof of the mouth and pharyngeal cavities. Next, with forceps, pull away the membrane that covers the roof of the mouth and the pharynx. In the posterior region of the cavity between the gills will be noted two large arteries that pass posteriorly and toward the mid-line. They join in the mid-line to form a large single vessel that extends posteriorly. The two large arteries are the **radices aortae** (singular, radix aortae), which are formed by a combination of the efferent branchial arteries; the single large vessel formed by their combination is the **dorsal aorta.** Trace the radix aortae on the intact side toward the gills, picking away the tissue that covers it.

It will be necessary to remove parts of the gill arches to find the efferent branchial arteries. This can easily be done with scissors and forceps. It soon becomes evident that each radix is formed by a combination of two efferent branchial arteries from the gills. If the posterior efferent trunk is traced farther toward the gills, two arteries can be seen combining in this region to form it. There are, then, three efferent arteries on each side, the posterior two combining into a common trunk before joining with the first to form the radix aortae. The three pairs of afferent and efferent branchial arteries that are present in Necturus represent aortic arches 3, 4, and 6, which still remain complete in this animal. Arches 1, 2, and 5 have all been lost in the adult of Necturus. It should be recalled that in the dog-fish, arch 5 is complete, arch 2 is represented in the afferent branchial arteries, and arch 1, although not present in a typical condition, is probably represented by the afferent spiracular and the spiracular epibranchial arteries. Arch 5 is present in some salamanders, although it is lacking in the adult Necturus.

Just medial to the point where the first efferent branchial artery joins the posterior trunk to form one of the radices aortae, an **internal carotid** takes origin from the first efferent and passes forward along the lateral roof of the mouth. Since aortic arches 1 and 2 are absent, this efferent branchial represents part of aortic arch 3. It should be noted, therefore, that both the external and the internal carotids arise from aortic arch 3. This same association occurs in higher forms, although, in most of them, there is a common carotid (derived from the ventral aorta and possibly a part of aortic arch 3), which in turn gives rise to the external and internal carotids. Medial to the point of origin of the internal carotid, another small artery arises from the radix aortae and passes anteriorly and dorsally. This is the **vertebral artery,** which supplies some of the blood to the central nervous system.

Locate an artery arising from the combination of the second and third efferent branchial arteries and extending posteriorly. It is located in the trough that is formed when the lower jaw and the ventral region are pushed over to one side. This is a new artery, the **pulmonary,** which passes to the lung. Look for this vessel along the dorsal surface of the lung. The pulmonary artery arises from aortic arch 6, just as in higher vertebrates. These arteries in all groups are, therefore, at least partly homologous. The pulmonary artery carries unaerated blood to the lung; the blood is aerated and then returned to the left auricle

of the heart by the **pulmonary vein,** which is located along the
ventral lung surface.   Find the vein on the lung, and then look
for its entrance into the left auricle.   In specimens with a distorted heart, the actual point of entrance is difficult to find.
Add the pulmonary vein to drawing 4.

Somewhat posterior to the point where the radices aortae combine to form the dorsal aorta, the latter vessel gives off the **subclavian artery,** which passes toward the forelimb.   Near the base
of the leg, this vessel branches into a cutaneous artery to the
skin and a branchial artery that proceeds on into the forelimb.
The cutaneous artery connects with the cutaneous vein by
capillaries; thus is formed a complete circulation in the skin for
respiration.   In addition, the cutaneous artery supplies the skin
and some of the muscles in that region with aerated blood.

**Drawing 5.   Efferent Branchial Arteries and Associated Ves-
sels—Ventral View.**   This drawing may easily be added to the
drawing of the arteries of the abdominal cavity (drawing 3).
If it is not, place the drawing in center of page.   **Labels:** Arteries—radix aortae, efferent branchial, vertebral, internal carotid,
pulmonary, subclavian, cutaneous, branchial.

THE UROGENITAL SYSTEM

Like the dogfish, amphibians have a mesonephric type of kidney, but in this group the organs are somewhat more compact.
There is, as usual, a close association between the urinary and
reproductive systems, which is also true of the higher vertebrates.
The student should study the systems of both sexes.

The Male.   Locate again the **kidneys,** one on each side of the
middorsal line.   These organs are quite elongate in the male and
from the ventral view are covered by the rather large **testes.**
Lift one of the testes, and observe the mesentery attached to its
dorsal surface.   This is the **mesorchium.**   Look through the
mesorchium toward the light, and observe a number of small
white tubules passing from the testes into the kidney.   These
are the **vasa efferentia,** which convey sperm from the testes into
the kidneys.   On the outer margin of the kidney, find the tightly
coiled **mesonephric duct,** or Wolffian duct.   From the kidneys,
both sperm and excretory products pass into the mesonephric
duct and thence to the **cloaca.**   Thus, as in the dogfish, these
ducts in the male are both excretory and reproductive in function.   Trace these ducts posteriorly to their openings into the
cloaca.   Slit the cloacal opening on one side to locate the ducts

in this region. Observe the entrance of the large intestine into the cloaca, and locate the membranous **bladder** that arises as a ventral outpouching from the wall of the cloaca. The mesonephric ducts in Amphibia do not join directly to the bladder, and it is thought probable that the excretory material is forced into the bladder by pressure caused by the contraction of the cloacal muscles. The bladder in Amphibia and reptiles is probably not entirely homologous to the bladder of mammals (see drawing directions 6, below).

The Female. Locate again the granular **ovaries** near the posterior end of the pleuroperitoneal cavity, one on each side of the middorsal line. Dorsal to the ovaries, find the **kidneys.** The kidneys in the female are not so elongate as those in the male. The mesentery of the ovary is the **mesovarium.** Dorsal to the ovaries on each side, and extending most of the length of the body cavity, is a tightly coiled **oviduct,** or Müllerian duct, supported by a mesentery, the **mesotubarium.** Trace one of the oviducts anteriorly, and locate its anterior opening, the **ostium,** near the anterior end of the liver. The tissue surrounding the opening is quite thin and is usually somewhat collapsed. Eggs break from the ovaries into the body cavity and eventually find their way through the ostia into the oviducts and thence to the cloaca. From the cloaca the eggs pass into the water. Fertilization in Necturus is external, and the young salamanders develop in the water. Follow the oviducts posteriorly, and note that they join the cloaca. The **mesonephric ducts,** or Wolffian ducts, in the female are quite small and difficult to find. It is usually easier to find them near the posterior end of the kidney. Expose this, and cut through the cloaca on the same side, exposing the posterior end of the oviduct. Then look for the mesonephric duct just dorsal to the oviduct. The mesonephric duct joins the cloaca just dorsal to the opening of the oviduct on that side. Locate the **bladder,** which is a membranous outpouching from the mid-ventral wall of the cloaca. As in the male, there is no direct connection between the mesonephric ducts and the bladder. In the female, these ducts are excretory only.

Drawing 6. Urogenital System—Ventral View. Indicate whether male or female. Draw only the system of your specimen, but study the system of both sexes. Include a diagram of the cloaca and the posterior end of the intestine. The intestine and the bladder should be drawn to one side since, in normal position, they would cover other structures. **Labels:** Male—kidney, testis, vas efferens (sketch in, if not seen), mesonephric duct, bladder, mesorchium, cloaca, intestine. Female—ovary, kidney, mesovarium, oviduct, ostium, mesonephric duct, cloaca, bladder, intestine.

THE NERVOUS SYSTEM

The nervous system will not be discussed in detail. In elementary courses, the frog or the toad is often studied in considerable detail, and this system is quite similar in the two animals. Besides, a detailed study would be of doubtful profit because of the small size of the structures involved.

The Brain. Strip the skin from the dorsal surface of the head, and remove the underlying muscle until the skull surface is exposed. Then, with a scalpel carefully shave thin strips from the dorsal part of the skull until the brain surface is exposed. Observe how much harder the skull of Necturus is than that of the dogfish. This is because of the presence of true bones that have become included in the skull, in contrast with the cartilage of the dogfish. These bones are also present in the skull of many of the bony fish. When the surface of the brain is uncovered, observe the blackish membrane, the **pia mater,** that adheres to the brain surface. A **dura mater** outside the pia mater is also partly differentiated, but the two are not easy to distinguish. As for the dogfish, it is probably better to use the term **primitive meninx** for both these membranes rather than to attempt making a distinction between them. To identify the divisions of the brain, pull away these membranes with forceps.

The anterior region of the brain is the **telencephalon,** which is incompletely divided into an anterior division, the **olfactory lobes,** and the posterior **cerebral hemispheres.** Posterior to the cerebral hemispheres is the very small **diencephalon,** the roof of which contains a **chorioid plexus,** which may have been destroyed in the dissection. The cavity under the chorioid plexus is the **third ventricle** of the brain. The **mesencephalon,** or midbrain, is the next division, the dorsal portion of which consists of the **optic lobes.** Posterior to the optic lobes is the very small **cerebellum,** which appears to form the anterior rim of the **fourth ventricle,** the cavity of the last brain division. The comparatively small cerebellum is probably the outstanding feature of the amphibian brain. As in other forms, it is the dorsal portion of the **metencephalon.** Posterior to the cerebellum is the **medulla oblongata,** or myelencephalon, which contains the fourth ventricle, mentioned above. The fourth ventricle contains a chorioid plexus in its roof, unless it has been previously destroyed. If still present, the plexus should be removed. The medulla oblongata passes indistinguishably into the posterior **spinal cord.** The cranial nerves will not be studied since they are quite small and resemble those of the dogfish.

Drawing 7. The Brain—Dorsal View. Make drawing about 5 inches long, and place in center of drawing plate. **Labels:** olfactory lobe, cerebral hemispheres, diencephalon, optic lobe, cerebellum, fourth ventricle, third ventricle, medulla oblongata, spinal cord.

The Spinal Nerves. The spinal nerves originate from the spinal cord and pass to various parts of the body. Some of them are difficult to find. In life, these nerves are whitish in color, but in injected specimens they frequently become pinkish and hard to differentiate from the muscle fibers. With forceps pull away the peritoneum and the muscles on the inner dorsal body wall, and observe the pinkish or whitish nerves that pass across and among the muscle fibers toward the lateral portions of the body. Observe also the **ribs,** which will appear as the muscles are pulled away. These are true ribs, although not so well developed as in higher forms.

Opposite each limb, several spinal nerves combine to form a nerve plexus, which doubtless helps in the coordination of the muscles of the limbs. The **brachial plexus** is formed from a combination of spinal nerves 3, 4, and 5. Look for this plexus just anterior to the subclavian artery. Nerves arise from this plexus and pass to various parts of the anterior limb. The **lumbosacral plexus** occurs opposite the hind limb and is usually more difficult to locate than the brachial plexus. If the specimen is not to be used for further study, remove the organs from the posterior part of the body. Locate that part of the vertebral column to which the pelvic girdle is attached. A portion of the girdle passes from the base of the hind leg medially to the vertebral column. Carefully pull away the peritoneum and the muscles anterior to the anterior edge of this portion of the pelvic girdle, and find the plexus in this region. Keep in mind that in injected specimens the nerves are likely to be yellowish or pinkish in color and thus difficult to distinguish from surrounding muscles. A drawing is not required unless so indicated by the instructor.

The **autonomic nervous system** of Necturus is represented by two dorsal threadlike strands, one on each side of the vertebral column. This system is somewhat better developed than that of the dogfish but is still quite difficult to study.

CHAPTER VI

THE TURTLE

Phylum—Chordata
Subphylum—Vertebrata
Class—Reptilia
Order—Chelonia (Testudinata)

Many instructors prefer to spend a relatively short time on the study of the turtle, since because of the shell it is perhaps not so easy to study as other forms. There are, however, several important evolutionary changes that have occurred in reptiles. Thus, by a brief study of this animal, more complicated systems of higher forms can be better understood. In the following exercises, these evolutionary changes will be emphasized.

The directions are based upon the use of a single injected specimen per student or per pair of laboratory partners. For this work, any of several species of turtles are satisfactory.

EXTERNAL ANATOMY

Most of the body of the turtle is enclosed in a shell. Correlated with this fact are several peculiarities, which will be pointed out from time to time.

The **shell** is composed of two regions, a dorsal **carapace** and a ventral **plastron.** The two portions are connected laterally by a bony **bridge.** The outer surfaces of the carapace and the plastron are covered by structures called **scutes.** These scutes are epidermal in origin, while the **plates** that they cover originate from the dermal layer of the skin. The plates cannot be seen externally but can be seen internally on the dorsal surface of the plastron and on the ventral surface of the carapace. The exposed parts of the body are protected by **scales,** which are epidermal in origin.

Examine the head. At the anterior end of the snout are two **external nares,** or nostrils. On each side of the head is an **eye,** which is probably covered by the upper and lower **lids.** Carefully remove the lower lid, and look near the anterior corner of the eye for a thin **nictitating membrane,** or third eyelid. This

108

structure is likewise present in birds and in some mammals. It serves to protect the eye although the eye may remain open. Posterior to the eyes and at about the same level are two rounded areas of skin, one on each side, the **tympanic membranes.** These structures cover the openings into the inner ear and correspond to the so-called "eardrum" found in higher animals. In the turtle, there are present only an inner and a middle ear, although in some reptiles this membrane is in a depression. This constitutes the beginning of an external ear, which is more fully developed in mammals.

Examine the edges of the **jaws,** and note the absence of teeth. The horny edges of the jaws, however, can inflict painful lacerations.

There are five **digits** on each of the limbs, although only four of them on the hind legs possess **claws.** The claws and a portion of the horny jaws are epidermal structures.

Observe the **cloacal opening** at the base of the tail on the ventral surface. A drawing is not required unless the instructor directs that one be made.

INTERNAL ANATOMY

For a study of the internal anatomy, the bridge connecting the carapace and the plastron should be cut through on both sides with a bone saw, and the plastron carefully disconnected from the muscles underneath and removed. In specimens that have been injected through the heart, this has usually been done already. Completely remove the plastron, and note the **plates** on its dorsal surface.

Several points should be observed before any additional dissections are made. There are practically no muscles occurring between the plastron and the visceral organs; the plastron thus furnishes most of the protection in this region. Two bony frameworks covered by muscles project from the front legs toward the mid-ventral line. These bony structures constitute the **pectoral girdle.** Note that there are no visible ribs and that there is no sternum, or breastbone. The ribs are fused with the undersurface of the carapace and so cannot be seen for the time being. Although no sternum is present in the turtle, a complete thoracic rib basket first occurs in some reptiles. A sternum first appears in some Amphibia and, in most reptiles, is joined in the mid-line by the ribs, thereby forming a complete basket. Ribs are not well developed in Amphibia and are thus not connected to the sternum in this group.

With forceps carefully pull away the muscles from one side of the pectoral girdle. This will reveal two projections. The anterior projection is a portion of the **scapula,** the main part of which cannot be seen at present. This portion of the scapula is the **acromion,** and it is probably homologous to the acromion in the mammalian scapula. The posterior projection of the pectoral girdle is the **precoracoid,** a structure not present in most higher mammals. A rather strong ligament extends between the ends of the acromion and the precoracoid. The scapula proper occurs somewhat dorsally and will not be studied at present. A **clavicle** is also present in the pectoral girdle, but it is fused with the undersurface of the plastron. A marked peculiarity in connection with the pectoral girdle should be noted: since the ribs are fused with the carapace, the girdle occurs *inside* the ribs.

Near the mid-line between the projecting halves of the pectoral girdle are two tubes passing posteriorly. The ventral one is the **trachea,** leading to the lungs; it is quite tough because of the presence of strengthening rings of cartilage. Near the heart, the trachea divides into two **bronchi,** one of which passes to each lung. The other tube, usually dorsal to the trachea, although it may be on one side, is the **esophagus,** which connects with the stomach. The trachea and the esophagus run dorsal to the **heart,** which occurs in the mid-ventral region. In injected specimens, part of the heart and the large arteries leading from it are different in color from the surrounding organs and are thus easily seen. The heart is normally surrounded by a membrane, the **pericardium,** but this has probably been destroyed in injected specimens, except dorsal to the heart, where a small portion of it may be seen. The cavity containing the heart and formed by the pericardium is, as usual, the **pericardial cavity.**

Posterior to the heart, the visceral organs are covered by a semitransparent membrane, the **peritoneum,** which also lines the walls of the **pleuroperitoneal cavity,** in which are contained the visceral organs. This cavity is the posterior part of the coelom, the pericardial cavity being the anterior portion. The peritoneum is also continuous with the mesenteries that are attached to the visceral organs. Posterior to the heart, there are two large veins within the peritoneum, which extend longitudinally. These are the **ventral abdominal veins,** which are probably homologous to the lateral abdominal veins in the dogfish and the ventral abdominal vein in Necturus. These veins collect some of the blood from the posterior part of the body and pass anteriorly into the liver.

Make a transverse cut with scissors across the peritoneum containing the ventral abdominal veins, also cutting through the middle of these vessels. Then fold back the anterior flap thus formed, so that other organs may be identified, if possible leaving stubs of the veins attached to the liver. Leave the posterior portion of the peritoneum as it is for the present. As the peritoneum is removed around the heart, note that it is fused in the dorsal region with the remnants of the pericardium. This fused area represents the **transverse septum** in lower forms. Now observe the **liver.** It is divided into right and left lobes. The **gall bladder** usually appears as a darker colored spot in the substance of the right lobe. The **bile duct** passes from the gall bladder posteriorly through the **lesser omentum** and to the duodenum but is sometimes hard to find.

Carefully remove the *left* lobe of the liver by picking away the pieces with forceps. This will expose the **stomach,** which lies dorsal to this liver lobe. In female specimens, the enlarged **ovaries** frequently occupy a large portion of the posterior region of the abdominal cavity. They are usually somewhat granular, irregular-shaped structures that contain eggs in various stages of development. If necessary, remove the ovary on the left side, but leave the other for future study. Coiled **oviducts** are associated with the ovaries; if necessary, the left one may be removed. Passing posteriorly from the stomach is the tightly coiled **small intestine,** the anterior portion of which is the **duodenum.** Note that there is no definite pyloric sphincter separating the stomach and the intestine. The **pancreas** is bound with mesentery to the anterior end of the duodenum, and the bile duct from the liver opens in this region. The posterior end of the intestine is the **large intestine,** or colon. At the beginning of the large intestine, there is a small outpouching in some species, the **caecum;** also, near this region, the **spleen** occurs. This structure is a small rounded body that is usually somewhat reddish in color. It is a part of the circulatory system.

Look under the posterior flap of the peritoneum, and note the **bladder,** a somewhat triangular-shaped structure attached to the peritoneum by one of its walls. The size and shape of the bladder will vary, depending upon the amount of liquid it contains. Sometimes it is greatly enlarged; if so, it should be punctured and the liquid drained off. Observe that the bladder opens into the posterior end of the large intestine. Since the urogenital ducts also open here, this region is the **cloaca.**

Other structures that are present will not be studied until after a brief consideration of the circulatory system.

Drawing 1. Digestive System and Associated Structures. This drawing should be made without the shell, and the organs should be spread somewhat. Dot in the lobes of the liver, so that the organs underneath may be seen. Some of the structures called for in the list of labels may have to be added later, after additional studies have been made. **Labels:** trachea, bronchus, esophagus, pleuroperitoneal cavity, liver, gall bladder, bile duct (sketch in, if not seen), stomach, duodenum, small intestine, large intestine, spleen, cloaca, bladder.

THE CIRCULATORY SYSTEM

Only the major veins and arteries will be noted. Study the heart first. In specimens that have been injected through the heart, the shape and structure will necessarily be somewhat abnormal. There are three complete chambers in the heart, a ventricle and two auricles. In this respect the turtle resembles the amphibians, differing in that there is a partial septum within the ventricle, which somewhat anticipates the completely separated ventricles in birds and mammals. This ventricular septum is essentially complete in crocodilians, but the aerated and unaerated blood still mix, even in these animals, when the two parts of aortic arch number 4 combine to form the dorsal aorta. The aorta is formed the same way in the turtle.

The **ventricle** is the large, somewhat cone-shaped structure from which conspicuous blood vessels arise. In injected specimens, part of the ventricle is likely to be differently colored from the other parts of the heart; in some cases, a string will be tied around a portion of it to prevent the injection material from being lost. Anterior to the ventricle on each side is an **auricle.** Look dorsal to the heart by pushing the ventricle anteriorly. This will reveal the **sinus venosus,** a thin-walled triangular-shaped sac that connects with the *right auricle.* The sinus venosus receives the unaerated blood that is returned by the large veins from the body and empties into the right auricle. Note the large arteries arising from the ventricle and passing anteriorly. Just anterior to the region where these arteries split and pass to each side of the body, a small dark body occurs, partly surrounded by the vessels. This is the **thyroid gland,** a gland of internal secretion of great importance in mammals.

Principal Veins of the Heart. In injected specimens, some of the larger veins of the heart may be partly destroyed, but most of them should appear. Three large veins return blood from the body into the sinus venosus, the two **precaval veins** and the **postcaval vein.** The precaval veins are sometimes called anterior venae cavae or descending venae cavae; the postcaval vein, the posterior vena cava or ascending vena cava. The latter terms are especially used for comparable veins in man.

Turn the ventricle forward, and locate the precaval veins first. Both of these veins return the blood from the anterior part of the body. The left precaval vein (from this view) passes under the anterior part of the left auricle and enters the left side of the sinus venosus. The right precaval vein enters on the right side in a comparable position, except that it does not pass across as much of the auricular surface as does the left precaval vein. A single hepatic veins can sometimes be seen, passing from the liver into the posterior wall of the sinus venosus. Its point of entrance is somewhat between the points of entrance of the precaval veins. The postcaval vein comes from the liver and enters the sinus venosus on the right side. Within the liver, several hepatic veins join the postcaval as it passes through its substance. If the entrance of the postcaval vein into the sinus venosus cannot be seen at present, do not dissect for it, but wait until the vein has been located in the pleuroperitoneal cavity. When this is done, trace it into the liver, and then with forceps carefully pick away the substance of the right liver lobe near the sinus venosus until the entrance of this vein into the right side of the sinus venosus is seen. The postcaval vein sometimes enters the sinus venosus somewhat on the dorsal side and so, from this view, is frequently not visible without some dissection.

A brief consideration should now be given to the formation of the postcaval and precaval veins. It is to be remembered that in Necturus a postcaval vein is present but that no precaval veins occur. In the turtle, the precaval veins are primarily homologous to the anterior cardinal veins and the common cardinal veins that occur in Necturus and the dogfish. Although precaval veins are not present in Necturus, they are present in tailless Amphibia (frogs and toads). In the turtle, the anterior ends of the posterior cardinal veins, which are persistent in Necturus, have disappeared, so that the postcaval vein now returns most of the blood from the posterior part of the body. The postcaval vein in Necturus and the turtle is formed from some of the hepatic veins and sinuses and the embryonic subcardinal veins. It is sometimes stated that the postcaval vein is partly formed from the old posterior cardinal veins, since, in the embryo, these two groups of vessels become continuous. The posterior ends of the posterior cardinal veins of the adult dogfish are thus formed from the embryonic subcardinal veins.

A brief study will now be made of some of the main branches of the larger veins. Cut across the large intestine just anterior to the attachment of the bladder. Then, by holding up the cut end, carefully free the anterior end of the large intestine from the mesentery that binds it to the dorsal body wall, being careful not to cut any blood vessels. Eventually, the intestine should be freed sufficiently so that it can be pushed forward somewhat, exposing the middorsal line of the abdominal cavity. Within this region there are two large blood vessels, the **dorsal aorta** and the **postcaval vein.** If the injection has been done properly, the dorsal aorta will be colored, usually yellow or red, and the postcaval vein will be bluish. Sometimes the postcaval vein may likewise be injected. It normally lies to the right of the dorsal aorta; and as it passes anteriorly, it curves toward the right and enters the right lobe of the liver. The dorsal aorta continues in the mid-line as it passes forward. Trace the postcaval anteriorly until it enters the liver; if the entrance of this vessel into the sinus venosus has not as yet been found, it should be examined now, according to the directions above. The posterior end of the postcaval vein will be studied later (see drawing directions 2, page 118).

The Posterior Veins. Locate again the ventral abdominal veins on the posterior flap of the peritoneum, and trace the left one posteriorly. Near the level of the pelvic girdle (the pointed bony structure covered with muscles and attached to the hind limbs) the ventral abdominal vein turns laterally and after a short distance gives off a **pelvic vein** medially onto the surface of the girdle. This vein is usually associated with an artery, which, if injected, may show up better than the vein. Before tracing the ventral abdominal vein farther, carefully remove the tissue on the left side between the pelvic girdle and the carapace, being careful not to injure any vessels in this region.

Then split the peritoneum between the two abdominal veins, disconnect the bladder from the peritoneum, and push it over to the right side. This will probably reveal the two saclike **accessory bladders,** one on each side of the urinary bladder, that open into the cloaca posterior to the opening of the urinary bladder. Now disconnect the pelvic vein and the associated artery from the pelvic girdle, and push them over to the left, keeping in mind the relationships of these vessels. This dissection will reveal the **kidney** and, in the male, the yellowish **testis** attached to the kidney by a mesentery (**mesorchium**). These structures occur somewhat dorsal and lateral to the pelvic girdle, very close to the posterior end of the abdominal cavity.

Follow the ventral abdominal vein posteriorly, picking away the surrounding tissue with forceps. It will probably soon be necessary to remove part of the pelvic girdle. If this is done, take scissors and, beginning at the anterior point of the girdle, cut posteriorly for about 1 inch. Then make a right-angle cut from the left side that meets the posterior end of the previous incision. This will loosen a portion of the girdle on the left side, which can then be pulled loose with forceps. As the ventral abdominal vein passes posteriorly, it receives several small branches from the surrounding tissue that need not be identified, except for one vein that usually appears quite clearly in most specimens. This is the **crural vein,** which comes into the outer surface of the abdominal vein from the thigh. After receiving the crural vein, the main ventral abdominal vein then turns sharply dorsally and continues toward the carapace in close association with an artery (branch of epigastric artery).

At this point, examine the kidney again. Push the bladder and other organs over to the side to locate this organ. Look on the outer margin of the kidney, and locate the **renal portal vein,** which passes to it, sometimes slightly on the dorsal side. The renal portal vein is a branch from the **external iliac,** which is the posterior continuation of the ventral abdominal. On the surface of the ·kidney, the renal portal vein receives a posterior branch, the **internal iliac,** but this vein is frequently hard to find. The external iliac vein continues into the tail, where it is called the **caudal vein.**

The relationships of these vessels are somewhat difficult to work out because of the shell, and their dissection need not be attempted unless the instructor has directed that it be made. If so directed, proceed as follows: Continue to follow the ventral abdominal vein as it passes dorsally, picking away the obscuring tissue. As it nears the carapace, this vein receives the **femoral vein** on its outer surface from the leg. Other smaller branches occur in this region but are frequently not evident. The point at which the ventral abdominal vein receives the femoral can be easiest located by studying the artery that accompanies the vein. The artery usually shows up better than does the vein, if it is injected. This artery branches very near the same place where the femoral vein enters the ventral abdominal. Posterior to the entrance of the femoral vein, the ventral abdominal is then called the **external iliac vein**; it may be said, therefore, that the ventral abdominal vein is formed from a combination of the external iliac and the femoral, since the blood in the veins is flowing toward the heart. The external iliac vein proceeds dorsally and somewhat posteriorly from the point of the attachment of the femoral, and eventually the renal portal vein (previously noted on the outer margin of the kidney) arises from the anterior margin of this vein and passes forward into the kidney. Other branches from the thigh join the external iliac vein as it passes posteriorly into the tail, where it is called the caudal vein.

A short comparison should now be made between the renal portal systems of the animals that have so far been studied. In reality, it will be seen that, despite certain complications in higher forms, they are all quite similar. It will be remembered that in the dogfish the caudal vein passes anteriorly and splits into the two renal portal veins, which break up into capillaries in the kidneys. These capillaries then join other small veins, which in turn pass into the posterior cardinal veins, which return the blood to the heart. It has been mentioned previously that embryonically the renal portal veins are derived from the posterior ends of the embryonic posterior cardinal veins, while the posterior ends of the posterior cardinal veins as found in the adult dogfish are formed from embryonic vessels termed the subcardinal veins, which replace the original posterior ends of these vessels. In Necturus and the turtle, the system is quite similar. The caudal vein passes anteriorly and divides into the renal portal veins, which break up into capillaries in the kidney. In the turtle, these veins are called external iliac veins for a short distance. Capillaries then join the posterior end of the postcaval vein, which has been derived from the embryonic subcardinal veins. The renal portal and associated vessels in the turtle and Necturus are somewhat more complex than in the dogfish, since, in these animals, the veins from the hind limbs are connected with the renal portal system. It should be mentioned at this point that the renal portal system begins to lose its previous importance in reptiles, becomes quite degenerate in birds, and is not present in the adult of mammals. In those groups where the system is degenerate or absent, the circulation through the kidneys is accomplished by branches from the dorsal aorta and the postcaval vein (renal arteries and veins).

Before returning to the anterior part of the body, look between the kidneys, locate again the postcaval vein, and observe the small **renal veins** passing from the kidney into the postcaval. It should be observed that the postcaval vein ends at the kidneys. In mammals, which do not possess a renal portal system, the postcaval vein extends the full length of the body cavity and receives the veins from the legs.

The turtle has a hepatic portal system of veins quite similar to the systems in Necturus and the dogfish. The vessels are difficult to find, however, and will consequently not be studied in detail. When the arteries of the abdominal cavity are studied, some of these veins may be seen in close association with the arteries.

Branches of the Precaval Veins. Trace the main branches of one of the precaval veins. These branches are the same on both sides, and hence only one need be followed. In most cases, the left precaval vein contains more blood and is therefore better for study, but individual specimens vary. Cut away the projecting end of the pectoral girdle on the side that is selected for examination. In specimens in which the arteries have been injected, some of the branches have probably been destroyed. As the precaval vein is traced anteriorly, pick away the obscuring tissue. The vein is formed by a combination of four veins, and their points of entrance into the precaval vary somewhat in different specimens. Start laterally in locating the vessels and work medially. The most lateral vessel is the small **scapular vein** from the shoulder region. This is a comparatively small vessel, sometimes difficult to find. The largest vein of the four is the **subclavian,** which is just medial to the scapular. This vessel brings blood from the arm (axillary vein) and the neck region (external jugular vein). These branches are difficult to find. The **internal jugular vein** carries blood from the sides of the neck and the brain. It may best be found by first looking lateral to the trachea and finding a white nerve in this region. This nerve is the vagus (cranial nerve X), and the internal jugular vein runs parallel to it. The most medial branch of the precaval vein is the **thyroscapular.** This vessel receives a small branch from the thyroid gland and a larger branch from the shoulder region.

Other veins occur in the turtle, but they are difficult to find and will not be studied.

Drawing 2.   The Main Veins—Ventral View.   A diagram of the body, including the shell, should be sketched in to indicate approximate relationship of the vessels.   Sketch in the kidneys, but do not include other organs except the chambers of the heart.   As soon as one part of this study is completed, make the corresponding portion of the drawing before continuing.   Show precaval veins on both sides, but include the branches on only one side and only the base of the precaval of the opposite side.   **Labels:** sinus venosus, ventricle, right auricle, left auricle.   Veins— precaval, postcaval, ventral abdominal, pelvic, crural, renal portal, renal; if the posterior veins are studied in more detail, add external iliac, femoral, caudal; scapular, subclavian, internal jugular, thyroscapular.

The Anterior Arteries.   Three main arteries spring directly from the ventricle of the heart.   These are, from left to right, the **pulmonary artery,** the **left systemic arch,** and the **right systemic arch.**   The right and left systemic arches are sometimes called the *right* and *left aortas.*

It will be necessary to turn the ventricle somewhat over to the left to see the origin of the right systemic arch, since from the present view it is covered by one of its branches.   Trace first the pulmonary artery.   This artery divides into **right** and **left pulmonary arteries,** one of which passes to each lung.   Look on the dorsal side of the main pulmonary trunk, and observe this branching close to its emergence from the ventricle.   Trace the left pulmonary artery as it proceeds across the body, turns dorsally, and passes into the left lung.   The actual point of entrance into the lung should not be noted until later.   Separate slightly the left pulmonary artery and the left systemic arch, and observe that the two vessels are intimately connected by tissue.   This tissue is all that remains of the **ductus arteriosus,** or the ductus Botalli.   In embryonic life this is a direct connection between the pulmonary arteries and the systemic arches that allows blood to pass from the pulmonary to the systemic without going through the lungs.   Since the lungs are not functioning in the embryo, pulmonary circulation is not essential.   The ductus arteriosus degenerates about the time the egg hatches, and pulmonary circulation then starts functioning. A similar condition obtains in the mammalian embryo. The bit of tissue that in the adult connects the pulmonary artery with the systemic arch is called the **ligamentum arteriosum,** or the ligament of Botallus, since no duct is now present. The right pulmonary artery passes to the right lung in essentially the same manner as the left pulmonary passes to the left lung, and it is connected to the right systemic arch by a ligamentum arteriosum.

At this point the **left pulmonary vein** should be noted. It is probably easiest to locate near the heart, just dorsal to and usually in contact with the left precaval vein. Push the precaval vein forward, and find the pulmonary vein. Trace it toward the heart, and observe that it empties into the left auricle. The **right pulmonary vein** from the right lung joins the left pulmonary just before its entrance into the heart.

Let us now briefly consider the method of passage of the blood through the heart of the turtle. It was stated earlier that the heart of the turtle is composed of two complete auricles and a ventricle that is partly divided by a ventricular septum. In injected specimens, the heart is unfortunately damaged so badly that a study of the heart structure is not feasible. It should be kept in mind that the final development of the four-chambered heart in birds and mammals prevents the mixture at any time of the aerated and unaerated blood. Even in Necturus and the turtle, there is an attempt, so to speak, to keep the two types of blood separated. Aerated blood from the lungs is received by the left auricle from the pulmonary veins, while unaerated blood passes into the sinus venosus from the large veins of the body and thence into the right auricle. There is thus no mixture of the two types of blood in the auricles. The blood from the left auricle then empties into the left side of the ventricle, and the blood from the right auricle passes into the right side of the ventricle. Since the ventricular septum is incomplete, there is probably a certain amount of mixture of the two types of blood in the ventricle, but the partial septum and the position of the openings of the arteries into the ventricle keep this mixture to a minimum. The opening of the right systemic arch occurs somewhat toward the left side of the ventricle, and the openings of the left systemic arch and the pulmonary arteries are somewhat toward the right side of the ventricle. The structure of the heart and the position of the openings of the arteries cause the right arch to receive relatively pure blood, and this passes to the brain by way of the brachiocephalic and carotid arteries.   The pulmonary arteries passing to the lungs receive relatively unaerated blood from the heart, while the left systemic arch carries somewhat of a mixture.   Since the two systemic arches combine to form the dorsal aorta, this vessel and its branches likewise contain mixed blood.   It is thought probable that, in those reptiles which have a relatively complete ventricular septum, practically no mixture of blood takes place in the heart itself but that the mixture of necessity occurs when the two systemic arches combine to form the dorsal aorta.   The system that occurs in the turtle and other reptiles, which prevents the mixture of pure and impure blood to some extent, definitely anticipates the condition that is carried to completion in birds and mammals. The combination of the two systemic arches to form the dorsal aortá mentioned above will be seen presently.

The Brachiocephalic Artery and Its Branches.   The **brachiocephalic artery** is the large vessel which arises from the base of the right systemic arch and sends branches toward the head. Again, turn the ventricle over to the left, and note the origin of this vessel.   Near the base of the brachiocephalic artery, small **coronary arteries** originate, then pass to the walls of the heart.   Pick away the tissue surrounding the main trunk and its branches.   It will probably be necessary to disconnect the thyroid gland from the arterial branches on one side, since it somewhat obscures vessels that are dorsal to it.   When the connective tissue has been cleared away, it will be noted that the main brachiocephalic trunk splits into four branches near the thyroid gland.   The **right** and **left subclavian arteries** are the larger lateral branches, and the **right** and **left common carotid arteries** are the more medial smaller branches.   In some species or individual specimens the carotids may arise from the subclavians.   First trace one of the subclavians, preferably the left subclavian, but preserve as many of the veins in this region as possible.   A small **thyroid artery** is given off to the thyroid gland shortly after the origin of the subclavian.   As the subclavian passes forward, several small branches are usually given off and pass to the surrounding tissue, but these need not be identified.

Near the point where the trachea divides into the two bronchi, a large artery arises from the subclavian and passes forward into the neck parallel to the trachea.   This is the **ventral cervical artery.**   Follow it anteriorly, and note that it sends small branches into the trachea, esophagus, and other structures in the neck. It also supplies the **thymus gland,** a yellowish body located in the neck. In some injected specimens, this gland may have been partly destroyed. Distal to the origin of the ventral cervical artery, the subclavian is called the **axillary artery.** This vessel passes laterally and gives off a large **suprascapular artery,** which almost immediately divides into branches that pass into the shoulder. Near the origin of the suprascapular, the axillary makes a loop, turns posteriorly and dorsally, and may eventually turn again somewhat anteriorly. It eventually gives off three large branches. The **dorsal cervical** is the most anterior branch; it passes anteriorly into the neck. The **vertebral artery** is the middle branch; it runs posteriorly and dorsally to the vertebral column. The third branch, the **brachial,** is really the continuation of the axillary artery. It turns at this point abruptly laterally and proceeds on into the front limb. Near the place where the axillary artery splits into the above three branches, a fourth branch, the **marginocostal,** also arises, but this does not show up well in some specimens. It passes laterally and posteriorly from its point of origin.

The common carotid arteries pass anteriorly along the sides of the neck. Try to locate a vein in close contact with the carotid in the anterior region. This is the internal jugular vein, which sometimes shows up better here than it does posteriorly. The vagus nerve, previously located near the internal jugular vein, is also closely associated with these vessels and should be observed again. It appears as a yellowish or whitish strand. As the common carotid artery is traced forward, the conspicuous **hyoid apparatus** will probably be seen on the ventral surface of the neck near the region where the skull attaches to the vertebral column. This structure consists of a body from which four winglike horns project posteriorly. It functions in the support of the larynx, or voice box, and has probably been derived from some of the posterior gill arches that occur in lower vertebrates. Near the ventral surface of the base of the skull, the common carotid divides into a lateral **external carotid** passing to the side of the head and a medial **internal carotid** entering the skull and supplying the brain (see drawing directions 3, page 124).

The Systemic Arches and Associated Vessels. Return now to the heart, and locate again the right and left systemic arches as they leave the ventricle. Observe that both pass anteriorly, then loop dorsally, and finally turn posteriorly. As the right arch has only one major branch, the brachiocephalic, it need not be traced farther. Trace the left systemic arch, which passes laterally and dorsal to the stomach. Disconnect the stomach from the mesentery (**mesogaster**) that binds it to the dorsal body wall, and push it over to the right. At this point, the actual entrance of the left bronchus, left pulmonary artery, and left pulmonary vein into the left **lung** should be noted. The lung is the saclike structure into which these branches open and, in well-injected specimens, usually has a reddish appearance. The left pulmonary vein is in close association with the bronchus and the artery. It should be observed that all except the posterior end of the lung occurs between the peritoneum and the carapace, being separated from the pleuroperitoneal cavity by the peritoneum. Only the posterior end can be said to occur within the cavity. This condition somewhat anticipates the complete separation of the pleuroperitoneal cavity into pleural and peritoneal cavities, which occurs in birds and mammals.

Some distance posterior to the point of entrance into the lung of the above-named structures, three large arteries arise from the left systemic arch. There is some variation in the way these branches arise, and they can be best identified by noting the organs that each supplies. The **gastric artery** passes to the stomach and liberally supplies this organ with branches. It normally passes posteriorly along this organ toward the duodenum. The **coeliac artery** supplies the duodenum, pancreas, posterior part of the stomach, and associated structures. After its origin from the systemic arch, it divides into two large branches; this division may take place almost immediately. The **superior mesenteric artery** is usually the largest of the three arteries that arise from the left systemic arch; it passes posteriorly into the mesentery of the intestine, where it breaks up into branches that supply the walls of this organ. During the study of these arterial branches, the student should also look for venous branches that represent vessels of the hepatic portal system. At the point where the left systemic arch gives rise to the superior mesenteric artery, it becomes abruptly smaller and passes medially a short distance, where it combines with the right systemic arch in the middorsal line to form the large **dorsal aorta** (see drawing directions 3, page 124).

The aortic arches of the turtle will now be compared with comparable vessels in Necturus. It will be recalled that in the latter animal a ventral aorta extends anteriorly from the ventricle and divides into three afferent branchial arteries, which pass into the gills. Three efferent branchial arteries carry the blood from the gills to the radices aortae and thence to the dorsal aorta. These afferent branchial and efferent branchial arteries in Necturus represent aortic arches 3, 4, and 6. In both Necturus and the turtle, six aortic arches are present in the embryo, but 1, 2, and 5 are completely absent in the adult of both animals. In the embryo of the turtle, a ventral aorta, as well as the six aortic arches, is present, but the ventral aorta does not occur in the adult. The ventral aorta divides into three parts, the pulmonary artery and the right and left systemic arches. These vessels, as indicated previously, open independently into the ventricle. This same splitting occurs in the conus arteriosus. A somewhat intermediate condition between Necturus and the turtle is present in tailless amphibians. In these animals, the systemic arches, the carotids, and the pulmonary arteries all arise from a common opening into the ventricle. In the turtle, there is only a single complete pair of aortic arches in the adult, in contrast to the three pairs in Necturus. These are the systemic arches, which combine dorsally to form the dorsal aorta. The systemic arches are derived from aortic arch 4. As in other animals where these vessels are present, the carotids are derived from aortic arch 3 and the dorsal and ventral aortas, while the pulmonary artery originates from aortic arch 6. Additional changes in the condition of the aortic arches and associated vessels occur in mammals and birds.

Study now some of the posterior branches of the dorsal aorta. First cut off the remaining projection of the pelvic girdle, half of which has already been removed. Look between the kidneys, and observe the **renal arteries** to the kidneys and the **genital arteries** to the reproductive glands. Posterior to the kidneys the dorsal aorta gives off paired branches; it will therefore be necessary to study only one vessel on one side. It would be best to make the study on the side opposite that which was used for the venous branches in the leg, so that the veins may be saved for review. It will be seen that the posterior end of the large intestine and the urogenital organs, especially in the male, are bound together by mesenteries. These should be separated so that it is possible to push the intestine over to the side, and the urogenital organs against the dorsal body wall. Posterior to the kidneys, a large artery is given off from the dorsal aorta on each side. This vessel is the **epigastric artery,** which passes laterally toward the carapace. Branches of this vessel have already been seen in association with the external iliac and ventral abdominal veins. Near the point where the femoral vein joins the external iliac to form the ventral abdominal vein, the epigastric artery divides into several branches, usually about three. A small posterior branch passes into the leg in company with the femoral vein. Another branch passes laterally and anteriorly toward the carapace, somewhat parallel to a small vein (epigastric) from the ventral abdominal vein. The third branch from the epigastric artery passes ventrally and then turns anteriorly in intimate association with the ventral abdominal vein. The anterior end of this branch occurs on the pelvic girdle parallel to the pelvic vein, but has probably been destroyed by this time.

Follow the dorsal aorta posterior to the origin of the epigastric artery. It soon divides into two large trunks, the **common iliac arteries.** A short distance posterior to this point, each common iliac divides into **external** and **internal iliac arteries.** The internal iliac artery runs somewhat ventrally and anteriorly toward the bladder and the large intestine and supplies blood to these organs and other structures in this region. The external iliac artery continues on into the hind leg.

Drawing 3. The Main Arteries—Ventral View. Make outline of the body as was done for the venous system. Draw in the chambers of the heart and the kidneys, but do not include other organs. After a section is completed, draw in the vessels before starting the next study. The instructor may prefer to divide this drawing into two parts because of the large number of labels involved. **Labels:** sinus venosus, ventricle, right auricle, left auricle. Arteries—pulmonary, left systemic arch, right systemic arch, brachiocephalic, coronary, subclavian, common carotid, thyroid, ventral cervical, axillary, suprascapular; if axillary is traced farther, add dorsal cervical, vertebral, brachial; dorsal aorta, gastric, coeliac, superior mesenteric, renal, epigastric, common iliac, external iliac, internal iliac.

THE UROGENITAL SYSTEM

The study of the urogenital system will probably destroy many blood vessels in the posterior region. Hence, the instructor may prefer to give a test or to hear recitations on the circulatory system before this work is started.

Select the side for study on which the urogenital structures are more nearly complete, and remove additional pieces of the pelvic girdle on that side. Cut posteriorly through the center of the girdle in the mid-ventral line; then cut through the base of the leg to be studied 1 inch or so lateral to the previous cut. The large leg bone, the **femur,** will soon be encountered in making the latter cut. It is easier to cut with bone scissors, but with patience a scalpel or large dissecting scissors will serve.

When the bone is severed, about 1 square inch of pelvic girdle and surrounding tissue will be loosened, except for an attachment to the vertebral column. Disconnect this section from all attachments to structures in the abdominal cavity. Then, with the left thumb, lift up the section somewhat, while at the same time working a scalpel under the edge. A bony attachment to the vertebral column will soon be encountered. This attachment should be cut and the section removed.

Both male and female systems should be studied. The kidney of the turtle is of the **metanephric** type, in contrast to the mesonephric kidney of the other animals that have been studied.

The Male. Identify again the **testes,** the round yellowish bodies ventral to the kidneys. The study should be made especially on the side from which the section of the pelvic girdle has been removed. Posterior to the testis on this side will be seen a tightly coiled tube that is attached to the testis by a mesentery. This coiled tube is the **epididymis.** Passing from the testes through the mesentery into the epididymis are a number of small tubules, the **vasa efferentia.** These tubules are difficult to see, but if the mesentery is held between the eye and the light they are usually evident. Posterior to the tightly coiled epididymis, a comparatively straight tube, the **vas deferens,** becomes continuous with it and passes posteriorly. Carefully pick away the material between the vas deferens and the intestine, and observe that the vas deferens passes into a chamber at the posterior end of the intestine. This is the **cloaca.**

The ureter, or **metanephric duct** from the kidney, is obscured by the coils of the epididymis. Carefully separate the epididymis from the ventral surface of the kidney. This will reveal a large vein along the ventral kidney surface, the renal portal vein. Some of its branches may also be observed. The ureter is parallel to this vein and may sometimes be covered by it. If the ureter is not seen at once on one side or the other of the vein, the vein should be removed, and the tube located dorsal to the vein. Trace the metanephric duct posteriorly, and note that it enters the cloaca near the opening of the vas deferens.

Posterior to the kidney and also attached to the cloaca (one on each side) are **accessory bladders** that have probably been seen before. Observe again the **urinary bladder** attached to the ventral cloacal wall. The accessory bladders may vary considerably. They may be small rounded thick-walled structures or, if distended with liquid, may be much larger and thin-walled. The accessory bladders open into the cloaca posterior to the opening of the urinary bladder. The exact function of the accessory bladders is not known, but in some marine turtles they are thought to be used as accessory respiratory organs.

Now carefully remove the remaining part of the pelvic girdle from the opposite side. Pick away the obscuring tissue and muscles so that the cloaca can be seen. Within the cloaca may now be observed a large dark-colored structure, the **penis,** or copulatory organ. The wall of the cloaca is quite thin in the ventral region and may be accidentally removed while exposing this region. If this thin wall has not already been removed, take it out now, so that the penis will be fully exposed. Disconnect the cloacal wall from one side, and turn the penis so that its dorsal surface can be seen. On the dorsal side there occurs a deep groove, the **urethral groove,** through which sperm pass to the body of the female during copulation. Each division of the penis on each side of this groove is called a **cavernous body.** Turn back to the ventral surface, and cut longitudinally through the penis in the mid-ventral line. Then spread the two halves, and observe the cloaca, which will be revealed dorsal to the penis. Note also that the cavernous bodies are quite spongy in nature and contain numerous open spaces. This type of structure allows for the accumulation of blood during the copulatory act, which causes the penis to remain rigid. If material is present in the cloaca, it should be washed out.

Just dorsal to the base of the penis there occurs a large opening, the **anus.** This is the posterior opening of the digestive tract, which in these animals opens into the cloaca. In some vertebrates, the anus opens directly to the outside, and thus no cloaca is present. Pass a probe through the anus, and note that the probe emerges through the previously cut end of the intestine into the abdominal cavity. Just ventral to the anus is the large opening of the urinary bladder. In its walls occur the openings of the ureters and of the vasa deferentia. Enlarge this opening so that its walls can be examined. Look for a small projection on each side, from which the vasa deferentia open. The ureters open somewhat medial to these papillae, but the openings are difficult to find. The most posterior openings into the cloaca are those of the accessory bladders. The cloaca opens to the outside by way of the **cloacal opening** under the base of the tail, which has been previously observed (see drawing directions 4, page 128).

The Female. The **ovaries** have already been seen as irregular-shaped bodies ventral to the kidneys. If they are very large, one of them has probably been removed. The **oviducts,** or Müllerian ducts, have also been observed, and possibly one of them has been removed. Study these structures on the intact side, and remove a portion of the pelvic girdle as directed for the male. Trace one of the coiled whitish oviducts anteriorly, and at its anterior end locate an opening, the **ostium,** by which the eggs enter the oviducts to pass to the outside. Posteriorly the oviducts open into the cloaca.

Carefully uncover the **cloaca,** the common chamber into which open the digestive and urogenital systems. This region appears to be the posterior end of the intestine. Identify again the **urinary bladder** attached to the anterior end of the cloaca, and note that the two oviducts also join the cloaca in this region, one on each side of the bladder. Posterior to the attachments of the bladder and the oviducts are two **accessory bladders,** one on each side, that may have been seen previously. Their size depends upon whether or not they are distended with liquid. Turn back now to the kidney on the side from which the ovary has been removed. Expose the ventral kidney surface, and locate a large vein on it. This is the renal portal vein, which may be seen to branch in this region. As is true of the male, the **metanephric duct,** or ureter, occurs parallel to this vein and may sometimes be dorsal to it. Look on each side of this vein; if the small tube is not found, remove the vein, and look dorsal to it. Trace the metanephric duct toward the cloaca, and observe that it opens into this structure somewhat dorsal to the entrance of the oviducts. Examine the posterior portion of the cloaca, and find a dark spot on its ventral surface, which is inside the cloaca but which can be seen through the cloacal wall. This dark spot is the **clitoris,** which is simply a thickened region of the cloacal wall. It is homologous to the penis of the male but, so far as is known, has no function in the female turtle.

Now make a longitudinal slit through the ventral cloacal wall from the entrance of the oviducts posteriorly to the clitoris, spread the two portions, and locate the openings mentioned below. Wash out any material that may be present. Somewhat anterior and dorsal to the entrance of the oviducts is a large opening, the **anus,** the posterior opening of the digestive tract. Push a probe into it, and observe that it emerges into the abdominal cavity from the intestine that was previously cut. Locate the openings of the oviducts somewhat posterior and ventral to the anus. These openings occur on little projections, or papillae. The openings of the metanephric ducts are somewhat difficult to find. They occur somewhat in front of the oviductal openings. Find where the urinary bladder and the accessory bladders enter the cloaca. These are the most posterior openings that occur in the cloaca. Material from the cloaca passes to the outside through the **cloacal opening,** which has previously been seen on the ventral surface of the base of the tail.

Drawing 4. Urogenital System—Ventral View. In the male, draw penis to one side so as to show structures underneath. In both sexes, dot in the accessory bladder on one side, and in female draw ovary and oviduct on one side only, unless the structures are very small. Draw only the system of your specimen, but study the systems of both sexes. Indicate whether male or female. **Labels:** Male—kidney, testis, epididymis, vas efferens (sketch in, if not seen), vas deferens, metanephric duct, accessory bladder, urinary bladder, penis, cloaca, cloacal opening. Female—kidney, ovary, oviduct, ostium, metanephric duct, urinary bladder, accessory bladder, cloaca, cloacal opening.

The urogenital system of the turtle will now be briefly compared with the systems of the animals previously studied. It has been indicated before that in the vertebrate series there are present three types of kidney: the pronephric, the mesonephric, and the metanephric. The pronephric kidney is characteristic of the embryos of most vertebrates and the adults of a few cyclostomes. The mesonephric kidney is found in the embryos of higher vertebrates and the adults of some cyclostomes, fish, and Amphibia. The metanephric kidney is present only in the adults of reptiles, birds, and mammals. The turtle, therefore, is the first animal studied in this manual to have a metanephric kidney.

In animals having a metanephric kidney the first two types of kidney occur in sequence in the embryo. Certain parts of these embryonic kidneys are utilized by the urogenital system of the adult reptile, bird, or mammal, while the other portions degenerate.   The portion that is most persistent is the original pro-nephric duct.   It forms first in connection with the pronephric kidney in the embryo.   When most of the pronephros degen-erates, the duct is then partly taken over by the mesonephric kidney and functions as the mesonephric duct.   In the male of reptiles, birds, and mammals, the vasa deferentia are derived from the embryonic mesonephric ducts, which thus become wholly reproductive in function.   These ducts degenerate in the female of these animals or may remain as nonfunctional remnants. The epididymis (sometimes considered to be the anterior end of the vas deferens) comes from a portion of the embryonic meso-nephric kidney.   The metanephric duct, which in the turtle is wholly excretory in both male and female, is mostly a new tube, except that in its embryonic origin it arises from the posterior end of the embryonic mesonephric duct.

THE NERVOUS SYSTEM

Only a portion of the nervous system will be studied, although the additional parts of the system will be briefly discussed.

The Brain.   Although the skull of the turtle is quite hard, the bones are relatively thin, and the removal of the dorsal surface of the skull is surprisingly easy if sufficient care is exer-cised.   Remove the skin and muscles from the top and sides of the head and the dorsal anterior portion of the neck.   It soon becomes evident that the skull possesses a striking posterior projection, the spaces on each side of which are filled with muscles.   This projection is the **occipital process,** formed by the **supraoccipital bone.**   This bone is not present as a distinct unit in the adult mammalian skull but forms part of the occipital bone.

Carefully shave and chip away the dorsal surface of the skull. If the thumb is placed against the skull and the fingers of the same hand are used to pull the scalpel across the skull toward the thumb, the force of the cutting strokes can easily be con-trolled.   In making the dissection, great care should be exercised to avoid getting the chips of bone in the eyes.

In injected specimens, blood vessels associated with the brain will soon appear, so that one can see when he approaches the dorsal brain surface.   When the dorsal surface of the brain is exposed, it will be noted that it is covered by a membrane, the **dura mater,** which somewhat obscures the contours of the brain.

This membrane is quite tough, and great care should be exercised in its removal. It is helpful to moisten the membrane somewhat if it has become dry during the dissection. When this membrane is removed, the chances are that some blood vessels will stick to it. The blood vessels will represent a chorioid plexus from the roof of the diencephalon. Look on the undersurface of the dura mater after it has been removed, and see if you can find a small bit of tissue adhering to the surface, partly surrounded by the blood vessels. This bit of tissue represents an outgrowth from the roof of the diencephalon and is the **epiphysis,** or pineal body. It is sometimes difficult to identify with certainty. In higher vertebrates, this structure is considered to belong to the endocrine system, although its definite function has not been established.

After the removal of the dura mater, the dorsal brain surface is still covered by a delicate membrane, the **pia mater,** which is sometimes difficult to distinguish from the wall of the brain itself. The pia mater of reptiles should probably not be considered as being entirely homologous to the pia mater of mammals, since in the latter group there are two membranes closely associated with the brain. These are the pia mater and the arachnoid, both of which have probably been derived from the pia mater as found in reptiles These membranes in reptiles, derived from the primitive meninx of lower forms, are considerably more distinct than in the mammals.

Identify the parts of the brain, beginning at the anterior end. A pair of **olfactory lobes** are separated by a groove from a posterior, much larger pair of **cerebral hemispheres.** Note that even in the turtle the cerebral hemispheres constitute by far the largest part of the brain, somewhat anticipating, so to speak, the continued enlargement of this region in mammals. Posterior to and somewhat enclosed by the posterior ends of the cerebral hemispheres is the **diencephalon,** probably represented by a concavity if the roof has been removed. This concavity is the **third ventricle** of the brain. Two **optic lobes,** the dorsal portions of the mesencephalon, occur just posterior to the diencephalon and the cerebral hemispheres. The single **cerebellum** is behind the optic lobes. Note that this region is larger than the cerebellum of Necturus. The **medulla oblongata** is the most posterior part of the brain and occurs behind and somewhat ventral to the cerebellum. A chorioid plexus occurs in the roof of the medulla, and a hollow space under the roof represents the **fourth ventricle** of the brain. Posterior to the medulla is the **spinal**

cord, although it is not possible definitely to delimit these two structures.

Drawing 5. The Brain—Dorsal View. Make drawing about 4 inches in length. **Labels :** olfactory lobe, cerebral hemispheres, diencephalon, third ventricle, optic lobe, medulla oblongata, fourth ventricle, cerebellum.

Although the brain is the only portion of the nervous system that will be studied in the turtle, a few words should be added regarding other parts. There are twelve pairs of cranial nerves, as opposed to the ten pairs found in the dogfish and Necturus. They are quite small and usually hard to identify in such a small specimen. One of these additional nerves, the spinal accessory (XI), is connected to the vagus (X) but becomes an independent nerve in mammals. The twelfth nerve, the hypoglossal, is probably derived from a spinal nerve of lower forms that has become incorporated within the skull in reptiles. The first ten cranial nerves are essentially the same as in the dogfish and Necturus. The presence of twelve cranial nerves is also characteristic of birds and mammals.

Spinal nerves also occur, originating from the spinal cord and passing to various parts of the body. Some of the anterior nerves combine to form the brachial plexus opposite the front limb, while the lumbosacral plexus is formed opposite the hind limb by a combination of some of the posterior nerves. Nerves from these plexuses pass into the limbs.

The **autonomic nervous system** consists of a pair of small longitudinal ganglionated nerve cords passing posteriorly, one on each side of the spinal column, and connected at intervals with the spinal nerves. Branches from this system innervate various visceral organs. An autonomic system is also present in the dogfish and Necturus but is not well developed. Even in the turtle, the fibers are sometimes difficult to find.

The respiratory system of the turtle is of special interest, since this is the first animal to be studied here that does not depend at least partly upon the water for oxygen. Although most turtles are somewhat aquatic, they must obtain their oxygen from the air and must return to the land to deposit their eggs. It should be remembered that the skin of Necturus and other amphibians is somewhat pervious to water, and some respiration is thus carried on through the skin. These animals must also keep moist to a certain extent, since otherwise the body moisture will pass to the outside and the animals will die. The skin of the turtle and other reptiles is impervious to water. Body fluids will therefore not evaporate through the skin, and hence the animals are not necessarily bound to a moist environment. The turtle depends on the lungs for obtaining oxygen, since no respiration can take place through the skin, and, as was noted, the lungs are considerably better developed than are those of Necturus.

CHAPTER VII

THE CAT

Phylum—Chordata
Subphylum—Vertebrata
Class—Mammalia
Order—Carnivora
Genus—Felis

The members of the class Mammalia are in many respects the most specialized of vertebrate animals and in many systems exhibit distinct advancements over the condition of lower forms. Cats are usually relatively easy to obtain in quantity and are thus studied most frequently as representative of this class. Considering all the factors involved, the cat is probably the most satisfactory example of the class that could be obtained for a course of this kind.

In making a detailed study of the cat over a long period of time, it is almost imperative that two cats be available for each student or for each pair of students.   It is believed that it would even be better for more than two students to work on a specimen than to attempt to work out all the systems on a single specimen. It is suggested that the muscular system, internal organs, and urogenital system be studied in one specimen, and that the second animal be used for the rest of the work.   Embalmed cats are far superior to other types of specimens; if at all possible, they should be used.   The specimen used for the exercises on the muscular, digestive, and urogenital systems need not be injected, but the arteries should be injected in the animal used for the circulatory system.   If only a single cat is available for a study of all systems, the circulatory system should be studied just after the work on the general identification of the internal organs.   The exercises on the skeleton should be completed first, since this is essential to a complete understanding of the muscles and their functions.

THE SKELETAL SYSTEM

The skeleton of mammals is almost completely ossified.   In vertebrate animals there is a series in the development of the

133

skeleton, from the completely cartilaginous skeleton in the Chondrichthyes to the skeleton composed almost entirely of bone in the higher forms. Bony elements gradually replace the cartilage until the majority of the skeleton is of true bone. In some respects, the skeleton of mammals is considerably simplified as compared with the skeleton of lower forms. This is brought about by a dropping out and fusing of bones and is to be especially noted in the skull. Even in mammals, the skeleton is cartilaginous in the embryo but is gradually replaced by the bony elements of the adult.

The **notochord** passes through a number of changes both evolutionary and embryological. It is a complete structure, as was seen in Amphioxus and the lamprey, and in the adults of these animals it furnishes the chief support for the body. In the dogfish, the notochord is still persistent but is partly replaced by the vertebrae. In vertebrates above the Chondrichthyes fish, the notochord forms in the embryo but is then gradually replaced by the vertebrae, so that, in most of the higher forms, none of the notochord persists, or only remnants of it are present. In the skeleton of the adult cat, there is nothing that can be definitely identified as any portion of the notochord, although this structure occurs in the embryo.

The vertebrate skeleton consists of three divisions: the **axial** skeleton, including the skull, the vertebral column, the notochord, and other associated structures such as the ribs and sternum if present; the **appendicular** skeleton, consisting of the pectoral and pelvic girdles and the bones of the limbs; and the **visceral** skeleton, composed of the branchial, or gill, arches and their derivatives in higher species. In fish, the elements of the latter division are concerned primarily with the formation of the jaws and with support for the gills. In land-dwelling vertebrates, which have lost the gills, these arches lose their former importance as gill supports. In mammals, the remnants of the visceral skeleton have helped primarily in the formation of the middle ear bones, the hyoid apparatus, and cartilages associated with the larynx and the trachea. The visceral skeleton will not be studied in detail in the cat, but parts of it will be noted from time to time.

There are several terms that will often be used and that should therefore be learned before a study is made of the skeleton. A **foramen** (plural, foramina) is a hole through a bone or between bones for the passage of nerves and blood vessels. Foramina are present in many parts of the skeleton but are more numerous in the skull. A **fossa** (plural, fossae) is an impression or indentation upon a bone, usually for muscle attachment. A **process** is a projection of bone from a larger bone.

A prepared and mounted skeleton is most satisfactory for the study of the skeletal system.

The Axial Skeleton. In the cat, the axial skeleton consists of the vertebral column, the skull, the ribs and sternum, and the notochord, which is present only in the embryo. Because of the complexity of the skull, it is suggested that it be studied separately. For this reason, although it is a part of the axial division of the skeletal system, the skull is discussed after the material on the complete skeleton has been presented. The vertebral column will be studied first. In the cat, there are several types of vertebrae. From anterior to posterior, these are the **cervical,** or neck, **vertebrae;** the **thoracic vertebrae;** the **lumbar vertebrae;** the **sacral vertebrae;** and the **caudal,** or tail, **vertebrae.**

Before the individual vertebrae are studied, certain general parts of a vertebra should be mentioned. Many of the vertebrae are modified and so will not have all the parts to be named, although one type or another will possess most of them. The large hole that passes through the vertebrae is the passage for the spinal cord. This in an individual vertebra is the **vertebral foramen.** The canal formed by all the foramina is sometimes called the **neural canal.** Ventral to the vertebral foramen is usually a thickened region called the **centrum.** This region replaces the notochord or surrounds it in those animals in which a portion of the notochord is still present. Dorsal to the vertebral foramen is an arch of bone, the **neural arch;** a **neural spine** may project dorsally from it. The vertebrae articulate with each other by processes called **zygapophyses.** Those on the anterior face of the vertebrae are the **prezygapophyses** while those on the posterior end are the **postzygapophyses.** In some animals, in the tail region there occurs an arch ventral to the centrum, the **hemal arch,** which encloses blood vessels. This was seen in the dogfish, and possible remnants of this arch occur in the caudal vertebrae of the cat.

The Cervical Vertebrae. There are seven cervical, or neck, vertebrae in the cat, and this is the number present in all except a few mammals. The first two are more modified than are the others and are called the **atlas** (anterior) and the **axis.** The atlas articulates with the skull, and its modifications are doubtless correlated with this fact. In skeletons that have been studied for a number of years, these two vertebrae may have become detached from the anterior end of the vertebral column.

Study the atlas first. It is a flattened vertebra with a projecting **transverse process** on each side. In normal position, these processes are lateral. If the atlas is detached, it should be arranged normally. The *anterior* end of the vertebral foramen is the larger, and the two holes that are present within it should be *dorsal*. The first spinal nerves, the vertebral arteries, and the vertebral veins pass through these holes in the atlas.

Above the vertebral foramen is the neural arch containing the two holes mentioned above. On each side is a transverse process, the base of which is penetrated by a hole. This hole is the **vertebrarterial canal,** or transverse foramen, through which pass the vertebral artery and the vertebral vein. These transverse processes are probably rudimentary ribs. The constitution of the ventral border of the vertebral foramen is not agreed upon by all workers. It may represent a portion of the centrum of the atlas, but most of the centrum of this vertebra has become fused to the axis and will be identified later.

Drawing 1.   The Atlas—Anterior View.   In skeletons in which the atlas is attached, this is the only drawing that can profitably be made. If the atlas is detached, a posterior drawing may also be made. **Labels:** transverse process, neural arch, vertebral foramen, vertebrarterial canal.

The axis, the second cervical vertebra, may likewise be disconnected in some specimens. If so, orient it correctly. On one side of this vertebra is a bladelike neural spine. This portion should be dorsal, while the larger end of the spine should be anterior, which causes it somewhat to overhang the atlas. The neural spine is the dorsal extension of the neural arch. Just below the posterior point of the neural spine, but still on the neural arch, are two projections by which the axis articulates with the next posterior vertebra. These projections are **postzygapophyses.**   If atlas and axis are joined in correct position, look into the ventral portion of the atlas and observe a small projection, the anterior extension of the axis. This is the **odontoid process,** and embryological studies have revealed that it represents the centrum of the atlas, which has become secondarily fused with the axis. This process is fused with the anterior end of the true centrum of the axis. If the atlas is not articulated with the axis, the odontoid process forms a conspicuous anterior projection from the ventral portion of the axis. From the lateral surface, the centrum of the axis is represented by the region somewhat lateral and ventral to the vertebral foramen. From the posterior part of the centrum there project small **transverse processes,** through the base of which is a hole, the **vertebrarterial canal.** These transverse processes are also probably rudimentary ribs.

Drawing 2. The Axis—Lateral View. Make drawing from the side. **Labels:** neural spine, postzygapophysis, odontoid process, centrum of axis, transverse process.

The last five cervical vertebrae are quite similar to one another. They have vertebral foramina, centrums, neural arches, neural spines, prezygapophyses, postzygapophyses, transverse processes (rudimentary ribs), and vertebrarterial canals. Identify these structures on each of the vertebrae.

Drawing 3. Representative Cervical Vertebra—Anterior View. If the vertebral column is not disarticulated, this drawing must of necessity be somewhat diagrammatical and should be so labeled. Indicate which vertebra is involved. **Labels:** vertebral foramen, centrum, neural arch, neural spine, prezygapophysis, postzygapophysis, transverse process, vertebrarterial canal.

The Thoracic Vertebrae. There are 13 thoracic vertebrae, to each of which is attached a pair of **ribs.** The first 10 thoracic vertebrae are quite similar. They possess elongate neural spines directed posteriorly and arising from neural arches. Both prezygapophyses and postzygapophyses are present. The prezygapophyses occur on the anterior dorsal surface of the neural arch, while the postzygapophyses are on the posterior surface of the neural spine near the base. Transverse processes occur that articulate with the ribs, although it is probable that these transverse processes are not homologous to those of the cervical vertebrae. They are not considered to be rudimentary ribs. Centrums are also present in these vertebrae.

Drawing 4. Thoracic Vertebra—Lateral View. Draw one of the first 10 thoracic vertebrae, and indicate which one is selected. **Labels:** neural spine, prezygapophysis, postzygapophysis, transverse process, centrum.

The eleventh, twelfth, and thirteenth thoracic vertebrae differ somewhat from the anterior 10. The neural spines are directed anteriorly and are somewhat shorter; a true transverse process is not present, but dorsal to the rib attachment are two projections.   The anteriorly directed projection arises from the prezygapophysis and is the **mamillary process,** while the posteriorly directed process is the **accessory process.**

Consider now the ribs and their attachments to the thoracic vertebrae.   The attachments to the first 10 vertebrae are similar. Each rib articulates at two points, with the transverse process and with the centrum.   The articulating surface on the transverse process is called a **costal facet,** while the raised portion of the rib that articulates on it is the **tuberculum** of the rib.   The end of the rib attaches between the posterior end of the centrum of one vertebrae and the anterior end of the centrum posterior to it.   The end of the rib that attaches between the centrums is called the **capitulum,** while each surface on the centrums to which the capitulum articulates is a **demifacet.**   Since the last three thoracic vertebrae have no transverse processes, the ribs articulate only with the centrums.   The tubercula are thus greatly reduced or absent in the last three ribs.

The Ribs.   There are three general types of ribs in the cat, classified according to the method of attachment to the sternum. The first nine ribs are attached independently to the sternum and are thus called **true ribs.**   The last four do not join the sternum independently; the ends of the tenth, eleventh, and twelfth are usually attached to each other before joining the sternum.   These ribs are **false ribs.**   The last false rib is a **floating rib,** since its ventral end is free and not attached to the sternum or to other ribs.

Study one of the ribs.   As indicated above, the end of the rib that articulates with the centrums of the vertebrae is the head, or capitulum, while the tubercle that articulates with the transverse process is the tuberculum.   Between the capitulum and the tuberculum is a small somewhat constricted area called the **neck.**   That portion of the rib from the tuberculum to the cartilaginous attachment to the sternum is the **shaft,** while the region of the shaft that possesses the greatest curvature is the **angle.**   The cartilaginous part of the rib attached to the sternum is the **costal cartilage.**   Costal cartilages also occur on the false ribs.

Drawing 5.   Rib—Anterior View.   Make drawing of one of the first nine ribs, and indicate which one is selected.   Include the costal cartilage.   **Labels:** tuberculum, capitulum, neck, angle, shaft, costal cartilage.

Ribs first appear in fish, but neither these animals nor the

Amphibia have well-developed ribs. Ribs are connected to the sternum for the first time in some reptiles, forming a complete thoracic basket. As was mentioned in Chap. VI, The Turtle, this animal possesses skeletal modifications correlated with the shell. The ribs in the turtle are fused to the carapace, a sternum is not present, and a complete thoracic basket does not occur.

The Sternum. The sternum is the bony jointed structure to which are attached the ventral portions of the ribs. It will be noted that it is composed of eight divisions called **sternebrae.** The first sternebra, to which the first pair of ribs attaches, is the **manubrium.** The most posterior sternebra is the **xiphisternum,** from which extends a posterior piece of cartilage, the **xiphoid,** or ensiform, **cartilage.** The latter projection is frequently broken off in old skeletons. A drawing of the sternum is not required unless the instructor states that one is to be made.

The sternum first appears in the tailless Amphibia and is present in most reptiles. As indicated previously, it is absent in the turtle, and this is doubtless correlated with the presence of the shell.

The Lumbar Vertebrae. There are seven lumbar vertebrae in the cat. They occur between the thoracic vertebrae and the fused region of the vertebral column (sacrum), to which the pelvic girdle is attached. Each possesses the following structures: neural spine (directed anteriorly), neural arch, vertebral foramen, mammillary processes, accessory processes (except on the seventh and sometimes the sixth), prezygapophyses, postzygapophyses, centrum, and prominent transverse processes directed anteriorly. The transverse processes may be partly composed of rudimentary ribs. Identify these structures on the vertebrae.

Drawing 6. Lumbar Vertebra—Anterior View. Unless spinal column is disarticulated, drawing will be somewhat diagrammatical and should be so labeled. Draw one of the first five vertebrae, and indicate which one is used. **Labels :** neural spine, neural arch, vertebral foramen, mammillary process, accessory process, prezygapophysis, postzygapophysis, centrum, transverse process.

The Sacral Vertebrae. The three sacral vertebrae are fused intimately into a single structure called the **sacrum.** This fusion is doubtless correlated with the fact that the pelvic girdle attaches to the vertebral column at this point. These vertebrae are separate in the embryo. Note the three pairs of **sacral foramina** on the dorsal surface of the sacrum for the passage of spinal nerves. There are also two pairs on the ventral surface. A drawing of the sacrum is not required.

The Caudal Vertebrae. The caudal vertebrae vary in number and structure. In most common cats, the number is 21 to 23, but there may be more or less than this number. In the Manx cat, the number is reduced, there usually being only 3 or 4 present.

In old skeletons, the end vertebrae are frequently missing. Near the base of the tail, most structures are present on the caudal vertebrae—neural arch, transverse processes, prezygapophyses, postzygapophyses, vertebral foramen, and centrum. In addition, on the anterior ventral surface of some of the vertebrae, there is a small anteriorly directed arch of bone. This arch is formed by two so-called "chevron bones" and may represent a hemal arch such as is found in some lower vertebrates. The chevron bones are frequently absent in mounted specimens. The structures mentioned above become smaller posteriorly and eventually disappear, so that the most posterior caudal vertebrae are composed almost entirely of the centrum, or body, of the vertebrae. Drawings of the caudal vertebrae are not required.

Look at the vertebral column as a whole, and note definite openings occurring between the vertebrae. These are the **intervertebral foramina** for the passage of the spinal nerves.

The Appendicular Skeleton. As was indicated above, the appendicular skeleton consists of the bones of the pectoral and pelvic girdles and the bones of the front and hind limbs. Study first the pectoral girdle and the front limbs.

The pectoral girdle of the cat consists of only two parts on each side, a large flattened triangular-shaped **scapula,** or shoulder blade, and a small slender **clavicle,** or collarbone. The mammalian pectoral girdle thus contains fewer bones than do the pectoral girdles of species previously studied. The clavicle in life is not attached to any part of the skeleton; therefore it will not be present unless tied to another bone. In many prepared skeletons, the clavicles are attached with wire to the lower part of the scapulae, and this holds them more or less in their normal positions. In life, the clavicles are held in place by the surrounding tissue. In man and many other mammals, the clavicle is normally attached to the skeleton.

Study the scapula. It is the large flattened bone that articulates with the large upper bone of the front leg. In its normal position, it occurs just external to the front ribs, with the widest part directed dorsally. This bone is important from the standpoint of muscle attachments and has several borders, processes, and fossae. There are three borders: the front edge is the **anterior border,** the posterior edge the **axillary border,** while the dorsal edge is the **vertebral border.** On the outer, or lateral, surface there occurs a strong ridge near the center. This ridge is the **spine** of the scapula. The ventral projection of this spine is the **acromion,** which is comparable to the process of the same name in the turtle. Just above the acromion and projecting laterally from the spine is the **metacromion.** The surface of the scapula in front of the spine is the **supraspinous fossa,** while posterior to the spine is the **infraspinous fossa.** All the inner, or medial, surface of the scapula is the **subscapular fossa.** The ventral end of the scapula articulates with the large bone of the front leg. The concavity in the scapula into which this large bone fits is the **glenoid fossa.** At the anterior edge of the glenoid fossa is a small projection of bone. This is the **coracoid process,** which is homologous with the coracoid bone of lower forms, in which it is usually a separate bone.

Drawing 7. Scapula—Outer Surface. Make drawing 5 to 6 inches in length, with the anterior border to your left and the vertebral border dorsal. **Labels:** anterior border, vertebral border, axillary border, spine, acromion, metacromion, supraspinous fossa, infraspinous fossa, glenoid fossa, coracoid process.

Although it is obvious that the front leg of the cat does not function as an arm in the sense that man's arm does, the two structures are morphologically quite comparable, and therefore terms will be used that would be applicable to a true arm. The **humerus** is the large bone of the upper arm that fits into the glenoid fossa of the scapula. The rounded enlargement that fits into this fossa is the **head** of the humerus. Medial to the head and continuous with it is a small projection, the **lesser tuberosity.** Somewhat anterior and lateral to the head and divided from it by a depression is the **greater tuberosity.** Both these structures are for muscle attachments. The lower, or distal, end of the humerus is divided into two parts, a medial **trochlea** and a lateral **capitulum.** In normal position, the trochlea articulates with the ulna (longest bone in lower arm) while the capitulum articulates with the other lower armbone, the radius. Just above the trochlea is a roughened projection, the **medial epicondyle.** Proximal to this epicondyle, the humerus is pierced by an elongate hole, the **supracondyloid foramen,** through which in life pass an artery (brachial) and a nerve (medial). Above the capitulum is a small projection corresponding to the medial epicondyle. This is the **lateral epicondyle.**

Drawing 8. Humerus—Posterior View. Indicate whether right or left. **Labels:** head, greater tuberosity, lesser tuberosity, trochlea, capitulum, medial epicondyle, supracondyloid foramen, lateral epicondyle.

Below the humerus are the two bones of the lower arm, or forearm, the **radius** and the **ulna.** The ulna is the longer—is, in fact, the longest bone of the arm. Study the ulna first. The proximal end extends above the end of the humerus as the **olecranon,** which corresponds to the elbow of man. Below the olecranon is a deep concavity into which fits the trochlea of the humerus. This is the **semilunar notch.** The distal end of the ulna is somewhat pointed into the **styloid process,** which articulates with one of the wristbones. Note that the radius passes across the front of the ulna and attaches to the wristbones on the inner, or thumb, side of the arm. The **head** of the radius possesses a concavity by which it articulates with the capitulum of the humerus. Below the head on the posterior surface is a raised area, the **bicipital tuberosity** for muscle attachment (biceps brachii). The distal end of the radius is somewhat irregular for articulation with the wristbones.

Drawing 9. Radius and Ulna—Anterior View. Draw the two bones separately, but on the same page. **Labels:** Ulna—olecranon, semilunar notch, styloid process. Radius—head, bicipital tuberosity.

7 carpals

Below the radius and the ulna is a series of seven **carpals,** or wristbones. Each of these has a specific name; but since they are difficult to differentiate in mounted specimens, they will not be individually identified. In man there are eight wristbones.

5 metacarp

Distal to the carpals are the five elongate bones of the hand, the **metacarpals.** Below the metacarpals are the **digits,** consisting of segments called **phalanges.** The inner digit consists of two phalanges; the others have three each. The digits are numbered and named beginning with the short inner digit. The short inner digit is 1, the **thumb** or pollex; 2 is the **index;** 3, the **medius;** 4, the **annularis;** and 5, the **minimus,** or little finger. At the end of each digit is a horny **claw.** A drawing is not required.

Turn next to the pelvic girdle. This structure articulates

with the sacrum. In the embryo, the pelvic girdle is composed of three bones on each side, the **ilium, ischium,** and **pubis.** In the adult, however, the three bones on each side are fused together to form a single bone. The two composite bones formed by this fusion are then fused in the mid-ventral line between the two bones of the upper hind leg to form the pelvic girdle. Each half of the pelvic girdle is called the **innominate bone** and is formed from a fusion of an ilium, ischium, and pubis on one side. Although the bones are closely knit together to form the innominate bone, the general limits of the embryonic bones may be identified. Study one side of the girdle. The large bone of the upper leg fits into the **acetabulum,** a depression, or hole, in the outer surface of the innominate bone. Between the bones of the upper leg there occurs a large hole on each side through the girdle, the **obturator foramen** for the passage of nerves and blood vessels. That portion of the girdle which articulates with the sacrum is the **ilium.** The bone extends ventrally and posteriorly and forms a portion of the anterior and dorsal wall of the acetabulum. This bone corresponds to the hipbone of man. The anterior dorsal curved edge of the ilium is the **crest** of the ilium.

The **ischium** is posterior to the acetabulum, and its anterior end contributes to most of the posterior wall of this depression. A projection from the inner posterior side of the ischium extends medially, posterior to the obturator foramen, and fuses with a like projection from the opposite side. The region of fusion of the two bones in the mid-ventral line is the **ischial symphysis.** A portion of the ischium extends anteriorly along the ischial symphysis. This is the **ramus** of the ischium, which meets the pubic ramus anteriorly. The pubic ramus will be identified presently. The ischium thus forms the posterior wall of the obturator foramen and in addition part of the lateral and medial walls. The posterior border of the ischium possesses a roughened curved area, the **ischial tuberosity.**

The dorsal end of the **pubis** forms part of the anterior and ventral border of the acetabulum. From the acetabulum, a portion of the pubis projects medially and fuses with a similar projection from the opposite pubis at the **pubic symphysis** in the mid-ventral line. A portion of the pubis, the **ramus** of the pubis, extends posteriorly along the pubic symphysis and meets the ramus of the ischium previously mentioned.

Drawing 10. Innominate Bone—Ventrolateral View. Make drawing as though this bone were flat, and include all the lateral and ventral portions. Put in center of page in more or less normal position with ilium dorsal and to your left. In labeling the three bones that make up this structure, enclose the approximate limits of each in a bracket, and run lead line to the bracket. **Labels:** acetabulum, obturator foramen, ilium, ischium, ischial symphysis, ramus of ischium, pubis, pubic symphysis, ramus of pubis, crest of ilium, ischial tuberosity.

The **femur** is the large bone of the upper part of the hind leg, the **head** of which fits into the acetabulum of the innominate bone. Lateral to the head of the femur is a smaller tubercle, the **great trochanter,** while below the head on the posterior, or ventral, surface is a much smaller **lesser trochanter.** Above the lesser trochanter and occurring between the head and the great trochanter is a rather deep depression, the **trochanteric fossa** for muscle insertion. At the distal end of the femur on each side is an enlarged condyle, the **lateral condyle** on the outer surface and the **medial condyle** on the medial, or inner, surface. These two condyles are separated on the posterior surface by a deep depression, the **intercondyloid notch.** On the anterior surface between the two condyles is a deep groove, the **patellar surface,** against which the patella, or kneecap, articulates. The **patella** occurs just in front of the knee joint. In prepared skeletons it may be absent or may be attached to one of the other bones at the joint with glue or wire. It is a **sesamoid bone,** a bone developed in association with a tendon. In life it is surrounded by the tendon of the quadriceps muscle and aids in its functioning. A kneecap is also present in birds, but not in lower vertebrates. Other sesamoid bones also occur in the cat in other joints of the arm and leg, but they are not so easy to identify as the patella.

Drawing 11. Femur—Posterior View. Make drawing of left femur. **Labels:** head, great trochanter, lesser trochanter, trochanteric fossa, lateral condyle, medial condyle, intercondyloid notch.

There are two bones of the lower leg or shank, a large **tibia** and a smaller lateral **fibula.** The tibia is actually the longest bone in the body. The articular surfaces of the proximal end of the tibia are **condyles** (**lateral** and **medial**). The distal end is prolonged on one side, forming a short process, the **medial malleolus.** The proximal end of the fibula is enlarged into a head, while from one side of the distal end the **lateral malleolus** protrudes, forming a slight projection.

Drawing 12. Tibia and Fibula—Anterior View. Use left leg. Draw bones separately, but put on same sheet. **Labels :** Tibia— lateral condyle, medial condyle, lateral malleolus, medial malleolus. Fibula—head, lateral malleolus.

Below the tibia and the fibula are the seven bones of the ankle, or **tarsal bones.** In prepared skeletons, most of these are difficult to identify individually, so they will not be studied in detail. They are essentially the same as those in the ankle of man. Two of the tarsal bones are relatively easy to identify. The **calcaneus** (fibulare), or heel bone, occurs as a rather large projection posterior to the distal ends of the tibia and the fibula. It is the largest bone of the ankle. Dorsal to the middle of the calcaneus and between it and the end of the tibia is another large bone, the **astragulus,** or talus. Five other anklebones are present, but these will not be identified. A drawing is not required.

Below the ankle are the **metatarsals,** or bones of the foot. There are four complete metatarsals, and a rudimentary stub of a fifth occurs at the base of the inner complete metatarsal. Like the bones of the hand and fingers, the metatarsals are numbered, beginning medially. Thus the rudimentary metatarsal is the remnant of metatarsal 1. The metatarsal and digit missing correspond to metatarsal 1 and the great toe on the foot of man. Three **phalanges** occur in each of the four **digits.** At the end of each digit is a horny **claw.**

It should be noted that the cat walks on its toes rather than with the complete foot on the ground. There are several gradations in mammals, from the condition in which the animal walks with its whole foot on the ground, to the other extreme in which the animal walks on the tips of its toes. The cat is somewhat intermediate, in that it walks on the toes but not on the extreme tips as do ungulates (cows, horses, etc.). The foot of the cat is *digitigrade;* those animals which walk on the tips of the toes are said to be *unguligrade.* The most primitive walking position is with the foot flat on the ground. This type of foot is *plantigrade,* the type possessed by man.

The Skull. The skull is much easier to study if it is detached from the skeleton and if the lower jaw is removed. The bones are quite completely fused, although the regions where two bones come together are usually indicated by irregular lines called **sutures.** These sutures show up better in some specimens than in others, and the exact limits of some of the bones are rather difficult to find even in excellent specimens. In studying the skull, many students have a tendency to outline the limits of the bones with pencil. This will not be allowed, since the skulls get dirty even with the best of care, and pencil marks in a short time obscure the original sutures so that many of the bones cannot be identified. Use a probe for tracing out the outlines of the bones.

Start the identification at the dorsal anterior region of the skull. In this region above the front teeth is a large opening that is partly separated internally. These are the **external nares,** which are more completely separated in life into two openings. Dorsal to the external nares are two **nasal bones.** Posterior and dorsal to the nasal bones are two large bones that occupy nearly half the dorsal surface of the skull. These are the **frontal bones,** which correspond to the bone of the human forehead, there being only a single frontal bone in man. Each frontal bone has a lateral projection that points toward a similar projection arising from an arch of bone along the lateral region of the skull. The projection from the frontals constitutes the **zygomatic processes of the frontals.** The lateral arch of bone is the **zygomatic arch,** and the projection from this arch that points toward the zygomatic process of the frontal is the **frontal process,** or orbital process. There are several elements in the zygomatic arch that will be mentioned later.

Between the frontal bone and the zygomatic arch on each side is a large cavity, which is somewhat divided into anterior and posterior regions by the zygomatic process of the frontal and the orbital process from the zygomatic arch. The anterior division of this cavity is the **orbit,** which formerly contained the eye. The surfaces of the bones bounding the orbit form somewhat of a concavity, which is the **orbital fossa.** The surfaces of the bones surrounding the cavity posterior to the orbit also form a fossa, the **temporal fossa.** The two fossae are separated by the zygomatic process of the frontal and the orbital process of the zygomatic arch. The temporal fossa extends posteriorly along the sides of the skull to a ridge at the posterior region (superior nuchal line). In life, the temporal muscle is attached to the surface of the temporal fossa, and it fills the cavity posterior to the orbit. It should be noted that the frontal bone extends ventrally into this region and thus contributes to both the orbital and temporal fossae. The dorsal boundary of the temporal fossa is marked by a slightly raised line, which extends from the posterior edge of the zygomatic process posteriorly along the surfaces of the frontal and the bone posterior to it.

On the dorsal surface of the skull, posterior to the frontal bones, are a pair of **parietal bones,** which form most of the dorsal posterior region of the skull and which contribute a portion of their surfaces to the temporal fossae. The lateral limits of these bones can easily be determined. Posteriorly they extend to a definite ridge, which passes across the back of the skull from one side to the other. This ridge is the **superior nuchal line,** or lambdoidal ridge. Muscles of the vertebral column attach along this ridge. Passing anteriorly from the center of the superior nuchal line is another somewhat smaller ridge, the **sagittal crest.** The posterior end of the sagittal crest is on the surface of a small bone, the posterior edge of which touches the superior nuchal line. This bone is the **interparietal,** which is sometimes difficult to differentiate from the parietals.

At the time of birth in man, several so-called "soft spots," or fontanels, occur in the skull, the largest of which are the anterior fontanel and the posterior fontanel. These soft spots are caused by a lack of bony material in these areas. The anterior fontanel occurs on the dorsal surface of the skull at the region where the frontal bone (a single bone in man) and the parietals come together. The posterior fontanel is between the parietals and the occipital bone below the superior nuchal line, to be identified presently. The anterior fontanel especially can be felt with the fingers in the newly born; although it gradually closes, it may persist for a year and a half or more. The posterior fontanel, being a smaller opening, closes somewhat earlier.

Before proceeding farther posteriorly, return to the anterior part of the orbit and identify the **lachrymal bone.** This is a small triangular-shaped bone in the front of the orbit, in contact with the base of the zygomatic arch in this region. A hole, or foramen, occurs at the anterior edge of the lachrymal bone and will be identified presently. The limits of the lachrymal bone are usually easily distinguished.

Posterior and ventral to the superior nuchal line is a large bone in which occurs a large opening. The bone is the **occipital,** and the opening is the **foramen magnum,** through which in life the spinal cord passes. On each side of the foramen magnum is a projection, an **occipital condyle;** these articulate with the atlas of the vertebral column. Lateral and somewhat anterior to the occipital condyles, the occipital bone forms a small projection on each side that is closely applied to a rounded elevation. This projection is the **jugular process.** The rounded elevations will be identified later.

Bones of the Upper Jaw.   Return to the anterior end of the skull.   Below the external nares is a pair of bones bearing teeth and fusing in the mid-line.   These are the **premaxillae,** or premaxillaries.   On the outer sides of the external nares a projection from each of the premaxillae passes dorsally; these are called the **frontal processes of the premaxillae.**   On the anterior edge of the roof of the mouth are two rather large openings.   These are the **incisive foramina** (anterior palatine foramina), which open into the nasal cavity.   The **palatine processes of the premaxillae** surround these openings anteriorly and laterally.   The posterior limits of these processes on the roof of the mouth are indicated by a suture just posterior to the incisive foramina.

The **maxillae** occur lateral and posterior to the premaxillae on each side and bear all the teeth other than those on the premaxillae.   Examine a maxilla on one side.   It possesses several processes.   The **frontal process of the maxilla** passes dorsally alongside the nasal bones up to the frontal.   The **zygomatic process of the maxilla** is a small toothlike projection that occurs on the ventral edge of the zygomatic arch.   It will be noted that the portion of the maxilla in which the teeth are embedded is raised into a slight ridge.   This ridge is the **alveolar process,** or alveolar border.   The **palatine process of the maxilla** occurs in the roof of the mouth posterior to the palatine processes of the premaxillae.   The extent of these processes on each side is fairly large, and the irregular sutures that mark their limits are not always clear.   The anterior edge of the two processes, one from each side, meet in the mid-line of the roof of the mouth just posterior to the palatine processes of the premaxillae.   The processes then extend posteriorly on each side next to the teeth.   The mid-region of the roof of the mouth between the posterior ends of these two processes is occupied by other bones, the **palatines.**   The latter occupy somewhat of a triangular area of the roof of the mouth, with the broadest part of the triangle directed posteriorly.   They extend posteriorly and include the openings dorsal to the posterior edge of the roof of the mouth.   These openings are the **posterior nares,** which communicate with the external nares.   The sutures that separate the palatines from the palatine processes of the maxillae are somewhat difficult to find in some cases.   Two small openings occur in the roof of the mouth, and these mark the lateral limits of the palatines in that region.   These openings occur on the sutures that separate the two bones, and it is frequently possible to trace the sutures from these openings.   A portion of the palatine on each side extends dorsally into the orbit. This orbital portion of the palatine includes two holes, or foramina, which will be identified later.

The palatine processes of the premaxillae, the palatine processes of the maxillae, and a portion of the palatine bone form the **hard palate,** which constitutes a secondary roof of the mouth. This structure first occurs in reptiles. It serves to prevent food from getting into the nasal passages and also causes most of the air that is taken into the nares to pass posteriorly into the pharynx through the posterior nares rather than into the mouth cavity.

Obviously, because of duplication of names, the name of a process alone means little unless the bone from which the process arises is indicated. Thus the use of the term palatine process might mean either the palatine process of the premaxilla or the same process of the maxilla. Duplicate names occur for other processes, also. In all cases, therefore, the name of the bone from which the processes arise should not be omitted.

Two other bones contribute to the upper jaw, the **malar,** or jugal, and the **temporal.** The malar bone makes up most of the zygomatic arch. Its anterior end is dorsal to the posterior end of the maxilla. This bone has two processes, the **frontal process of the malar,** previously identified, which points dorsally toward the zygomatic process of the frontal, and the **zygomatic process of the malar,** which extends posteriorly from the orbital process as the ventral edge of the zygomatic arch. Note the longitudinal ridge on the surface of the malar bone. The masseter muscle, which functions in closing the mouth, attaches to this ridge.

The temporal bone is quite complex It is formed from a fusion of three bones as found in lower vertebrate animals, the squamous, petrous, and tympanic bones. In the embryo and the young cat, these three bones are relatively distinct; in the adult, they are fused into a single bone. The temporal is considered to have three regions corresponding to these three original bones. The **squamous** portion of the temporal consists of the **zygomatic process of the temporal,** which makes up the posterior dorsal portion of the zygomatic arch, and a flattened part on the side of the skull to which the zygomatic process is attached. The zygomatic process of the temporal is just dorsal to the zygomatic process of the malar. On the undersurface of the zygomatic process of the temporal is an indentation, the **mandibular fossa,** for the articulation of the lower jaw. The zygomatic

process of the temporal attaches to a flat region on the posterior
lateral surface of the skull ventral to the parietal bone, which,
as indicated, is also a portion of the squamous region of the
temporal bone. Posterior and ventral to the zygomatic process
of the temporal is a large rounded elevation that contains a
large opening near its dorsal side. This rounded elevation is
the **tympanic bulla,** which composes the **tympanic** portion of the
temporal bone. It has been mentioned previously as being in
contact with the jugular process of the occipital. The large
opening in the tympanic bulla is the **external auditory meatus.**
This is the opening of the external ear; internally, it leads into
the cavity of the middle ear (tympanic cavity) within the tympanic bulla. In life, this cavity contains three middle-ear bones,
difficult to study in work of this kind. They help to transmit
sound waves from the tympanum, or eardrum, to the inner ear.
The petrous portion of the temporal bone consists of an inner
petrous part and an outer mastoid region. The **petrous** part
contains the inner ear and cannot be seen from an external view.
The **mastoid** part of the petrous portion is a small, somewhat
triangular-shaped bone that projects ventrally over the tympanic bulla just posterior to the external auditory meatus. The
ventral tip of the mastoid bone forms the **mastoid process.** In
man, in whom the mastoid bone forms a ridge just behind the
ear, the condition of mastoiditis is caused from an infection
within the air spaces of this bone.

The Sphenoid Bones. Although the sphenoid bone of man is
a single bone, there are two sphenoid bones in the cat, each of
which consists of two or more parts. The posterior sphenoid
bone is sometimes called the **sphenoid proper;** the anterior bone
is the **presphenoid.** The sphenoid bone is on the ventral surface
of the skull between the tympanic bullae, and the suture separating the sphenoid from a portion of the occipital in this region
is not always distinct. The suture occurs near the anterior ends
of the tympanic bullae; it is often possible to find it by turning
the skull so that bright light falls on this region. The several
parts of the sphenoid bone are distinct in young cats and in
some instances are partly separated in the adult. Just in front
of the ventral portion of the occipital bone is the **basisphenoid**
region of the sphenoid, which occupies all the surface between
the tympanic bullae anterior to the occipital and which extends
as far anteriorly as the level of the two hooklike projections from
the ventral portion of the skull. The anterior end of the basisphenoid is somewhat pointed, so that between the projections,

it occupies only a small portion of the middle region. In front of the tympanic bullae and lateral to the basisphenoid are the **alisphenoid** regions of the sphenoid bone, sometimes called the **wings** of the basisphenoids. The alisphenoids extend dorsally on each side into the posterior part of the orbit. In this region of the orbit are to be seen four holes, or foramina, the most posterior of which is just anterior to the base of the zygomatic arch. The three posterior foramina, to be identified later, are within the alisphenoid bone. Dorsal to these foramina, a projection of the alisphenoid extends dorsally and articulates with the anterior edge of the temporal, the ventral portion of the frontal, and a ventral projection from the parietal. In the roof of the mouth, the alisphenoids extend anteriorly on each side of the basisphenoids and in this region are called the **pterygoid processes.** These processes also include the posterior ends of the rather prominent ridges, one on each side, which end posteriorly in the hooklike processes mentioned previously. Each of these hooklike projections is called a **hamulus.** The anterior ends of the alisphenoids extend as far anteriorly as the posterior end of the palatines. The lines of demarcation between the anterior end of the basisphenoid and the alisphenoids sometimes appear quite clearly. In the mid-line within the basisphenoid and near its anterior end is to be seen a small hole. Just lateral to this hole on each side is a small slitlike foramen. These foramina, to be identified later, lie on the dividing line between the basisphenoid and the alisphenoids in that region.

In the mid-line just in front of the anterior end of the basisphenoid is a very slender bone, the **presphenoid,** which extends anteriorly between the anterior ends of the alisphenoids and the posterior ends of the palatines. A rather large portion of this bone extends dorsally on each side into the orbit as the **orbitosphenoid.** Look into the lower posterior part of the orbit to see this portion, which is usually a separate bone in lower vertebrates. Within the orbit, the posterior portion of the orbitosphenoid contains the most anterior of the four foramina, mentioned in the preceding paragraph, that occur in the posterior part of the orbit. The ventral limits of this bone in the orbit are somewhat difficult to identify; they occur along the dorsal border of a depression (external pterygoid fossa) in the ventral portion of the orbit.

Drawing 13. The Skull. Three drawings should be made of the skull, one dorsal, one ventral, and one lateral. Because of the large number of labels, each drawing should be made on a separate sheet. It is not practical to include on any one drawing as many labels as might be desired; thus, most of the processes and foramina have been omitted from the required list of labels. Some of these may be added if so desired by the student or instructor, but crowding of the labels should be avoided. It would be best to identify most of the bones and their processes before attempting to make any of the drawings.

Labels: Dorsal view—external nares, nasal, frontal, zygomatic process of frontal, parietal, superior nuchal line, interparietal, occipital, premaxilla, temporal, maxilla, zygomatic process of temporal, malar, frontal process of malar.

Lateral view—premaxilla, nasal, frontal, parietal, occipital condyle, temporal, occipital, tympanic bulla, external auditory meatus, maxilla, lachrymal, hamulus, pterygoid process of alisphenoid. Later add teeth—incisor, canine, premolar, molar.

Ventral view—incisive foramen, premaxilla, maxilla, palatine, presphenoid, alisphenoid, basisphenoid, occipital, tympanic bulla, occipital condyle, foramen magnum.

Foramina and Fossae of the Skull. Some of the foramina and fossae of the skull have already been identified. Identify the foramina first.

As indicated previously, a foramen (plural, foramina) is a hole through a bone or between bones for the passage of nerves and blood vessels. Start at the anterior end of the skull. Most of the foramina occur in pairs, but only one on one side will be described unless they are quite close together.

External Nares. The external nares have already been identified as the openings at the anterior end of the skull bordered by the premaxillae and the nasal bones.

Incisive Foramina. The incisive foramina have already been identified. They occur in the anterior end of the hard palate. They are bordered anteriorly and laterally by the palatine processes of the premaxillae and posteriorly by the palatine processes of the maxillae. These openings connect the nasal passages with the mouth.

Infraorbital Foramina. The infraorbital foramina (one on each side) occur at the anterior end of the zygomatic arches within the maxillary bones. These openings are evident when one looks at the skull from the anterior view. The infraorbital nerve, a branch of the fifth cranial nerve, and the infraorbital artery from the external carotid pass through these foramina.

Nasolachrymal Canal. The opening of the nasolachrymal

canal occurs in the anterior side of the orbit, just dorsal to the infraorbital foramen. This opening is almost wholly surrounded by the lachrymal bone, but in most specimens the anterior edge is bordered by the frontal process of the maxilla. The canal itself passes through the maxilla and connects to the nasal passages. It serves for the passage of tears from the orbit into the nasal passages.

Posterior and ventral to the opening of the nasolachrymal canal are two foramina. The dorsal and somewhat posterior of these holes is the **sphenopalatine foramen.** The anterior and ventral opening is the **posterior opening** of the posterior palatine canal. A nerve and an artery pass through each of these openings. The **anterior opening** of the posterior palatine canal occurs in the hard palate at the anterior edge of the palatine bone. The two first-named foramina likewise occur in a portion of the palatine bone.

In the ventral posterior portion of the orbit are four foramina arranged, roughly, in a row. From anterior to posterior these are the **optic foramen,** the **orbital fissure,** the **foramen rotundum,** and the **foramen ovale.**

The optic foramen is within the orbitosphenoid portion of the presphenoid bone and is the opening through which the optic nerve enters the orbit.

The orbital fissure occurs somewhat between the alisphenoid and orbitosphenoid, the walls being thus formed by both these bones. Through the orbital fissure pass the third, fourth, and sixth cranial nerves, a part of the fifth, and an artery.

The foramen rotundum occurs in the alisphenoid. Through it passes a branch of the fifth cranial nerve.

The foramen ovale likewise transmits a branch of the fifth cranial nerve. It also occurs within the alisphenoid.

Turn now to the ventral surface of the skull. The foramen magnum in the occipital bone should be noted again. Anterior to the foramen magnum and touching the medial posterior edge of the tympanic bulla is the large **jugular foramen.** Through this opening pass a vein and the ninth, tenth, and eleventh cranial nerves. Within the opening of the jugular foramen and piercing the medial wall is a small opening, the **hypoglossal foramen,** through which passes the twelfth cranial nerve. Observe again the large external auditory meatus at the base of the bulla. At the anterior edge of the bulla is an opening that passes into the bulla itself. This is the opening by which the Eustachian tube passes into the middle ear within the bulla. This opening, plus the small tube that passes anteriorly and medially from the opening, is sometimes called the **canal for the Eustachian tube.**

The opening of the **pterygoid canal** is quite small and sometimes difficult to find. It occurs just anterior to an anterior projection of the tympanic bulla and is on the dividing line between the basisphenoid and alisphenoid. A branch of the fifth nerve passes through this opening.

Just posterior to the external auditory meatus and at the tip of the mastoid process is the **stylomastoid foramen.** The seventh cranial nerve passes through this opening.

As previously explained, a fossa is a depression, or indentation, in a bone. Muscles are usually attached in these areas. The orbital and temporal fossae have already been observed. Although one frequently thinks of these fossae as being the large cavities enclosed between the zygomatic arch and the side of the skull, strictly speaking the fossae are the depressions on the surfaces of the bones concerned. Study these fossae again. They are somewhat continuous with each other, but they are considered to be separated by the orbital process of the malar and the zygomatic process of the frontal. At the ventral and posterior limits of the orbital fossa is the optic foramen. Eye muscles are attached along the orbital fossa. The temporal muscle is attached to the temporal fossa in life, and the orbital fossa and the orbit surround the eye and associated structures. The temporal fossa extends posteriorly along the side of the skull to the superior nuchal line.

The **external pterygoid fossa** is an elongate depression in the surface of the skull ventral to the orbital fossa. It extends from the sphenopalatine foramen posteriorly to the orbital fissure. In life, a muscle (external pterygoid muscle) attaches in this depression. Ventral and somewhat posterior to the posterior end of the external pterygoid fossa is a somewhat smaller fossa, the anterior wall of which is partly formed by the hamulus. This is the **internal pterygoid fossa,** where in life the internal pterygoid muscle is attached.

On the ventral surface of the zygomatic process of the temporal bone, identify again the **mandibular fossa,** in which the lower jaw articulates.

The Lower Jaw and the Teeth. The lower jaw of mammals consists of only two bones, as opposed to several in the lower jaws of other vertebrates.   Each half of the jaw consists of a **dentary bone,** with several processes; the dentaries are fused anteriorly by a symphysis to form the complete jaw.   Each dentary is divided into two general regions, an anterior, horizontal portion in which the teeth are embedded, called the **body** of the mandible; and a posterior, somewhat vertical portion, called the **ramus.**   Although there is no sharp line of demarcation between these two divisions, the projections on the posterior end of the dentary are considered to be on the ramus.

Study the outer surface of one of the dentaries.   At the posterior end there are several processes.   The dorsal part of the ramus is the **coronoid process.**   Below the coronoid process is a transverse projection, the **condyloid process,** which in life articulates with the mandibular fossa of the skull.   This articulation causes the coronoid process to project dorsally into the temporal fossa.   The ventral process at the angle of the jaw is the **angular process.**   Anterior to the condyloid process is a large depression, the **coronoid fossa,** where, in life, jaw muscles are attached.   Near the anterior end of the dentary there are two foramina (sometimes only a single one), the **mental foramina.**   From these foramina emerge an artery and a nerve, which pass within the lower jaw and supply the teeth.   The artery and the nerve enter the lower jaw on the inner surface near the posterior end of the dentary at the **mandibular foramen.**   The artery (inferior alveolar, or dental) is a branch of the inferior maxillary, which, in turn, branches from the external carotid artery.   The nerve (inferior alveolar) comes from the trigeminal nerve, cranial nerve V.

The teeth of the majority of mammals differ from those of the lower vertebrates in several respects.   The teeth of most mammals are **heterodont;** that is, they are differentiated into various types, as contrasted with those of most lower vertebrates, which are all of the same general type.   They are **thecodont,** which means that each tooth is set into a separate socket, or alveolus.   They are also **diphyodont,** a condition in which there are only two sets of teeth, the so-called "milk teeth" and the permanent teeth.   (Perhaps for man the term triphyodont might be used, since, upon the removal of the permanent teeth, these are immediately replaced by a third set, the "store-bought" teeth.)

In identifying the teeth, both a skull and a lower jaw (or one-half a lower jaw) should be at hand.   With one exception, the teeth of the upper and lower jaws of the cat are the same.

Start at the front edge in making the identifications. In this region, there are six small **incisor teeth** in both the upper and the lower jaw. Lateral and posterior to the incisors is a single elongate **canine** on each side. The number of **premolars,** or bicuspids, the teeth posterior to the canines, varies in the two jaws. In the upper jaw on each side there are three premolars; in the lower jaw, only two. In some cats, there may occasionally be an accessory first premolar, especially in the upper jaw. The last tooth in both upper and lower jaw on each side is a **molar tooth,** that of the upper jaw being quite small. There are usually 30 permanent teeth in the adult cat, while there are 26 milk, or temporary, teeth in the kitten. Man normally has 32 permanent teeth and 20 milk teeth. The third molar in man is the "wisdom tooth," which frequently does not appear. In such a case, if all the wisdom teeth failed to appear there would be only 28 permanent teeth.

Drawing 14. The Lower Jaw—Lateral View. This drawing could possibly be included on the same sheet as the ventral view of the skull but would be better on a separate plate. **Labels:** coronoid process, condyloid process, angular process, coronoid fossa, mental foramen, symphysis. Teeth—incisor, canine, premolar, molar.

The number and type of teeth vary considerably in different species of mammals; but, aside from occasional individual variation, the number is constant for each species. It has been found that the number and type of teeth are very important in the classification of the different species of mammals. Those biologists who are interested in the identification and classification of mammals make use of this fact and indicate the number and type of teeth present in each species by a **dental formula.** Since the teeth are the same on both sides of the jaws, only those teeth on a single half are indicated. Thus a complete dental formula would include only the teeth present in half the upper and half the lower jaw on the same side. Dental formulas are written in the form of fractions; the numerator refers to the teeth in half the upper jaw, and the denominator refers to the teeth in half the lower jaw. The numbers that are used indicate the number of teeth of each type present, beginning with the incisors.

The dental formula of the cat is $\dfrac{3\text{-}1\text{-}3\text{-}1}{3\text{-}1\text{-}2\text{-}1}$. This means that in half the upper jaw there are 3 incisors, 1 canine, 3 premolars, and 1 molar. The lower numbers refer to the same type of teeth in half the lower jaw. The formula is sometimes written 3/3, 1/1, 3/2, 1/1. The dental formula of man is $\frac{2\text{-}1\text{-}2\text{-}3}{2\text{-}1\text{-}2\text{-}3}$.

With reference to the jaws and the articulation of the lower jaw to the skull as found in mammals, the three bones of the middle ear are important. The three middle-ear bones are the malleus (hammer), the incus (anvil), and the stapes (stirrup). As indicated previously, the lower jaw of mammals consists of only two dentaries, one on each side, as opposed to several bones in the lower jaws of reptiles. The extra bones found in reptiles either have been lost or have been reduced in size and incorporated within the middle ear as the middle-ear bones. Thus the articular of reptiles forms the malleus, and the quadrate (bone of upper jaw fused to skull) forms the incus. The third ear bone of mammals, the stapes, is at least partly homologous to the columella, the bone of the middle ear that occurs in amphibians and reptiles. In fact, some writers speak of the latter as the stapes rather than as the columella.

In lower vertebrates, the articulation of the lower jaw is between the articular of the jaw and the quadrate mentioned above. With the conversion of these bones into middle-ear bones in mammals, the articulation is now between the dentary and the squamous portion of the temporal. This articulation occurs at the mandibular fossa on the ventral posterior portion of the zygomatic arch. It should be noted that many of the bones discussed above are considered to be homologous to parts of the visceral skeleton as found in lower forms.

EXTERNAL ANATOMY

The body of the cat is covered with **hair,** which is derived from the epidermis. Hairs are peculiar to mammals, and their homologies with comparable structures in lower forms have not yet been established. Examine the head. Observe the **eyes,** protected by the **lids,** the **external nares,** or nostrils, and the **pinna,** or ear. The cat has a third eyelid, the **nictitating membrane,** attached at the corner of the eye; it is sometimes quite noticeable in living cats when they lazily open and close their eyes. Pull apart the upper and lower lids, and find the nictitating membrane. It is to be remembered that one of these structures is also present in the turtle. Peer into the opening partly surrounded by the pinna.　This is the **external auditory meatus,** previously identified in the skull.　The external auditory meatus and the pinna constitute the external ear of mammals. Mammals are the only animals with pinnae, although, as mentioned in Chap. VI, The Turtle, the beginning of an external auditory meatus appears in some reptiles.　The external auditory meatus is derived from the first pharyngeal cleft of the embryo, which forms at the same place as the first gill slit of lower vertebrates.

The **vibrissae,** or whiskers, around the mouth function as sensory hairs.　Examine the upper lip under the nose, and observe that the cat normally has a slight harelip, since there is a slight indentation present.　In the formation of this portion of the face in both the cat and man, pieces from opposite sides normally meet and fuse in the mid-line, this fusion being more complete in man than in the cat.　In man, in some cases, parts of the hard palate do not fuse completely; this condition is known as "cleft palate."　Harelip in man is caused by the incomplete fusion of the two sides of the lip.　The term is derived from the fact that a noticeably split lip is a normal feature in rabbits and hares.

A definite **neck** occurs, with seven cervical vertebrae, which were observed in the study of the skeleton.　This number of neck vertebrae is characteristic of most mammals, including such long-necked beasts as the giraffe.　Posterior to the neck, the body is divided into an anterior **thorax** and a posterior **abdomen.**　The posterior limit of the former is marked by the posterior edge of the ribs.　On the ventral surface of the body in female cats are several pairs of **teats,** or nipples.　The milk, or mammary, glands open to the outside by way of these structures. The presence of mammary glands is another feature found only in mammals.　The homology of these structures is obscure.

The limbs have already been studied in connection with the skeletal system.　Identify again the various parts.　Under the base of the tail is the **anus,** the posterior opening of the digestive tract.　Ventral to the anus occur portions of the urogenital system.　In the female, the opening plus the surrounding folds of skin called the **labia major** is known as the **vulva.**　In the male, the most conspicuous part of the urogenital system in this region is the **scrotal sac,** or scrotum, inside of which the testes appear as rounded protuberances.　Ventral to the scrotum and somewhat anterior is an opening from which the **penis** can be protruded. The skin surrounding the opening is the **foreskin,** or prepuce; in most cases, the penis will not be visible externally. Note, therefore, that there is no definite cloaca in the cat, since the urogenital and digestive systems open separately to the outside. This condition also obtains in most mammals. A drawing of the external anatomy is not required unless the instructor directs that one be made.

THE MUSCULAR SYSTEM

A considerably more detailed study will be made of the muscular system of the cat than of that of the animals previously studied, for it is much more complicated. Many of the muscles are comparable to those of lower vertebrates, but others either are additions or are considerably modified from the condition previously seen. In some cases, single muscles of lower forms have become a complex of several related muscles. The muscular system in the cat and in man is quite similar, with modifications in one animal or the other due to the different methods of walking, standing, etc.

A few explanations should be given before this work can be successfully undertaken. It should be kept in mind that muscles work by *contraction* only—they never push. Thus a muscle or a group of muscles will move a certain part of the body in one direction, while another muscle or group will move the part back to its original position. Muscles, therefore, usually occur in opposing pairs or groups. Each muscle has an origin, insertion, and action. Muscles, of course, are attached at each end to portions of the skeleton. The origin of a muscle is its relatively immovable point of attachment; the insertion is the point of attachment that is more movable. In a few muscles, the origin and the insertion will change, depending upon which end stays fixed and which end moves. Thus the origin and insertion will vary, depending upon the action of the muscle at a particular time. The action of a muscle is the operation that it performs when it contracts.

Examining a portion of one's own anatomy may lead to a fuller understanding of some of these terms. Note the front edge of the upper arm. Most of this region is covered by a relatively large muscle, the **biceps brachii.** Now move the lower arm so that it approaches the upper arm, and note that the biceps brachii becomes shorter and larger in the center. This is especially noticeable if a book or some other object is held in the hand during the movement.   This movement demonstrates the most important action of the biceps brachii, which is to move the lower arm toward the upper arm.   This muscle is attached to the shoulder blade (scapula) and to one of the lower-arm bones (radius).   Since the scapula does not move much when the muscle acts, the scapula is the **origin** and the radius is the **insertion.**   On the back of the upper arm is the **triceps brachii,** the function, or action, of which is to straighten the arm. The action of this muscle is the opposite of that of the biceps brachii.

Individual muscles consist of muscle fibers, which are bound together in groups by whitish connective tissue called **fascia.** The fascia also encloses the muscles and connects the superficial muscles to the skin.   The true muscle tissue does not extend for the full length of the muscle; thus, the origin and the insertion of a muscle are made, not by the muscle tissue itself, but by a continuation of the connective tissue that encloses and is contained within the muscle.   If the point of attachment is relatively thin and cordlike, it is called a **tendon;** if broad and flat, with practically no concentration into a cord, it is called an **aponeurosis.**   The general term fascia is sometimes applied to an aponeurosis.   That portion of the muscle near the center consisting of true muscle tissues and the associated fascia is called the **belly** of the muscle.

Muscles are classified according to the type of action they perform.   Some muscles have only one type of action, while others may have two types.   The following are the most important types of muscle according to their actions.   The examples that are given are cat muscles, although the muscles of man are comparable.   Some of these muscles have an additional action, but these will be noted when the individual muscle is studied.

Flexor.   A muscle that bends a joint, thus causing one part of the body to move toward another part.   Example: the biceps brachii flexes the lower arm (causes it to move toward the upper arm).

Extensor.   A muscle that straightens a joint, thus causing one part of the body to move away from another part.   Example: the triceps brachii extends the lower arm (causes it to move away from the upper arm).

Adductor.   A muscle that moves a part of the body (especially a limb) toward the median line of the body.   Example: the sartorius muscle adducts the thigh.

Abductor. A muscle that moves a part of the body (especially a limb) away from the median line of the body. Example: the biceps femoris abducts the thigh.

Depressor. A muscle that lowers a structure. Example: the digastric muscle lowers the lower jaw.

Elevator. A muscle that raises ·a structure. Example: the masseter muscle raises (elevates) the lower jaw.

Rotator. A muscle that turns, or rotates, a portion of the body. Example: the acromiodeltoid raises and *rotates* the humerus.

Constrictor. A muscle that compresses or constricts a part. Example: the external oblique muscle constricts the abdomen.

A few additional remarks in connection with the study of muscles should be made. The origin, insertion, and action of the individual muscles are given under the discussion of a particular muscle. Do not actually trace out a muscle to see the origin and insertion, since to do so would likely destroy associated muscles. However, after the muscle study is complete, this may be done if the instructor so directs. Since muscles work only by contraction, a good idea of their action can be obtained if one studies the direction in which the muscle fibers extend. The individual muscles are at times difficult to separate in their entirety; but, by observing the direction of the muscle fiber passage, one can usually closely delimit them.

In all probability, both the front and hind legs of the specimens will be pulled somewhat out of their normal positions, but the terms indicating relationships such as *dorsal, ventral,* etc., will be based upon the normal position of the limbs. This should be carefully noted, for otherwise confusion will result.

In most courses the cats used as specimens will probably be embalmed and thus will not have to be placed in preserving fluid, a type of preservative greatly inferior to embalming. The specimen will be used for some time; for this reason, every effort should be made to keep it in good condition. It should be skinned in such a manner that the skin can be wrapped around the bare regions and tied in that position after the laboratory period is completed. It also helps to tie a piece of cheesecloth around the animal. After the muscles have been studied for a few periods, they will become somewhat dry, and a solution should be rubbed on to keep them pliable. A good simple solution may be made by mixing glycerin and water, about three parts of water to one part of glycerin. At the end of the laboratory period, after this or a similar solution has been rubbed on the exposed parts, the skin should be wrapped around the body as usual. Facilities for storage differ in different laboratories; the instructor will give specific instructions concerning the procedure.

Skinning. Turn the cat on its belly, and with scissors clip most of the hair away from the skin just above and along the backbone. Start clipping just behind the head, and continue posteriorly to the base of the tail. Then, with scalpel, make a shallow incision only partly through the skin along the clipped area from the back of the head to the base of the tail. The object of this first shallow incision is to avoid cutting into the muscles underneath. Then start near the anterior region between the shoulder blades, and make the slit deeper for a short distance, picking up the edge of the slit with the fingers from time to time until it can be seen that the skin has been completely penetrated in this short area. The skin is rather loosely connected to the underlying muscles by whitish connective tissue, so that one can usually see when this is accomplished. After breaking through the skin, extend the cut anteriorly and posteriorly, using the short incision as a guide to the depth of the incisions, until the skin has been penetrated along the original shallow incision.

The skin should be disconnected on one side only, preferably the cat's left side, since this side is easier to skin when the scalpel is held in the right hand. The **superficial fascia,** a whitish connective tissue, connects the skin to the underlying muscles. In large or fat cats, the superficial fascia is frequently invested with fatty material. On the muscles themselves and covered by the superficial fascia, another type of fascia occurs, the **deep fascia.** Disconnect the skin from the muscles with as little actual cutting as possible. The fingers and the end of the scalpel opposite the blade are excellent tools with which to work. It will be necessary to cut the nerves and blood vessels that will be seen passing from the body to the skin.

With fingers and the blunt end of the scalpel, start disconnecting the skin from the underlying muscles on the left side until it has been removed about halfway toward the ventral surface. Then, with scissors, make a lateral cut through the skin just posterior to the shoulder region. Carry this incision ventrally, disconnecting the associated fascia from the muscles, and then turn anteriorly under the arm. Since the arm muscles will not be studied for some time, as much skin as possible should be left on the arm. About 2 inches in front of the preceding lateral cut, make another lateral incision through the skin from the original dorsal incision. Continue this second lateral incision ventrally and somewhat posteriorly in front of the arm until it meets the previous cut under the arm. Now make a lateral cut through the skin from the original incision just in front of the hind legs, and carry it on ventrally. The skin along the side may now be disconnected around to the mid-ventral line. Great care should be taken to remove none of the muscles with the skin, except certain cutaneous, or skin, muscles that will stick to the skin when it is removed. These will not be studied. In some cats, especially if they are quite lean, some of the chest muscles that will be studied may also stick to the skin. Before any of the muscles that stick to the skin are removed, be sure to consult with the instructor to make sure that you have identified them correctly. The flap of skin which has been loosened should stay attached to the body, so that at the end of the laboratory period it may be wrapped about the exposed portions and tied in place. This will prevent the cat from drying out.

After the skin has been loosened around to the mid-ventral line, scrape the fat and other connective tissue from the muscle surfaces, being careful not to remove any of the muscle tissue itself.

In order to assist the student to keep in mind the relationships between groups of muscles, several of the following exercises will be composite drawings, including two or more studies. As soon as one study is completed, the muscles should be added to the drawing as indicated. Faint lines should be used to indicate the direction of the passage of muscle fibers, and heavier lines for the edges of the muscles.

Abdominal Muscles. After removing the skin and fat from the ventral region, note the white line in the mid-ventral line. This is the **linea alba,** a raphe that separates the muscles of the two sides. The term **raphe** will be used at times in connection with muscle attachment. It is a general term referring to a ridge, or crease, that indicates the line of fusion of symmetrical parts of the body. Ordinarily, there is a sheet of connective tissue at this point of fusion the edge of which helps to form the ridge or crease. As has been indicated previously, muscles on one side of the body seldom pass across to the other side but may be attached at the middorsal or mid-ventral lines of the body, where they frequently fuse with comparable muscles from the opposite side at a raphe.   The linea alba is thus a raphe to which a special name has been applied.   Other raphes, such as the mid-ventral thoracic raphe, are named according to their positions.

External Oblique Muscle.   On each side of the linea alba and extending anteriorly and dorsally around the side is a broad flat muscle, the fibers of which pass anteriorly and dorsally from the linea alba.   This is the **external oblique muscle.**

ORIGIN: Posterior ribs and the lumbodorsal fascia.   The lumbodorsal fascia is the tough shining sheet of connective tissue that covers the muscles on the posterior region of the back.

INSERTION: Pelvic girdle (pubis), linea alba, and mid-ventral raphe of the thorax.

ACTION: Constricts abdomen.

Internal Oblique Muscle.   Covered by the external oblique muscle are two other abdominal muscles, rather thin in some specimens, which makes identification somewhat difficult.   Carefully make a short slit with the scalpel across the fibers of the external oblique muscle, being careful not to cut into the muscles underneath.   Then separate some of the fibers of the external oblique from the muscle underneath.   The muscle thus partly exposed is the **internal oblique.**   At times, its fibers do not show up well, but they extend at almost right angles to those of the external oblique muscle, posteriorly and dorsally from the linea alba.

ORIGIN: Lumbodorsal fascia and pelvic girdle (crest of ilium).

INSERTION: Linea alba.

ACTION: Compresses abdomen.

Transverse Muscle.   Make the previous slit deeper so that it will pass through the fibers of the internal oblique.   The muscle under the internal oblique is very thin, but the fibers usually show up well.   This is the **transverse muscle,** the fibers of which run dorsally and slightly anteriorly from the linea alba, more dorsally and less anteriorly than do the fibers of the external oblique.

ORIGIN: From last four ribs, lumbar vertebrae, and pelvic girdle (ilium).

INSERTION: Linea alba.

ACTION: Constricts abdomen.

Rectus Abdominis Muscle.   A pair of **rectus abdominis muscles** occur one on each side of the linea alba, but they are covered by the ends of some of the muscles described above.   Cut through these ends for a short distance on one side of the linea alba, exposing one rectus abdominis muscle.   It can be distin-

guished from the preceding muscles by the fact that its fibers
extend longitudinally, parallel to the linea alba.

ORIGIN: Pelvic girdle (pubis).

INSERTION: Costal cartilage of first rib, and sternum.

ACTION: Compresses abdomen; retracts ribs and sternum.

Drawing 15. Muscles of the Side and Thigh—Lateral View.
Make a full-page outline of the side of the cat, including its thigh;
do not include the head, neck, upper arm, or lower leg. Show
the three layers of the abdominal muscles by leaving a "window"
in the outer layers, and indicate the lower layers by light lines
showing the direction of fiber passage. Sketch in a few of the
posterior ribs, and later add the intercostal muscles. **Labels:**
Abdominal muscles—external oblique, internal oblique, transverse, rectus abdominis, position of linea alba. Later add thigh
muscles—sartorius, gluteus medius, gluteus maximus, caudofemoralis, biceps femoris, semitendinosus, tensor fasciae latae.

The Pectoral, or Chest, Muscles. Turn the cat on its back
and study the muscles of the chest. There are four pairs of chest
muscles, but the exact limits of some are very difficult to find.
The limits are usually indicated somewhat by the direction of
fiber passage. In a few specimens, the limits are quite clear.
Scrape the muscles clean of fat and fascia so that the fibers are
well exposed.

Pectoantibrachialis. Start at the front margin of the shoulder,
and note a muscle in this region that passes across the anterior
edge of the shoulder toward the arm. This particular muscle is
not a chest muscle, but it is usually easily separable from the
first chest muscle, which is just posterior to and in contact with
it, and its name will be given later. The most anterior pectoral
muscle is the **pectoantibrachialis,** which is just posterior to the
above-mentioned muscle. Its fibers pass straight across from
the sternum to the arm. It is a bandlike muscle of about the
same width for its entire length. It is frequently separable from
the muscle posterior to it.

ORIGIN: Manubrium of sternum.

INSERTION: Ulna of forearm.

ACTION: Pulls arm toward chest; thus, an adductor muscle.

Pectoralis Major. The **pectoralis major muscle** is just posterior to and in contact with the pectoantibrachialis. It is somewhat fan-shaped with the widest part attached to the sternum.
This muscle passes toward the arm and becomes smaller, and
passes under (dorsal to) the pectoantibrachialis.

ORIGIN: Sternum and mid-ventral raphe of thorax.

INSERTION: Humerus of upper arm.

ACTION: Pulls arm toward chest.

Pectoralis Minor. It is usually difficult if not impossible to separate all the **pectoralis minor muscle** from the muscles described above. It is posterior to the pectoralis major, and its attachment to the sternum is as wide as or slightly wider than this end of the pectoralis major. It is fan-shaped, also; and as it passes toward the arm, it becomes smaller and passes under (dorsal to) the distal end of the pectoralis major.

ORIGIN: Sternum.

INSERTION: Humerus.

ACTION: Pulls arm toward chest.

Xiphihumeralis. The **xiphihumeralis muscle** is sometimes easy to separate from the pectoralis minor, since its proximal end is frequently slightly raised above the level of the anterior muscles. It is the most posterior chest muscle. It passes from the sternum anteriorly and dorsally under the pectoralis minor.

ORIGIN: Xiphoid process of sternum.

INSERTION: Humerus (bicipital groove).

ACTION: Pulls arm toward chest.

See drawing directions 16 (page 170).

Muscles of the Ventral and Lateral Portions of the Neck. The heads of some specimens will probably be applied so closely to the neck that it will be necessary to push the head back before the neck and throat muscles can be studied.

Slit the skin from the anterior end of the chest anteriorly along the middle of the throat, and carry the incision under the middle of the floor of the mouth to the tip of the lower jaw. Then peel back the skin on both sides so as fully to expose the throat and lower jaw. Also, remove the skin from the sides of the neck and some from the sides of the head. There is usually a large amount of fat and other material along the throat and sides of the neck; this should be removed. Do not cut the skin from the body. Instead, leave it attached, and at the end of the laboratory period wrap it around the exposed muscles and tie it in place.

Sternomastoid. At the side of the neck, note a large blood vessel passing anteriorly from the anterior edge of the shoulder. This is the external jugular vein. It passes across the first muscle to be studied. The muscle under (really dorsal to) the external jugular vein is the **sternomastoid.** From the region of the jugular vein, the sternomastoid passes obliquely posteriorly and meets the corresponding muscle from the opposite side in the mid-ventral line, the two muscles forming somewhat of a V shape at the base of the throat. From the sternum, to which these muscles are attached, they pass anteriorly and dorsally around the sides of the neck and attach to the superior nuchal line and mastoid process at the base of the skull.

ORIGIN: Manubrium of sternum and mid-ventral thoracic raphe.

INSERTION: Mastoid process and superior nuchal line.

ACTION: Individually turns head; together depress head.

Clavotrapezius. Lateral and dorsal to the sternomastoid is a somewhat larger muscle that passes from the shoulder region anteriorly and dorsally around the side of the neck. This is the **clavotrapezius.** Its limits can best be seen if the specimen is turned on its side. It covers most of the side of the neck. This muscle is one of the three trapezius muscles that occur in the cat. It will be mentioned more in detail when the other trapezius muscles are discussed.

Clavobrachialis. The **clavobrachialis muscle** is the one previously mentioned as being in contact with the anterior edge of the pectoantibrachialis. It is more or less of a continuation of the clavotrapezius from the clavicle ventrally (apparently laterally) across the shoulder region and the anterior margin of the upper arm. The clavotrapezius thus ends at the angle formed by the arm and neck, while the clavobrachialis occurs from this angle and along the anterior margin of the upper arm. These two muscles are sometimes considered to be a single muscle, the term cephalobrachial then being used. Here they will be considered as separate muscles.

ORIGIN: Clavicle; also fibers of the clavotrapezius muscle.

INSERTION: Ulna.

ACTION: Flexes forearm.

Cleidomastoid. The **cleidomastoid muscle** is dorsal to the clavotrapezius and the sternomastoid. The two latter muscles should be separated and their edges pulled apart somewhat to reveal the cleidomastoid. It is a bandlike muscle, the fibers of which pass longitudinally.

ORIGIN: Mastoid process (depending upon action).

INSERTION: Clavicle (depending upon action).

ACTION: Pulls clavicle anteriorly; also helps to turn and depress the head. The origin and insertion thus vary according to the action.

Muscles of the Throat, or Ventral Part of the Neck. *Sterno-hyoid.* One pair of throat muscles, the sternomastoids, has already been described. Turn back to the mid-ventral line where these muscles attach to the sternum. Dorsal to the sterno-mastoids are two longitudinal muscles, the ends of which can usually be seen in front of the anterior margins of the sterno-mastoids. The fascia that frequently occurs in this region should be pulled away. This will leave a slight depression in which can be seen the ends of the longitudinal muscles. These are the **sternohyoid muscles.**

Carefully cut through the attachments of the sternomastoids in the mid-ventral line until longitudinal muscle fibers are seen. The sternomastoids are partly divided into regions at their origin on the sternum, so that, unless one carefully observes the direction of fiber passage, the incision may not be made deep enough and the sternohyoids will not be fully exposed.

ORIGIN: First rib (costal cartilage).

INSERTION: Hyoid bone (to be seen presently).

ACTION: Draws hyoid posteriorly.

Sternothyroid. With forceps pick away the tissue lateral to the sternohyoid muscle on the cat's right side. Very shortly another small muscle will be exposed dorsal to the sternohyoid and also possessing longitudinal fibers. This muscle is the **sternothyroid.**

Before noting the origin, insertion, and action of this muscle, locate a few structures in this region. Separate the two sterno-hyoids in the mid-ventral line, spread them apart, and trace them anteriorly to their insertion. Feel in this region with the fingers, and try to find the **hyoid bone,** to which the sternohyoid muscles are attached. In some specimens this bone is easily located; in others, this is more difficult. The hyoid bone helps to support the tongue and larynx and has probably been derived from the hyoid arch and other visceral, or gill, arches found in lower forms. Just posterior and dorsal to the attachment of the sternohyoid muscles can be seen the **larynx,** or voice box. This structure is somewhat cartilaginous and is whitish in color. The ventral portion of the larynx is formed by the **thyroid cartilage,** which is the "Adam's apple" in man. The thyroid cartilage and other parts of the larynx have also been derived from visceral, or gill, arches of lower forms. Leading posteriorly from the larynx is the **trachea,** the tube that passes to the lungs.

ORIGIN: First ribs (costal cartilages) and sternum.

INSERTION: Larynx (thyroid cartilage).

ACTION: Moves larynx posteriorly.

Thyrohyoid. The **thyrohyoid muscle** is just anterior to the sternothyroid and appears to be a direct continuation of it. The thyrohyoid and the sternothyroid are together about the same length as the sternohyoid. The sternothyroid and thyrohyoid can easily be distinguished from each other by pulling them slightly with forceps and thus determining their points of attachment.

ORIGIN: Larynx (thyroid cartilage).

INSERTION: Hyoid bone.

ACTION: Raises larynx.

Digastric. With forceps pull away the fascia from the lower surface of the bones of the lower jaw and from between these bones under the floor of the mouth. The **digastric muscles** occur, one on each side, along the undersurface of the lower jawbone.

ORIGIN: Mastoid and jugular processes.

INSERTION: Ventral side of lower jaw.

ACTION: Depresses lower jaw, thus opening the mouth.

Mylohyoid. If sufficient connective tissue has been removed from between the two halves of the lower jaw, there should now be a distinct depression in this region. The **mylohyoids** extend transversely between the two parts of the lower jaw. The two muscles, one from each side, insert in the mid-ventral line between the two sides of the lower jaw, thus forming a complete sheet on the undersurface of the floor of the mouth.

ORIGIN: Inner side of lower jaw.

INSERTION: A median raphe on the undersurface of the floor of the mouth. Both muscles insert together.

ACTION: Raises floor of mouth.

Geniohyoid. Carefully slit through the insertions of the mylohyoids in the mid-ventral line, and fold back these ends. Two small muscles, the fibers of which run longitudinally, will thus be exposed. These are the **geniohyoids**.

ORIGIN: Inner ventral side of lower jaw near anterior end.

INSERTION: Hyoid bone.

ACTION: Pulls hyoid forward.

Masseter. A pair of muscles should now be located that, strictly speaking, should probably not be considered to be neck or throat muscles. If the skin has not been removed from the side of the head, remove it now as far dorsally as the middle of the top of the head. The **masseter muscle** is the large thick muscle occurring at the angle of the jaw.   Posterior to the masseter muscle can be seen glandular tissue constituting a salivary gland, the **parotid.**   Another gland, the **submaxillary,** occurs somewhat ventral to the parotid, also in contact with the masseter muscle. This gland is somewhat smaller than the parotid.   Other salivary glands occur in the cat, but they are more difficult to locate than those mentioned.   The masseter is the muscle in man that can be felt contracting at the angle of the jaw when one tightly closes the mouth.

ORIGIN: Zygomatic arch.

INSERTION: Lower jaw, especially in and around the coronoid fossa.

ACTION: Elevates the lower jaw, thus closing the mouth.

Temporal Muscle.   The **temporal muscle** occurs just above the ear and posterior to the eye.   It is a large thick muscle and occupies the temporal fossa and the hole surrounded by the posterior part of the zygomatic arch.

ORIGIN: Temporal fossa of skull.

INSERTION: Coronoid process of lower jaw.

ACTION: Elevates lower jaw in conjunction with masseter.

Drawing 16.   Pectoral, Throat, and Associated Muscles— Ventral View.   Make a full-page drawing of one side of the cat from the mid-ventral line to the side.   Include the upper arm, but omit the thigh.   This drawing should include the thoracic, neck, and head regions.   As indicated, some muscles will be included that, strictly speaking, do not belong to either the pectoral or the throat group of muscles.   **Labels:** Pectoral and associated muscles—pectoantibrachialis, pectoralis major, pectoralis minor, xiphihumeralis, external oblique, latissimus dorsi, spinotrapezius, linea alba, rectus abdominis.   Throat and related muscles—mylohyoid, thyrohyoid, sternohyoid, sternothyroid, sternomastoid, cleidomastoid, geniohyoid, clavotrapezius, clavobrachialis, masseter, digastric.

Muscles of the Shoulder and Upper Part of Back.   *Latissimus Dorsi.*   Turn the cat on its side, and observe a very large flat muscle extending along the side from the inner surface of the upper arm posteriorly to the large shiny fascia that covers the posterior region of the back.   This large muscle is the **latissimus dorsi,** and it partly covers the external oblique.   The fascia is the **lumbodorsal fascia.**

ORIGIN: Posterior thoracic and lumbar vertebrae (neural spines).

INSERTION: Humerus.

ACTION: Pulls arm dorsally and posteriorly.

Trapezius Muscles. The **trapezius muscles,** of which there are three in the cat, are sometimes considered as being divisions of a single muscle. They will here be considered as separate. Muscles in this region are sometimes difficult to differentiate, so that it may be necessary to pick away additional connective tissue in order to make identification easier. Remember that in most instances muscles can be somewhat differentiated by the direction in which their fibers extend. The trapezius muscles are in contact with each other in front of the latissimus dorsi and cover almost the entire surface along the vertebral column and somewhat laterally to this region.

Spinotrapezius. The **spinotrapezius muscle** occurs dorsal and anterior to the median portion of the latissimus dorsi, and somewhat overlaps it. It is the most posterior trapezius muscle. The ventral edge of the spinotrapezius is usually easily separable from the latissimus dorsi. The fibers of this muscle pass somewhat parallel to those of the latissimus dorsi. The posterior portion, which is attached to the spines of the vertebrae, is much wider than the anterior end; it is thus triangular in shape.

ORIGIN: Thoracic vertebrae (neural spines).

INSERTION: On the fascia of the supraspinatus and infraspinatus muscles, to be identified later, which occur on the scapula.

ACTION: Pulls scapula dorsally and posteriorly.

Acromiotrapezius. The **acromiotrapezius muscle** is anterior to the preceding. It is also somewhat triangular in shape, and the fibers run in a dorsoventral direction from the vertebral column to the scapula. It is a relatively wide muscle for its full length, so that it is not so truly triangular as is the spinotrapezius. Externally, it covers much of the anterior and dorsal region of the scapula. The scapula may be seen by moving the front leg.

ORIGIN: Cervical and thoracic vertebrae (neural spines).

INSERTION: Scapula (spine and metacromion process).

ACTION: Individually pulls scapula dorsally. The two muscles help hold the two scapulae in position.

Clavotrapezius. The **clavotrapezius muscle,** the most anterior of the trapezius muscles, partly covers the sides and the back of the neck. It has been previously identified as the anterior and dorsal continuation of the clavobrachialis. These two muscles are separated at the clavicle.

ORIGIN: Superior nuchal line of skull.

INSERTION: Clavicle.

ACTION: Pulls clavicle up and anteriorly.

Levator Scapulae Ventralis. The **levator scapulae ventralis muscle** occurs in contact with the anterior ventral border of the acromiotrapezius and can be distinguished from it by the fact that the fibers are directed more anteriorly than are those of the acromiotrapezius. It is a comparatively small, somewhat band-like muscle, passing anteriorly and dorsally under the clavo-trapezius muscle. The latter should be cut, and the levator scapulae ventralis traced anteriorly.

ORIGIN: Atlas (transverse process); occipital bone of skull.

INSERTION: Scapula (metacromion process).

ACTION: Pulls scapula forward.

Deltoid Muscles—Spinodeltoid. Two deltoid muscles occur in the cat. The **spinodeltoid** is ventral to the acromiotrapezius, and the fibers run anteriorly and ventrally across the upper arm. (The fibers will probably appear to extend only anteriorly if the cat's leg is pulled forward out of normal walking position.) The anterior edge of the spinodeltoid is in contact with the levator scapulae ventralis.

ORIGIN: Spine of scapula.

INSERTION: Humerus.

ACTION: Raises (flexes) humerus and rotates it.

Acromiodeltoid. The **acromiodeltoid** is anterior to the preceding and ventral to the levator scapulae ventralis. This muscle is somewhat triangular, and there may be a vein along its surface. The fibers of this muscle are directed ventrally.

ORIGIN: Scapula (acromion process).

INSERTION: Mostly on spinodeltoid muscle.

ACTION: Same as spinodeltoid.

Drawing 17. Muscles of Shoulder and Associated Regions— Lateral View. Make a full-page drawing from the side of the anterior two-thirds of the cat, including the upper arm. Draw the muscles as they are identified. **Labels:** sternomastoid, clavo-trapezius, clavobrachialis, acromiodeltoid, levator scapulae ventralis, acromiotrapezius, spinodeltoid, spinotrapezius, latissimus dorsi, external oblique, xiphihumeralis, pectoralis minor, pectoralis major, long head of triceps brachii, lateral head of triceps brachii.

The Deeper Muscles. The muscles studied in the preceding paragraphs are on the surface of the body and are, therefore, superficial muscles. Some of the deeper muscles should now be identified. Loosen the trapezius muscles so that they may be cut across to expose the muscles underneath. Cut across the acromiotrapezius muscle near the vertebral column. This will reveal the anterior border of the scapula. Then cut across the belly of the spinotrapezius, and spread the cut edges. Both the anterior and vertebral borders of the scapula will be thus exposed. Remove the connective tissue and fascia between the scapula and the vertebral column, being careful not to injure a muscle that occurs in that region.

Rhomboideus. Pull the front leg of the cat toward the ventral side of the body, and note the muscle that extends from the vertebral border of the scapula to the vertebral column. This is the **rhomboideus,** the fibers of which are somewhat convergent and not so compactly bound together as the fibers of a muscle usually are. Some of the posterior fibers of this muscle form a rather compact group. Instead of attaching to the vertebral border of the scapula as do most of the other fibers, they pass over the scapula and attach to the outer scapular surface. This posterior division of the muscle has the appearance of being a separate muscle but is still considered to be a part of the rhomboideus. The point of attachment of this portion to the outer scapular surface is partly covered by the latissimus dorsi muscle.

ORIGIN: Thoracic vertebrae (neural spines).

INSERTION: Vertebral border and outer surface of scapula.

ACTION: Pulls scapula toward vertebral column.

A lateral and anterior portion of the rhomboideus is also somewhat separated from other parts of the muscle. This is given the name **rhomboideus capitis.** This division of the muscle extends farther anteriorly under the clavotrapezius than do the other fibers and is a somewhat bandlike extension of the main muscle. It extends anteriorly along the side of the neck. Cut across the belly of the clavotrapezius, and trace out the limits of this division. Then loosen and cut across the rhomboideus capitis.

ORIGIN: Superior nuchal line.

INSERTION: Scapula.

ACTION: Rotates scapula and pulls it forward.

Splenius. The **splenius** is the large muscle that covers the side and dorsal part of the neck and that was more fully exposed when the rhomboideus capitis was cut. Its posterior edge is in contact with the rhomboideus proper.

ORIGIN: From fascia along the middorsal line of the neck.

INSERTION: Superior nuchal line.

ACTION: Raises head and turns it.

If the ventral portion of the acromiotrapezius muscle has not as yet been turned back exposing the muscles on the outer surface of the scapula, this should be done now. Then cut across the latissimus dorsi at about the level of the vertebral border of the scapula, and extend the cut along the scapular border. Loosen the anterior part of the latissimus dorsi, until practically the entire scapula with its muscles is exposed. The supraspinatus, the infraspinatus, and the teres major may then be found.

Supraspinatus. The **supraspinatus** is the muscle that was covered by the acromiotrapezius before the latter was cut. As the name implies, it occurs in the supraspinous fossa of the scapula and extends over the anterior border, where it is in contact with another muscle on the inner (medial) surface of the scapula. This muscle on the medial scapular surface will be identified later.

ORIGIN: Supraspinous fossa of scapula.

INSERTION: Humerus (greater tuberosity).

ACTION: Extends humerus.

Infraspinatus. The **infraspinatus muscle** occupies the infraspinous fossa of the scapula and is posterior to the supraspinatus muscle. (It is apparently ventral to the supraspinatus if the front legs are stretched forward.) This muscle was covered by the latissimus dorsi before the latter was detached.

ORIGIN: Scapula (infraspinous fossa).

INSERTION: Humerus (greater tuberosity).

ACTION: Rotates humerus.

Teres Major. The **teres major** is posterior (apparently ventral) to the infraspinatus. It, also, is covered, in life, by the latissimus dorsi.

ORIGIN: Scapula (axillary border) and fascia of associated muscles.

INSERTION: Humerus (medial surface).

ACTION: Lowers and rotates humerus.

Teres Minor. Separate the teres major and the infraspinatus, being certain that the posterior ventral surface of the latter is well exposed. The **teres minor** passes from the posterior ventral surface of the infraspinatus to the humerus and is sometimes quite difficult to find. The fibers of this muscle extend in a slightly different direction from those of the infraspinatus.

ORIGIN: Scapula (lower part of axillary border).

INSERTION: Humerus (greater tuberosity).

ACTION: Rotates humerus.

Subscapularis. The **subscapularis** is the muscle that was previously mentioned as being in contact with a portion of the supraspinatus. It occurs on the inner (medial) surface of the scapula and occupies the subscapular fossa. Most of this muscle can be seen on the inner scapular surface, anterior and ventral to the rhomboideus, if the connective tissue in this region is cleaned away and if the scapula is pulled somewhat away from the body.

ORIGIN: Subscapular fossa.

INSERTION: Humerus (lesser tuberosity).

ACTION: Adducts humerus; pulls it medially.

Serratus Ventralis Anterior. Cut across the rhomboideus so that the vertebral border of the scapula is now free from the body wall. From the ventral portion of the scapula, another muscle passes toward the body wall and attaches to the side of the body. Cut through the pectoral muscles, if this has not already been done, and note that this muscle spreads out into a fan shape between the scapula and the ribs posterior to the scapula. This muscle is the **serratus ventralis anterior.** The anterior portion is sometimes considered to be a separate muscle (levator scapulae), but the separation between the two is difficult to find.

ORIGIN: Anterior 9 or 10 ribs, and last 5 cervical vertebrae (transverse processes).

INSERTION: Inner surface of scapula.

ACTION: Pulls scapula toward ribs, anteriorly and ventrally.

Disconnect the latissimus dorsi for its entire length from the muscles underneath, and turn it over the back. The dorsal posterior portion of the serratus ventralis anterior is usually somewhat connected to the body wall by fat or loose connective tissue. This material should be cleared away, so that the next muscle to be studied will be exposed.

Serratus Dorsalis Posterior. The **serratus dorsalis posterior** is a thin sheet of muscle along the surface of the ribs posterior to the serratus ventralis anterior and partly covered by this muscle and the latissimus dorsi. It originates in the mid-line of the body by a thin aponeurosis; the ventral portion is attached to the ribs by several slips.

ORIGIN: Thoracic and lumbar vertebrae (neural spines).

INSERTION: Posterior ribs.

ACTION: Pulls ribs anteriorly.

Intercostal Muscles. There are a large number of **intercostal muscles** occurring between the ribs, which they assist in moving during respiration. Make a longitudinal slit in the external oblique muscle over the posterior ribs to find these muscles. There are two layers, external intercostal and internal intercostal muscles, but they are somewhat difficult to distinguish.

ORIGIN: Ribs.

INSERTION: Ribs.

ACTION: Pull ribs anteriorly (external intercostal muscles) and back (internal intercostal muscles).

Scalenus. Raise the previously cut ends of the pectoral muscles, and observe under them several muscles that pass longitudinally and somewhat combine anteriorly to form a single muscle. These are the **scalenus muscles.**

ORIGIN: Ribs.

INSERTION: Cervical vertebrae (transverse processes).

ACTION: Bend neck; pull ribs forward. Origin and insertion are thus interchangeable, depending upon the action.

The Epaxial Muscles. It should be remembered that the **epaxial muscles** are those along the body in the dogfish and Necturus which are separated from the ventral (hypaxial) muscles by a longitudinal septum. In the cat they have undergone considerable modification compared with the condition found in these two animals. Make a longitudinal slit through the lumbo-dorsal fascia about $1\frac{1}{2}$ inches anterior to the region where the hind legs join the body, and continue the slit anteriorly through the origin of the serratus dorsalis just posterior to the base of the neck. Turn back the fascia for about 1 inch, so as to reveal the muscles, the fibers of which extend more or less parallel to the vertebral column. As will be noted, the divisions between some of these muscles are rather indefinite. Begin the identification in the posterior region, where several divisions will be observed. Toward the posterior region of the body especially, these muscles will be enclosed in tough fascia, and this material will have to be removed at times before the divisions will be evident.

Multifidus Spinae. The **multifidus spinae** is the smallest and most dorsal division in the posterior region and is very closely applied to the vertebral column. It extends up to the region of the neck, where it divides into two divisions to be noted later. In the region of the thorax, this muscle is partly covered by other muscles, so that it cannot be seen externally. Do not as yet attempt to trace this muscle for its entire length, since to do so will destroy other muscles.

ORIGIN: Transverse processes of vertebrae.

INSERTION: Neural spines of vertebrae.

ACTION: Straightens and twists back.

Longissimus Dorsi. Grasp the ventral cut edge of the lumbo-dorsal fascia, and pull it ventrally. This will expose two muscles that are lateral to the multifidus; the fascia itself is attached to the dorsal edge of a third. These three muscles are in reality divisions of a single muscle, the **longissimus dorsi.** Follow these three divisions anteriorly, and observe that they do combine into a single muscle, which continues anteriorly and attaches to some of the vertebrae under the serratus ventralis anterior. It is sometimes difficult to trace this muscle for its entire length. In the region of the thorax, the longissimus dorsi is the middle of three longitudinal muscles that occur along the side. This anterior portion should be found, so that the identification of the additional muscles will be easier.

ORIGIN: Sacral and caudal vertebrae, and pelvic girdle (ilium).

INSERTION: Several vertebrae along the vertebral column.

ACTION: Extends vertebral column.

Spinalis Dorsi. In the thoracic region under the origin of the serratus dorsalis, which has already been cut, are to be seen two longitudinal muscles, one on each side of the anterior end of the longissimus. The dorsal muscle is the **spinalis dorsi.**

ORIGIN: Posterior thoracic vertebrae (neural spines).

INSERTION: Anterior thoracic and cervical vertebrae.

ACTION: Straightens (extends) vertebral column.

Iliocostalis. The **iliocostalis** is the muscle mentioned above as being ventral to the anterior end of the longissimus dorsi.

ORIGIN: Ribs.

INSERTION: Ribs.

ACTION: Pulls ribs together.

Semispinalis Cervicis. The **semispinalis cervicis** is the anterior end of the multifidus spinae, which was previously identified in the posterior region. It lies under the splenius. Slit the splenius, and observe that the semispinalis consists of two fairly definite divisions, a dorsal **biventer cervicis;** and a ventral, or lateral, **complexus.** It should be noted that, although the biventer cervicis is rather intimately connected to the spinalis dorsi, it is in reality an anterior extension of the multifidus spinae.

Close examination will reveal that, although some of the fibers of the spinalis dorsi and the biventer cervicis are mixed, they are essentially separate muscles. Posterior to the biventer cervicis, the multifidus is under the spinalis dorsi and in this region is sometimes difficult to identify as a definite muscle.

ORIGIN: Thoracic and cervical vertebrae.

INSERTION: Superior nuchal line of skull and atlas.

ACTION: Raises head.

Since so many of the muscles have been cut, a drawing is not required, although it is suggested that sketches be made to be used for review.

Muscles of the Upper Arm. Remove the skin from the cat's arm in such a way that it can be wrapped about the arm when the work is completed. Either arm may be used, but the left arm is probably better, since most of the previous work has been done on this side. It will be noted that some of the upper-arm muscles are covered by the insertions of the pectoral muscles, but these should not be exposed until later. Start the study with the cat on its back.

Triceps Brachii. The largest muscle of the upper arm is the **triceps brachii,** which, as the name implies, is divided into three somewhat distinct heads. This muscle occupies a part of the posterior and outer surfaces of the arm. The **long head** of the triceps is on the posterior edge of the upper arm, and it can be seen from both lateral and medial, or inner, surfaces. Raise the cat's arm so that the outer surface may be seen. The **lateral head** of the triceps is the large mass of muscle on the outer surface of the arm just in front of the long head. The separation point between these two heads occurs on the outer-arm surface and can best be seen distally. Separate these two heads, spread them apart, and locate the **medial head** between the two.

ORIGIN: Humerus.

INSERTION: Ulna (olecranon process).

ACTION: Extends forearm (straightens whole arm).

Extensor Antibrachii. Turn back to the inner surface of the upper arm. Just in front of and partly covering the long head of the triceps, from this view, is a thin ribbonlike muscle, the **extensor antibrachii.** This muscle should be disconnected from the triceps. The division between the two can usually best be seen near the posterior edge of the arm.

ORIGIN: Latissimus dorsi.

INSERTION: Ulna (olecranon process).

ACTION: Extends forearm in combination with the triceps.

Anterior to the extensor antibrachii, the other arm muscles are covered by the insertions of the pectoral muscles. Cut across the pectoral muscles near the region of the origin of the extensor antibrachii (unless this has already been done), and turn the stubs anteriorly.

Biceps Brachii. The **biceps brachii** occupies the anterior margin of the upper arm and is normally covered by the insertions of the pectoral muscles. It is a rather large spindle-shaped muscle.

ORIGIN: Scapula (glenoid fossa).

INSERTION: Radius.

ACTION: Flexes forearm (draws forearm toward upper arm).

Before an attempt is made to identify the next muscle, the clavobrachialis and the fascia connected to its posterior edge should be completely disconnected from the anterior and lateral surface of the arm. To do this, turn the cat on its ventral surface so that the outer surface of the arm may be seen. It should be noted that a large vein runs along the arm in this region. This is sometimes removed with the fascia, but it should be preserved if possible, since it occurs along the surface of the next muscle to be identified.

Brachialis. After completing the above operations, identify the **brachialis.** This is a rather small muscle that occurs on the outer surface of the arm, just anterior to the lateral head of the triceps. It is in contact with the distal end of the acromiodeltoid muscle and in some respects appears to be a direct distal continuation of this muscle.

ORIGIN: Humerus.

INSERTION: Ulna.

ACTION: Flexes forearm.

Most of the muscles of the forearm are concerned with the rotation of the lower arm and with the movements of the hand and digits. Since most of them are relatively small, they will not be studied at this time. Add the muscles called for to drawing 17, page 172.

The Muscles of the Thigh. *Sartorius.* Place the cat on its back, and remove the skin from its right leg. (If the right leg has been used for injecting the blood vessels or embalming fluid, use the left leg.) The skin should be removed in such a fashion that it can be wrapped around the leg at the end of the laboratory period. Observe the inner surface of the thigh. Most of this surface is covered by two long flat muscles. The general line of demarcation between these is partly indicated by blood vessels near the middle of the surface of the thigh. The muscle occupying the anterior half of the inner surface is the **sartorius,** which also extends partly over the anterior edge of the thigh onto the outer surface. The posterior muscle is the **gracilis,** which will be discussed later.

ORIGIN: Ilium (crest and ventral portion).

INSERTION: Proximal end of tibia and fibula.

ACTION: Adducts and rotates thigh; extends shank.

Tensor Fasciae Latae. On the proximal end of the anterior edge of the thigh, there usually occurs a large amount of fat and other connective tissue. This material should be removed with the fingers. When it has been removed, the limits of the sartorius on the outer surface of the thigh will become evident. Disconnect the sartorius from the underlying muscles, and cut it across the middle. This can easily be done by first disconnecting the front edge and inserting a finger under the muscle. It should now be noted that the muscles on the outer and anterior surface of the thigh are partly covered by a rather thin fascia. This fascia is the **fascia lata,** which must be partly removed before the underlying muscles can be identified. With scissors make a small longitudinal cut through this fascia on the anterior edge of the thigh. Then, before cutting farther, disconnect the fascia from the underlying muscles using the blunt end of the scalpel or the fingers. When the fascia has been lifted, it will be noted that there is a thin muscle attached to the fascia near the proximal end of the thigh. This muscle is the **tensor fasciae latae.**

ORIGIN: Ilium.

INSERTION: Fascia lata.

ACTION: Tightens fascia lata; helps extend leg.

Now continue the split in the fascia lata distally to the patella, or kneecap, disconnecting it from the underlying muscles. The fascia should then be pulled somewhat to one side.

Vastus Lateralis. The **vastus lateralis** was covered by the fascia lata and occupies most of the anterior edge of the thigh.

ORIGIN: Femur (great trochanter).

INSERTION: Patella.

ACTION: Extends shank (straightens whole leg).

Rectus Femoris. The **rectus femoris** occurs in close association with the preceding muscle and is sometimes hard to differentiate from it. It was mostly covered by the sartorius before this muscle was cut and lies somewhat nearer the inner surface of the thigh. The line of demarcation between this muscle and the vastus lateralis also occurs slightly toward the inner surface, although still on the anterior edge of the thigh. If the two muscles cannot readily be separated, the split in the fascia lata should be carried proximally until the origins of the two muscles are uncovered. These lie somewhat under the tensor fasciae latae, which will probably have to be split to uncover them. When the fat and other connective tissue near the junction of the thigh and the body have been picked away, the distinct origin of the two muscles can usually be readily observed. Separate these two muscles.

ORIGIN: Ilium (near acetabulum).

INSERTION: Patella.

ACTION: Extends shank (straightens whole leg).

Vastus Intermedius. The **vastus intermedius** occurs between the vastus lateralis and the rectus femoris. When these two muscles are widely separated, the vastus intermedius should be seen. It is in contact with the femur.

ORIGIN: Femur (shaft).

INSERTION: Patella.

ACTION: Extends shank (straightens whole leg).

Vastus Medialis. Locate the **vastus medialis** on the inner surface of the thigh, in contact with and posterior to the rectus femoris. The fascia lata is attached to its edge.

ORIGIN: Femur (shaft).

INSERTION: Patella.

ACTION: Extends shank (straightens whole leg).

It is to be noted that the last four muscles to be discussed have essentially the same insertion and action. They are often considered the divisions of a single muscle, the **quadriceps femoris.**

Gracilis. Locate again the **gracilis,** the large flat muscle covering most of the posterior inner surface of the thigh posterior to the sartorius.

ORIGIN: Ischium and pubis (symphyses).

INSERTION: Tibia.

ACTION: Adducts thigh; pulls thigh posteriorly.

It should now be seen that the gracilis does not cover all the posterior inner surface of the thigh but that there is a small anterior region where other muscles occur. Disconnect the edge of the gracilis nearest the sartorius from the underlying muscles.

Then work the fingers underneath, and note the line of demarcation between the gracilis and the muscles anterior to it. Cut across the middle of the gracilis, and fold back the cut edges. A rather large mass representing several muscles will thus be more clearly exposed. The limits between these muscles are not always apparent. Start at the proximal end of this group of muscles.

Pectineus. The **pectineus** is the first, very small section of the muscle mass and was not covered by the gracilis. It is often hard to find in small cats and may sometimes appear to be a portion of the next muscle.

ORIGIN: Pubis.

INSERTION: Femur (shaft).

ACTION: Adducts thigh.

Adductor Longus. Distal to the pectineus, the **adductor longus** appears as a slightly larger muscle. This muscle also was not covered by the gracilis before it was cut but may have been obscured by connective tissue.

ORIGIN: Pubis.

INSERTION: Femur.

ACTION: Adducts thigh.

Adductor Femoris. Distal to the adductor longus is a comparatively large triangular muscle, which appears to be composed of several groups of fibers. Most of the posterior region of this muscle was previously covered by the gracilis, but the upper anterior parts were not. This is the **adductor femoris.** It is usually rather easily separable from the muscle that is distal to it.

ORIGIN: Pubis and ischium (rami).

INSERTION: Femur (shaft).

ACTION: Adducts thigh and extends thigh.

Semimembranosus. Still farther distal to the adductor longus, and somewhat larger than it, is the **semimembranosus.**

ORIGIN: Ischium (tuberosity and ramus).

INSERTION: Femur.

ACTION: Extends thigh.

Semitendinosus. The **semitendinosus** is the most distal and posterior muscle of the thigh; the proximal end is partly covered by the semimembranosus when observed from this view. The distal end is usually rather easily separable from the semimembranosus. Trace this muscle as it passes toward the body, and determine its limits.

ORIGIN: Ischium (tuberosity).

INSERTION: Proximal end of tibia.

ACTION: Flexes shank.

Drawing 18. Muscles of Medial Surface of Thigh. Make a full-page drawing of the thigh, including enough of the shank to show the gastrocnemius. Make drawing with the gracilis and sartorius cut and with the edges laid back to show the muscles under them. **Labels:** pectineus, adductor longus, gracilis (cut), adductor femoris, semimembranosus, semitendinosus, gastrocnemius, rectus femoris, vastus medialis, patella, tensor fasciae latae, sartorius (cut).

Turn the cat on its ventral surface, and again examine the outer surface of the thigh. Determine again the extent of the tensor fasciae latae.

Biceps Femoris. This is the muscle which covers most of the outer posterior surface of the thigh; it will appear to be continuous with the fascia lata. With forceps break through the fascia lata just below the tensor fasciae latae. Then, with forceps or fingers, work between the fascia lata and the muscles underneath. As one proceeds distally, it will be noted that the biceps muscle can thus be easily disconnected.

ORIGIN: Ischium (tuberosity).

INSERTION: Tibia and patella.

ACTION: Abducts thigh; flexes shank.

Caudofemoralis. Locate the base of the tail, and clear away all fascia and connective tissue in that region. The **caudofemoralis** is a small muscle extending across the thigh from the base of the tail toward the proximal end of the biceps muscle. Clean away the connective tissue from this muscle so that it may be separated from the biceps. The distal portion is somewhat concealed by the biceps. Turn back the front edge of the biceps muscle, and notice that the caudofemoralis extends along it distally. Now separate these two muscles, and observe that a long tendon from the caudofemoralis extends distal to the knee.

ORIGIN: Caudal vertebrae.

INSERTION: Patella by the long tendon previously identified.

ACTION: Abducts thigh; helps extend shank.

Gluteus Maximus. The **gluteus maximus** is just anterior to the preceding and is sometimes difficult to separate from a muscle, the gluteus medius, that is anterior to it. With forceps clean away the fascia in this region, and identify the gluteus maximus as a small muscle partly overlying a larger muscle mass anterior to it. The gluteus maximus muscle is partly covered by the caudofemoralis.

ORIGIN: Sacral and caudal vertebrae.

INSERTION: Femur (great trochanter); fascia lata.

ACTION: Abducts thigh.

Gluteus Medius. The **gluteus medius** is the large mass of muscle anterior to and partly covered by the gluteus maximus.

ORIGIN: Ilium (crest); caudal and sacral vertebrae.

INSERTION: Femur (great trochanter).

ACTION: Abducts thigh.

Add the muscles called for to drawing 15, page 165.

Gastrocnemius. Most of the muscles of the lower leg or shank will not be identified, since the majority are relatively small and their limits are frequently hard to distinguish. Look on the posterior side of the shank, and observe a relatively large, somewhat spindle-shaped muscle that occupies most of this region. This is the gastrocnemius.

ORIGIN: Femur and associated fascia; sesamoid bones.

INSERTION: Calcaneus, or heel bone.

ACTION: Extends foot. When this muscle contracts in man, the individual rises on his toes.

Add the gastrocnemius muscle to drawing 18, page 183.

INTERNAL ANATOMY

In the cat the coelom has four complete divisions in contrast to the two divisions noted in the animals previously studied. These four sections are the two pleural cavities, each of which contains a lung; the pericardial cavity, surrounding the heart; and the peritoneal, or abdominal, cavity, which holds the various organs of the viscera. As the study progresses, the structures that form the walls of these several cavities should be observed. It should be noted that the single, pleuroperitoneal cavity that occurs in the animals previously studied has in the cat become divided into an anterior pleural region and a posterior peritoneal area. The pleural region is further separated into the two pleural cavities, each of which contains a lung. The pericardial cavity is between the two pleural cavities. It should be recalled that the separation into pleural and peritoneal regions is somewhat anticipated in the turtle, since, in that animal, most of the lung surfaces are outside the pleuroperitoneal cavity.

Locate the posterior end of the sternum in the mid-ventral line where the ribs from each side connect to it. With scissors cut through the posterior margins of the ribs about ½ inch to the left of the sternum, and carry the incision anteriorly parallel to the sternum as far forward as the level of the front legs. The cavity that has been cut into is the **left pleural cavity,** in which occurs the left lung. At the posterior end of the longitudinal incision, look through the slit, and locate a muscular partition that passes across the body and forms the posterior wall of the left pleural cavity. This is the **diaphragm,** a muscle that aids in respiration and that separates the pleural and pericardial cavities from the posterior peritoneal cavity. Now make a transverse slit through the ribs from the posterior end of the longitudinal incision toward the dorsal part of the body, being careful not to cut through the diaphragm. Make a similar transverse cut anteriorly, near the anterior end of the sternum, and bend back the ribs thus loosened so that the left pleural cavity will be opened.

Within the cavity the most noticeable structure is the **left lung,** a pinkish lobed structure. From anterior to posterior, the lobes are the **anterior, middle,** and **posterior lobes.** The pleural cavities are lined with a thin membrane, the **pleura,** which is also applied to the surfaces of the lungs. Near the mid-ventral line of the body, between the two pleural cavities, is the **pericardial cavity,** containing the **heart.** Locate the heart, which is sometimes so surrounded by fatty material that it is not possible as yet to distinguish details of structure. Passing from the heart to the mid-ventral line of the body is a thin partition, formed from a fusion in this region of the pleura of the right and left pleural cavities. This partition is the **mediastinal septum.** The two pleurae, one from each side, are thus fused ventral to the heart; but dorsally they separate, and a cavity is thus formed between them. The cavity between the two pleurae is the **mediastinum,** which encloses most of the organs or their parts in the mid-region, including the heart, the venae cavae, the aorta, the esophagus, the trachea, and the thymus gland.

The mediastinal septum may now be broken, and a flap cut on the right side through the ribs, comparable with that on the left side. (If this same specimen is to be used for a study of the circulation, the instructor may prefer to modify this dissection.) Observe the **right lung** in its pleural cavity. It is somewhat larger than the left lung and has more lobes. The difference in size is doubtless correlated with the fact that the main arterial trunks from the heart pass toward the left side. In man, the right lung, although somewhat shorter than the left, is broader and consists of more lobes.

The right lung likewise has the main divisions, **anterior, middle,** and **posterior lobes,** and the posterior lobe is again subdivided into two parts, the **lateral and medial lobes.** The lateral lobe is larger than the medial and, as the name implies, occurs lateral to the medial division. To find the medial lobe, push the lateral lobe toward the dorsal part of the body, and push the heart ventrally. In locating the medial lobe of the lung, one should see a large vein extending from the posterior part of the body, passing ventral to the medial lobe, and joining the anterior end of the heart. This is the **postcaval vein.**

Between the two lungs occur the heart, the pericardial cavity, and associated blood vessels. There will frequently be so much fat in this region that until it is removed the details of the heart cannot be seen. The heart is enclosed within a thin membranous sac, sometimes called the **pericardial sac,** which is composed of the **pericardium,** a membrane that is comparable to the peritoneum, which lines the abdominal cavity. Between the pericardial sac and the heart is a small space, the **pericardial cavity.** This cavity, as previously indicated, is a part of the coelom, or body cavity. The pericardium, in addition to surrounding the heart, is closely applied to the heart's surface, so that it is not easy to distinguish this portion from the wall of the heart itself. That portion of the pericardium forming the pericardial sac is called the **parietal pericardium.** The part fused with the heart is the **visceral pericardium.** The two divisions of the pericardium are continuous at the anterior end of the heart.

Some of the above details are difficult to distinguish if there is much fat associated with the heart, but they should be kept in mind as the heart is exposed. With forceps and scissors remove the fatty material and the pericardial sac from around the heart. Note that the heart is not decidedly on the left side of the body, as is commonly supposed, but practically in the mid-line. This is the case in man, as well. One receives the impression that the heart is on the left side because the ventricles, which beat more strongly than do the auricles, are to the left of the mid-line of the body. Near the anterior end of the heart, and sometimes partly covering it, is a mass of tissue that is usually somewhat pinkish in color, although the color varies somewhat. This is the **thymus gland.** The size and appearance of this structure vary in different specimens. It is quite large in a young cat but gradually degenerates as the animal becomes older. The same change takes place in the thymus gland of man. In some cases, it may be difficult to distinguish the gland from the fat in this region. This gland is usually regarded as one of the endocrine glands, but its specific function has not been definitely established. The pericardium about the bases of the arteries leading from the heart should be removed, as should also the thymus and the mediastinal septum, anterior to this. If the specimen is to be used for a study of the circulation, great care should be taken not to injure blood vessels in this region.

Study the heart. It consists of two posterior **ventricles,** inseparably fused into a thick muscular cone-shaped structure, and two anterior **auricles,** appearing as two small flaps attached to the anterior ends of the ventricles. The heart of the cat, and of all other mammals, thus consists of four complete chambers—two ventricles and two auricles. Aerated and unaerated blood never mix in these animals as they do in lower forms. Blood from the body empties into the right auricle, and then passes into the right ventricle. This blood has little oxygen, so before it is again pumped over the body it must be aerated. From the right ventricle, the blood passes to the lungs by way of the pulmonary arteries. Here it obtains oxygen and gives up carbon dioxide, which is expelled from the lungs. From the lungs, the aerated blood passes into the left auricle by way of the pulmonary veins. From the left auricle, the blood goes on into the left ventricle, and thence by way of the aorta to all parts of the body. There are thus, to all intents and purposes, two complete hearts and two complete circulations—the pulmonary circulation and the body circulation. Note that there is no sinus venosus present. This structure, so important in lower forms, has in mammals become incorporated into the right auricle as a small mass of tissue, the **sinuauricular node.** The rate of heartbeat is regulated by impulses from the central nervous system that pass to the sinuauricular node. More details of the circulation will be mentioned later, but the general plan should be kept in mind as the blood vessels are identified.

Identify the two main arteries that leave the heart, the pulmonary and the aorta. It will probably be necessary to pull away some of the tissue surrounding these vessels. The **pulmonary trunk** arises from the right ventricle near the ventral side of the heart. Its base occurs somewhat between the two auricles, and it then passes to the left and dorsally, where it divides into **right** and **left pulmonary arteries,** one of which passes to each lung. As indicated previously, these arteries carry unaerated, or "impure," blood to the lungs, where an exchange of gases takes place between the blood and the air within the lungs. The **aorta** is partially in contact with the pulmonary trunk, and it leaves the heart just dorsal to it. The aorta, which is somewhat larger than the pulmonary artery, can be seen just anterior to and dorsal to its base. The right auricle often overhangs the base of the aorta. The aorta comes from the left ventricle, and from it spring the main arteries of the body. It carries aerated, or "pure," blood.

Other structures in this region should be noted unless the specimen is to be used for the study of the circulation; in that case, the anterior circulation should be worked out first. Look near the inner ventral edge of the medial lobe of the left lung, and note that in this region there are points of attachment to this lobe. This is also true of the other lobes, but they can most easily be seen on the medial lobe. This is the region where the air tubes enter the lung. Clean away the tissue in this region, and work anteriorly. Just anterior to the region of attachment is a tube, the **bronchus,** which almost immediately joins a larger tube, the **trachea.** A bronchus from the other lung also joins the trachea at this point, although it is sometimes difficult to see where the bronchi end and the trachea begins. The trachea passes anteriorly to the larynx, or voice box. These tubes are somewhat strengthened by rings of cartilage. Push the left lung over to the right side, and note that it is attached to the wall of the thorax. This attachment is made by the **pulmonary ligament,** a mesentery that helps to hold the lung in place. When the lung is pushed over to the right side, a membranous partition is noted dorsal to it. This partition is made up of the pleurae, and the cavity enclosed between the two is the dorsal portion of the mediastinum, which has previously been mentioned. Within the mediastinum and through the pleura may be seen the dorsal aorta as it passes posteriorly, and, ventral to it, a larger tube, the **esophagus.**

Turn again to the diaphragm. This structure is of considerable importance in respiration and is found only in mammals. It is partly homologous to the transverse septum as found in lower forms but has become more complex by the addition of muscle fibers and other material. The center of the diaphragm is tendinous rather than muscular and is thus called the **semilunar tendon.** Several structures pierce the diaphragm, including the postcaval vein, the aorta, and the esophagus.

A study should now be made of the organs in the peritoneal cavity. With scissors cut through the ventral body wall to the left of the mid-ventral line, and make an incision from the pelvic region anteriorly to the diaphragm. Crosscuts should then be made to facilitate the identification of the organs; if necessary, the diaphragm may be disconnected from the inner body wall. The cavity thus revealed is the **peritoneal,** or abdominal, **cavity,** the posterior division of the coelom. The cavity is lined by the **peritoneum,** a very thin membrane that is continuous with the mesenteries that help to support the organs.

Identify some of the organs without removing them from their normal positions. The **liver** is the large, lobed, usually reddish structure at the anterior end of the cavity. It is attached to the diaphragm. Posterior to the liver, most of the organs are partly covered by a membrane, which is sometimes so invested with fat that one cannot see through it. This is a mesentery, the **great omentum,** which covers the intestine and sometimes part of the stomach. On the cat's left side, and usually not covered by the mesentery, is the **spleen,** an organ somewhat resembling the liver in texture, but usually slightly different in color. This organ extends to the left and dorsally. As indicated previously, the spleen is not a part of the digestive system but functions in connection with the circulatory system. It manufactures white blood cells and has other important functions.

Partly covered by the left side of the liver, and sometimes visible if slightly protruded, is the **stomach.** Raise the left side of the liver so that this organ may be more fully seen. Near the posterior end of the body cavity, close to the mid-ventral line, is the **urinary bladder,** which may contain fluid or may be empty. It is supported by three mesenteries that are attached to the ventral body wall, a single **median ligament,** attached to the median ventral surface of the bladder, and two **lateral ligaments,** often invested with fat and attached lateral to the median ligament.

Do not fully destroy the great omentum, but simply disconnect it from the underlying organs so that at the end of the laboratory period it may be pulled back over the organs; this will keep the organs moist. If the organs become too dry, some of the glycerin-water mixture or a comparable liquid should be rubbed on them at the end of the period.

Turn again to the liver. It has two major divisions, the **right** and **left lobes,** each of which is again subdivided into a **lateral** and a **median lobe.** The divisions of the left lobe are easily seen, since both occur ventrally; as the names imply, the lateral lobe occurs to one side of the median lobe. Only the median lobe of the right division can be seen ventrally, and it is itself somewhat lobate. Observe the **gall bladder** on the ventral surface of the right median lobe at the end of the cleft that partly divides this lobe. The lateral lobe of the right division occurs dorsally so that the lateral portion must be lifted somewhat in order to see it. A very small additional division of the liver is the **caudate lobe.** The left liver lobe should be lifted slightly so that this fingerlike projection may be observed. It protrudes posteriorly toward the stomach and is sometimes partly in contact with that organ.

The liver is held in place by two mesenteries, the **falciform ligament** and the **coronary ligament.** The falciform ligament passes from the anterior ventral portion of the liver to the ventral body wall and may have been partly destroyed in the dissection. The coronary ligament attaches the liver to the diaphragm. Move the liver so that the latter mesentery may be seen. Anterior to the liver the two ligaments are continuous with each other so that at this point the two are difficult to differentiate.

Raise the left lobe of the liver so that the stomach can be seen. Connecting the liver to the stomach and the anterior end of the intestine is a large mesentery, the **lesser omentum,** which is sometimes called the gastro-hepato-duodenal ligament. This mesentery is sometimes divided into the gastrohepatic ligament from the liver to the stomach and the hepatoduodenal ligament from the liver to the anterior end of the intestine. The limits of these two divisions are difficult to define. If the intestine is pushed over to the left side, the structures within this mesentery are easier to identify. The **bile duct,** sometimes greenish in color, passes from the liver to the anterior end of the intestine and will appear as a somewhat thickened portion of the mesentery. It occurs within the hepatoduodenal portion of the lesser omentum. At its anterior end, the bile duct is joined by a **cystic duct** from the gall bladder and **hepatic ducts** from the liver itself, but these ducts are sometimes hard to see.

Locate the stomach again, and find the entrance into it of the **esophagus,** on the anterior side. The anterior surface of the stomach is somewhat concave and is called the **lesser**

curvature. The posterior convex surface is the **greater curvature.** The anterior larger portion of the stomach, into which the esophagus opens, is the **cardiac region.** The opposite smaller end is the **pyloric division.** There is no definite line of demarcation between the two. The bulge that is to the left of the entrance of the esophagus is called the **fundus.** Note that the stomach is attached to the spleen by the **gastrosplenic ligament,** which is really a portion of the great omentum. The stomach curves over to the right and ends at a ring of muscle, the **pyloric sphincter.** (A sphincter muscle is one that closes an opening.) This structure is represented externally by a slight bulge and has the function of regulating the passage of food from the stomach into the intestine.

The anterior end of the **small intestine** is the **duodenum,** which passes to the right and posteriorly. Note the entrance of the bile duct into the anterior end of the duodenum. Along the medial edge of the duodenum is attached the **mesoduodenum,** a mesentery that passes to the body wall. Within this mesentery is the **pancreas,** the color of which will vary with the specimen. It is somewhat lobed, and a portion of it extends dorsally and to the left, dorsal to the stomach. A portion of the pancreas is usually in contact with or near the spleen.

One of the **pancreatic ducts** from the pancreas joins the bile duct just as it enters the duodenum. This duct can sometimes be found if the pancreatic tissue is pulled away in this region. Another accessory pancreatic duct enters the duodenum independently, but this is difficult to find.

Trace the duodenum posteriorly. It soon turns to the left across the body and passes somewhat anteriorly. The next division of the small intestine is the **jejunum.** Although there is no definite point of division between these two parts, the jejunum is considered to begin at the place where the duodenum turns posteriorly after forming a U shape. Note the mesentery attached to the intestine posterior to the duodenum. This is the **mesointestine** (sometimes called the mesentery proper). The most posterior division of the small intestine is the **ileum.** Again, there is no sharp division between this region and the jejunum. The ileum opens into the **large intestine** on the right side of the abdominal cavity. This junction can sometimes be easily found by pushing all the intestine, except the duodenum, over to the left and then looking just medial to the duodenum. At the point where the ileum opens into the large intestine, a short pouch, or **caecum,** is formed, since the ileum joins the large intestine somewhat on the side rather than directly at its end.   The point of entrance can easily be found by looking for this slight irregularity in the intestine.   This is the region where the appendix occurs in man; there is no definite appendix in the cat.

The colon, or large intestine, is indefinitely divided into the **ascending** (anterior region), **transverse,** and **descending colon.** The posterior portion of the descending colon is sometimes called the **rectum.**   The colon is attached to the dorsal body wall by a mesentery, the **mesocolon.**

A formal drawing is not required.   If the same specimen is to be used for all the work on the cat, the circulatory system should be taken up at this point.   Otherwise, follow the sequence outlined in the manual.

THE UROGENITAL SYSTEM

The cat, as well as the turtle previously studied, has a metanephric type of kidney in the adult, as opposed to the mesonephric kidney of the lower vertebrates.   In the embryo of the cat and other mammals, however, the other two types of kidneys—the pronephros and the mesonephros—develop first. From these embryonic kidneys, certain parts of the adult urogenital system are derived.   Other parts degenerate before the animal becomes adult or remain as nonfunctional structures. These points will be discussed later.

The kidneys and their ducts are essentially the same in both sexes.   Locate the **kidneys** on the dorsal body wall, one on each side of the middorsal line.   They are rather compact, somewhat bean-shaped structures, being more of a typical "kidney shape" than the kidneys of the animals previously studied.   Each kidney is covered by the peritoneum, which binds it to the body wall.   Disconnect one of the kidneys from the body wall by cutting the peritoneum.   The inner margin of the kidney is somewhat concave and is called the **hilum.**   The hilum is the region into which passes the renal artery and from which pass the renal vein and the **metanephric duct,** or ureter.   Locate this white duct as it passes from the hilum, and follow it posteriorly, picking away any obscuring tissue that may be present. Push the visceral organs over to one side, and note that the metanephric duct opens into the neck of the bladder.   From the bladder, another tube, the **urethra,** passes toward the outside.

This will be dissected later.   Be sure to study the systems of both sexes.

The Female.   The size of the parts of the genital system of the female will vary, depending upon the sexual state of the animal.   If the ducts contain embryos, they will be quite large. Locate the reproductive ducts posterior to the kidneys, which in this region are formed into the shape of a Y.   The anterior arms of the Y are the **horns of the uterus,** and the ureters from the kidneys pass dorsal to them as they proceed toward the bladder.   The embryos develop in the horns of the uterus, so that, in pregnant cats, this portion of the system will be quite large. It normally takes approximately two months for the embryos to develop in the cat.

Trace one of the horns of the uterus anteriorly.   The anterior end of this tube becomes quite small and convoluted and is called the **Fallopian tube.**   The anterior end of the Fallopian tube is somewhat enlarged into a funnel-shaped structure, within which occurs an opening, the **ostium.**   This anterior expansion partially fits over the **ovary,** a small mass of tissue in this region that is sometimes hard to separate from the end of the Fallopian tube.   Observe that there is no direct connection between the ovary and the Fallopian tube, a condition that obtains in the female of most vertebrate animals.

Posteriorly, the two horns of the uterus combine to form a single tube, the **body of the uterus.**   The body of the uterus is continued posteriorly as the **vagina,** although the exact limits of the two divisions are difficult to fix.   In order to trace these structures farther, it will be necessary to spread the legs and to cut through the ventral region of the pelvic girdle.   Trace the structures as they are called for, picking away any obscuring tissue.   Locate again the neck of the bladder, and note that a tube, the **urethra,** passes posteriorly from it, closely associated with the vagina.   The urethra occurs ventral to the vagina, and near the posterior end of the body these structures combine to form the **urogenital sinus,** which opens to the outside by way of the **urogenital opening,** previously seen from the external view. Identify again the **labia majora,** the folds of skin that surround the urogenital opening.   On the ventral wall of the urogenital sinus is a small projection, the **clitoris,** which is homologous to the penis of the male.   It is very small and is sometimes not very evident.

The parts of the urogenital system are held in place by mesen-

teries, some of which are divided into several parts. Only a
few of the more important will be identified. The **broad ligament**
is attached to the horns and body of the uterus and partly surrounds the ovary. The **round ligament** is a rather narrow mesentery attached to the anterior end of the horn of the uterus and,
passing posteriorly, fuses with the body wall. These two
mesenteries are connected. That portion of the broad ligament
which supports the ovary is sometimes called the **mesovarium.**
Further divisions of the broad ligament, made by some workers,
are difficult to delimit. The median and lateral ligaments of the
bladder have already been identified.

The cat is the first animal to be studied in which two complete
oviducts are not present. The urethra is also an innovation;
this structure will be discussed later. The Fallopian tubes, horns
of the uterus, body of the uterus, and vagina are formed from
oviducts, or Müllerian ducts, comparable to those found in other
vertebrates. In the cat, the posterior ends of these ducts are
fused into a single tube, which forms the body of the uterus and
the vagina. This fusion of oviducts is characteristic of most
mammals, although the degree of fusion varies in different
species. There are several types of uteri in mammals, the
different types being dependent upon the degree of fusion of the
oviducts. The uterus of the cat is of the **bipartite** type, which
represents a somewhat intermediate degree of fusion. Extreme
fusion is found in the **simplex** uterus, characteristic of man and
many other primates.

Drawing 19A.   The Female Urogenital System—Ventral View.
Make an outline of the posterior part of the body to show relationships of parts. Draw bladder to one side. **Labels:** kidney,
metanephric duct, hilum, urethra, horn of uterus, body of uterus,
Fallopian tube, ostium, ovary, vagina, urogenital sinus, bladder,
urogenital opening.

The Male. Locate again the two **testes** ventral to the anus,
which are contained within the **scrotum,** or scrotal sac. Remove
the scrotum from one testis, and observe a white cord that
passes anteriorly from the end of this structure. This is the
spermatic cord, which is composed of an outer covering derived
from the peritoneum, testicular blood vessels and nerves, and the
duct from the testis, the vas deferens. Trace the spermatic cord
anteriorly, and observe that it passes through the muscles of the
abdominal wall by way of a short canal. This hole in the
abdominal wall is the **inguinal canal.** The testes develop within

the abdominal cavity, where, in many vertebrate animals, they remain throughout life. In most mammals, however, the testes pass posteriorly into the scrotum along with nerves, blood vessels, vasa deferentia, and a fold of the peritoneum. The inguinal canal then forms about the spermatic cord. Occasionally, in man, a portion of the intestine passes through this canal into the scrotum, causing one type of hernia, or rupture.

Cut through one of the inguinal canals, and trace the spermatic cord anteriorly. The **vas deferens** emerges from the spermatic cord, passes over the ends of the metanephric duct, and enters the neck of the bladder distal to the entrance of the ureters. This entrance probably cannot be seen as yet.

Cut through the ventral part of the pelvic girdle, and spread the legs so that additional dissections can be made. Locate again the neck of the bladder, and dissect it free from the surrounding tissue. Then trace it posteriorly, and locate the entrance of the vas deferens. From the point of entrance of the vasa deferentia into the neck of the bladder, the tube that passes to the outside is called the **urethra.** At this point, an enlargement occurs, the **prostate gland;** this secretes a fluid into the urethra during copulation, which aids in the transfer of the sperm to the female. Follow the urethra posteriorly. Another secretory gland, **Cowper's gland,** appears as a slight enlargement somewhat posterior to the prostate gland. The urethra eventually passes into the **penis,** a slight enlargement at the posterior end of the body. The fold of skin that surrounds the penis and that has been observed externally is the **prepuce,** or foreskin. Cut into the prepuce, and examine the penis. The somewhat pointed end of the penis is called the **glans.** Note the small spines on the glans and the **urogenital opening** at its end. During copulation, the penis becomes greatly distended with blood, so that it projects posteriorly and to the outside.

Turn back to the testis, which was previously freed from the scrotum. Cut through the white tissue surrounding it, and examine its structure. On the dorsal surface of the testis is a tightly coiled tube, the **epididymis,** which passes posteriorly over the testicular surface. From the posterior end of the epididymis, the vas deferens passes forward into the spermatic cord. The epididymis is connected with the internal testicular tubules by minute tubules, the **vasa efferentia,** which cannot be seen in this dissection. The tightly coiled portion of the epididymis is sometimes considered to be the proximal part of the vas deferens. (In reality the epididymis is more complex and contains more divisions than indicated. In a study of this kind, however, it is inadvisable to go into more details.) Near the epididymis, a mesentery, the **mesorchium,** is attached to the testis. At the end of the testis, the **gubernaculum,** a short mesentery, attaches the testis to the posterior wall of the scrotum. The gubernaculum and the round ligament of the uterus are homologous.

The vas deferens in the male, as in the turtle, has been derived from the embryonic mesonephric, or Wolffian, duct. In the female, this duct forms in the embryo, but it usually degenerates, along with the mesonephric kidney, or remains as a nonfunctional vestige. The metanephric duct, or ureter, in both sexes is mostly a new structure, although it develops embryonically as an outgrowth of the posterior end of the mesonephric duct. The urethra, characteristic of many mammals, is a new structure, derived embryonically from the cloaca. It should be noted that functionally the urethra and the mesonephric duct of the dogfish and Necturus are quite similar. In the male, both ducts convey urine and sperm to the outside, while, in the female, only excretory products are transported. The two ducts, however, are not homologous.

Drawing 19B. The Male Urogenital System—Ventral View. Make an outline of posterior part of body to show relationships. Draw bladder to one side. **Labels:** testis, kidney, metanephric duct, hilum, inguinal canal, vas deferens, spermatic cord, prostate gland, urethra, Cowper's gland, penis, glans, epididymis.

THE CIRCULATORY SYSTEM

If a new specimen is furnished for the study of the circulatory system, the following directions for dissection should be followed. If the old specimen is used, these directions should, of course, be disregarded.

At first, cut open only the abdominal cavity, to prevent drying out. Do not skin the specimen; instead, make the incisions through both the skin and the muscles. At the end of the laboratory period tie a piece of cheesecloth or a towel about the specimen to prevent drying.

Make a longitudinal incision through the skin and the muscles slightly to one side of the mid-ventral line. Extend the cut from the posterior region anteriorly to the sternum. Then make cross incisions through skin and muscles so that the internal organs will be well exposed. Do not as yet go anterior to the diaphragm, the sheet of muscle that passes across the body near the posterior edge of the ribs. Follow the directions of the laboratory instructor for the removal of the great omentum. Some instructors prefer that the omentum be carefully removed so that it can be used to cover the internal organs at the end of the laboratory period. Others, who believe that this is not necessary, will probably direct that this mesentery be discarded completely.

The Veins of the Peritoneal Cavity. There is probably more individual variation in the veins than in any other system of the cat. For this reason, it is sometimes necessary to trace a vein to the organ that it drains in order to be sure of its identification. This is especially true of the branches of the hepatic portal system.

The Hepatic Portal System. A portal system has been previously defined as a system of veins that begins and ends in capillaries. The hepatic portal system is composed of veins from various parts of the digestive tract that combine to form the hepatic portal vein. The system starts with capillaries in the visceral organs, which combine to form larger veins. These larger veins join, forming the hepatic portal vein. The hepatic portal vein then passes into the liver, where it breaks up into capillaries. By this system of veins absorbed food material from the digestive tract is carried into the liver, where some of it is stored for future use. Hepatic veins in the liver carry the blood into the postcaval vein, from which it passes into the heart.

It should be remembered that blood in the veins is always flowing *toward* the heart, although in identification it is sometimes easier to locate a large vein first and then find the smaller branches that combine to form it. Small veins are sometimes spoken of as branches of the larger veins, although, if the direction of blood flow is taken into consideration, the smaller branches really combine to form the larger vessels.

Although the **hepatic portal vein** is rather large, it is sometimes difficult to locate the point at which it enters the liver because of the mesenteries and other tissue that surround it. Push the intestine and the stomach over to the left, and look on the dorsal surface of the lesser omentum. In some cats, the vein will appear without any dissection being made. If blood is present in the vein, it will appear bluish in color. If the vein does not show up, carefully pull away some of the tissue near the middle of the lesser omentum until it is found. Near the anterior end of the duodenum, three branches open into the hepatic portal.   Before the hepatic portal is fully exposed, these veins should be located. They may open individually into the hepatic portal, or two or more of them may join to form a common trunk, which in turn enters the hepatic portal.   These veins are best identified by first finding them on the organs that they drain.   When they are found, trace them to their junction with the hepatic portal. All three of these vessels are closely paralleled by an artery, which is easier to see than the vein.

Turn to the lesser curvature of the stomach, and locate an artery that branches over the stomach wall in this region.   Then look for small bluish venous branches that run parallel to the arterial branches.   In some cats, these branches will be difficult to find, since no blood will occur within them.   These branches combine and form the **coronary vein,** which passes toward the hepatic portal from the lesser curvature of the stomach.   With forceps pick away the tissue anterior to the lesser curvature, and try to find the main trunk.   The **gastroepiploic vein** brings blood from the greater curvature of the stomach and a portion of the lesser omentum.   It can usually be located along the greater curvature at the pyloric end of the stomach near the duodenum when the tissue in this region has been picked away with forceps. The best way to find the **anterior pancreaticoduodenal vein** is by carefully separating the pancreas from the duodenum near its anterior end.   This vein helps to drain the pancreas and the duodenum.

Posterior to the entrance of the above three veins, the hepatic portal receives a somewhat larger branch, the **gastrosplenic vein.** This vein enters the medial side of the hepatic portal and, at the point of entrance, is often surrounded by pancreatic tissue. Locate the point of entrance by examining that portion of the pancreas in contact with the hepatic portal on its medial, or inner, side.   Trace the gastrosplenic as it runs over to the left, picking away the tissue that surrounds it.   It is formed from several branches, some of which are quite small.   The following branches however, can be found in most specimens.

The **pancreatic vein** passes anteriorly and brings blood from a portion of the pancreas near the stomach.   Somewhat to the left of the pancreatic vein, the gastrosplenic is formed from two rather large branches, the **anterior splenic,** which comes from the anterior end of the spleen and the stomach, passes somewhat dorsal to the stomach, and joins the other branch on its anterior, or dorsal, edge; and the **posterior splenic,** which is larger than the former vessel and appears to be a direct continuation of the gastrosplenic across the body. It comes from the posterior end of spleen and stomach and receives several small veins from the pancreas. If these two vessels are traced out in their entirety, great care should be taken not to injure other associated blood vessels. Posterior to the entrance of the gastrosplenic vein, the hepatic portal is called the **superior mesenteric.** This vessel soon receives a large vein, the **inferior mesenteric,** which brings blood from the large intestine. This branch sometimes joins the superior mesenteric somewhat dorsally, so that some dissection may be necessary to locate its entrance. The inferior mesenteric as a variation occasionally joins the gastrosplenic rather than the superior mesenteric vein. The inferior mesenteric can probably best be located by looking alongside the descending colon in the mesentery, the mesocolon.

A **posterior pancreaticoduodenal vein** next joins the superior mesenteric. It returns blood from the posterior end of the duodenum and the pancreas and can be found by stretching the mesentery of the duodenum, the mesoduodenum. Some of the branches of this vessel usually anastomose with branches of the anterior pancreaticoduodenal vein. Numerous additional branches from the intestine will be seen joining the superior mesenteric vein posterior to the posterior pancreaticoduodenal vein. These branches are all known as **intestinal veins,** which carry blood from the intestine.

All drawings of the circulatory system should be full-page, unless otherwise indicated.

Drawing 20. Hepatic Portal System—Ventral View. The organs should be diagramed and spread somewhat to show relationships. **Labels:** Veins—hepatic portal, coronary, gastrosplenic, gastroepiploic, anterior splenic, posterior splenic, superior mesenteric, inferior mesenteric, posterior pancreaticoduodenal, anterior pancreaticoduodenal, intestinal.

The Postcaval Vein and Its Branches in the Peritoneal Cavity. The **postcaval vein** enters the right auricle of the heart and returns most of the blood from the posterior part of the body. Its actual point of entrance into the right auricle cannot be seen until later.

Locate the postcaval vein as it emerges into the abdominal cavity from the right lateral lobe of the liver. It occurs near the middorsal line and in some specimens may be partly surrounded by tissue. Although for clarity the postcaval vein is sometimes spoken of as giving rise to branches, it should be remembered that the blood actually flows into the postcaval from the branches. In the liver, several **hepatic veins** join the postcaval, but these should not be identified until later, since many of them are within the liver tissue. The branches within the abdominal cavity that are received by the postcaval vein will vary somewhat on the two sides, owing to the fact that embryonically the postcaval is formed from a composite of several vessels.

Identify first the branches on the cat's right side. Locate the right kidney and, at its anterior end, a small nodule of tissue, the **right adrenal gland.** The branch from the adrenal gland and the adjacent body wall into the postcaval is the **right adrenolumbar vein.** With forceps pull away the tissue until this vein is exposed. The adrenolumbar vein sometimes passes into the postcaval from near the center of the kidney and is then quite close to the renal. Posterior to this branch, the postcaval receives the **right renal vein** from the kidney. Posterior to the right renal, there occurs a small branch from the reproductive organ, the **gonadal vein.** In the female, this is the **right internal ovarian vein** from the ovary; in the male, the **right internal spermatic vein** from the testis. These veins can sometimes be found running posteriorly along the body wall parallel to the postcaval vein. They may be quite small, and they frequently do not appear. The gonadal veins on this side may occasionally enter the renal vein rather than the postcaval.

Now identify the veins on the cat's left side. The **left adrenolumbar vein** typically enters the common trunk that is formed by the veins below but may join the postcaval directly. The **left renal** and the **left internal ovarian** or **internal spermatic veins** join to form a common trunk before entering the postcaval. Posterior to the entrance of the above vessels, the **iliolumbar veins** join the postcaval. They collect blood from the body wall and can sometimes be seen on the surfaces of the muscles, although they are at times buried in the tissue. There are two of these veins, one from each side. An artery is parallel to each and is normally more evident than is the vein. Dissect a portion of the postcaval from the body wall, and find several **lumbar veins** joining its dorsal side and collecting blood from the muscles of the body wall. These veins are frequently not evident, since they are quite small. The posterior branches that are received by the postcaval vein occur dorsal to the arteries in this region and will thus not be studied until later.

Drawing 21. **Postcaval Vein and Branches—Ventral View.** This drawing should include the postcaval vein and its branches posterior to the diaphragm. Sketch in the kidneys, but omit the other organs. Be sure to leave enough space at the bottom of the sheet to add the posterior branches after they have been identified later. **Labels:** Veins—postcaval, hepatic (sketch in, if not seen), right adrenolumbar, right renal, left adrenolumbar, left renal, right gonadal, left gonadal, lumbar. Later add common iliac, sacral, internal iliac, external iliac, deep femoral, femoral, caudal.

A brief discussion of the origin of some of the veins of the cat is now in order. Perhaps the most noticeable difference between these and those of the turtle is the absence of the renal portal system in the cat. It was mentioned previously that even in some reptiles the renal portal system loses some of its former importance. In the turtle the postcaval vein extends only as far posteriorly as the kidneys, while the vessels from the hind legs and the tail are connected to the renal portal system. It should be remembered that the renal portal veins, where they are present, are derived from the posterior ends of the embryonic posterior cardinal veins. Since the renal portal veins are absent as such in the cat, the posterior veins from the legs and tail are now connected to the posterior end of the postcaval vein, which, in this animal, extends the length of the abdominal cavity. The anterior end of the postcaval vein in the cat is formed in essentially the same way as the postcaval vein in the turtle—from hepatic veins and sinuses and embryonic subcardinal veins. The latter vessels form the posterior ends of the posterior cardinal veins in the adult dogfish. The middle portion of the postcaval vein of the cat is derived from embryonic veins (supracardinal veins and others), while the posterior portion is from embryonic posterior cardinal veins. The posterior parts of the embryonic posterior cardinal veins, as indicated before, are at least partly homologous with the renal portal veins of the forms previously studied.

The Veins Anterior to the Diaphragm. Cut through the ribs slightly to the left of the sternum, and carry this incision to the anterior end of the left lung. Then cut laterally through the ribs on the left side just in front of the diaphragm and also near the level of the middle of the anterior lobe of the lung. Bend this flap laterally so that the organs will be in sight. Near the anterior end of the sternum, an artery and a vein can be seen passing ventrally to the sternum and then extending posteriorly along the sternum in the mid-ventral line.   These vessels should be preserved.   In order to facilitate the identification, a short transverse incision should be made through the sternum and the ribs on the right side anterior to the region where the artery and the vein join the sternum.   The parts of the heart should already have been identified during the study of the internal anatomy. Therefore, do not as yet remove the pericardium from the heart, since to do so might injure some veins in this region.   Push the heart and the left lung over to the left side, and find the postcaval vein as it enters the right auricle on the dorsal side of the heart. This vein receives two small **phrenic veins** from the diaphragm as it passes through this structure, but they are usually difficult to find.

The Precaval Vein and Its Branches.   The precaval vein returns blood to the right auricle of the heart from the anterior part of the body.   Note that there is a single vein, rather than two precaval veins which occur in some other animals.   During embryonic life two precaval veins are formed; but a cross vein develops between the two, the left innominate vein, and the left precaval then partly degenerates.   A portion of the left precaval vein remains to form the coronary sinus in the adult.   In some specimens, certain rather small veins will appear that are not evident in others.

Locate the right auricle, and find the large **precaval vein** that enters it from the anterior end of the body on the cat's right side. This vessel is also called the anterior vena cava and the descending vena cava.   It occurs somewhat dorsally, and the membranes and tissue surrounding it may have to be removed.   Push the heart toward the cat's left, and find a rather large vein entering the precaval from the dorsal side of the body very close to its entrance into the auricle.   This is the **azygous vein,** which receives several small branches, including the **intercostal veins** from between the ribs.   The azygous is considered to be the remnant of the embryonic right posterior cardinal vein plus an embryonic blood vessel (right supracardinal).

Before tracing the branches of the precaval vein, locate numerous **coronary veins** that occur over the dorsal and lateral surfaces of the heart.   It will be necessary to remove part of the pericardium to find these veins.   Do this carefully.   The coronary veins join the **coronary sinus,** which empties independently into the right auricle. This sinus occurs toward the dorsal surface of the heart and at the present stage of study is difficult to find without injuring other vessels. The coronary sinus is a remnant of the embryonic left precaval vein.

In identifying the branches of the precaval vein, use forceps to pull away the obscuring tissue. The first branch anterior to the azygous that is received by the precaval is the **sternal vein,** which brings blood from the mid-ventral region of the body. This vein and its branches are those which were previously mentioned as passing from the sternum dorsally across the body and which were seen when the dissection for this study was being made. The sternal vein is formed by a union of two **internal mammary veins.** The sternal and internal mammary veins are associated with arteries, which, if well injected, will show up better than the veins. The posterior ends of the internal mammary veins arise in the abdominal cavity, and they can sometimes be seen along the ventral abdominal muscles in this region. The sternal vein itself sometimes receives a small branch from the sternum, but this frequently does not appear.

Anteriorly, the precaval vein is seen to be formed by two large branches, the **innominate,** or brachiocephalic, **veins.** In order to see these branches well, it may be necessary to clip the artery passing to the sternum along with the sternal vein. If this is done, be sure to leave a recognizable stub for future use. In many cases, the precaval vein receives a rather large **right vertebral vein** into its dorsal side posterior to the occurrence of the innominate veins. This vessel sometimes joins the right innominate. Some dissection dorsal to the precaval is usually necessary to locate this vein. This vessel, together with the left vertebral vein to be seen later, collects blood from the spinal cord and the brain and runs in the vertebrarterial canals of the vertebral column. Branches from some of the back muscles also join the vertebral veins, but they are difficult to find without destroying other vessels.

The branches received by the innominate veins are essentially the same on both sides. As indicated, however, the left innominate rather than the precaval vein usually receives the left vertebral, while the right vertebral joins the precaval directly in most cases. Also, in some specimens, a branch that usually joins the vertebral vein on one side or the other may at times connect directly to the innominate; this is especially true on the left side. In most cases, this vein is the **costocervical.**

Trace one of the innominates on one side only, preferably on the cat's right side, since this dissection will uncover some arteries that should be followed on the right side. Anteriorly, the innominate vein will be seen to be formed by two large branches, a median **external jugular vein** and a lateral **subclavian vein,** which collect blood from the arm and shoulder region. First trace the subclavian, picking away the obscuring tissue. When the subclavian vein leaves the thorax, it is called the **axillary vein.** Since that is a rather indefinite designation in specimens that are being dissected, this vein will be considered the subclavian for the short distance that it does not receive branches; from the first branch distally, it will be called the axillary. It will probably be necessary to cut some of the pectoral muscles in tracing the vein; in so doing, be sure not to destroy any associated blood vessels. The axillary vein receives two branches very close together, a small **ventral thoracic vein** from the pectoral muscles, which enters the ventral edge of the axillary, and a much larger **subscapular vein,** which comes from the shoulder region and enters the anterior side of the axillary. The latter also receives a branch from the outer surface of the upper arm. The small ventral thoracic may be turned anteriorly if the pectoral muscles have been pushed forward in the dissection.

Distal to the entrance of these branches, the axillary sometimes receives several small unnamed branches and two somewhat larger veins, the **long thoracic** and the **thoracodorsal.** The sequence in which the two latter vessels enter the axillary varies somewhat. The long thoracic vein enters the posterior edge of the axillary. It collects blood especially from the pectoral muscles and is composed primarily of a single large trunk, which can usually be traced posteriorly along the inner surface of the pectoral muscles. The thoracodorsal vein enters the axillary near its dorsal side. It is formed from two branches of about equal size, one that passes anteriorly and joins the subscapular vein and another that extends posteriorly to the latissimus dorsi muscle. These two branches join to form the thoracodorsal vein just before its entrance into the axillary. The axillary vein continues into the arm and, distal to the above branches, is called the **brachial vein.**

Return now to the external jugular vein on the right side. The branches of the two external jugulars are similar except that the left jugular receives the **thoracic duct** near its base. This duct is a portion of the lymphatic system and, since its walls are quite thin, is usually difficult to find. Two external jugular veins on one side may occasionally occur as an abnormality in some specimens. If the sternomastoid muscle is slit longitudinally near the right side, the identification of the branches will be facilitated. Near its base, the external jugular vein receives a small medial branch, the **internal jugular,** which can be followed anteriorly as it passes somewhat parallel to the former. This vessel, which does not show up well in some specimens, returns some of the blood from the brain and the anterior region. Anteriorly, the external jugular vein receives the large **transverse scapular vein** from the shoulder region. This enters the external jugular vein from the dorsal, or lateral, side, and some dissection may be necessary to expose its entrance. It returns blood from the shoulder and adjacent regions and also receives a branch from one of the veins on the outer surface of the upper arm. The external jugular vein continues anteriorly along the surface of the sternomastoid muscle. Near the jaw, it is formed by a union of two veins, the **anterior facial** (anteriorly) and the **posterior facial vein.** These two branches return the blood from the face, the glands, and muscles of the jaw and head. They themselves receive small branches, but these will not be identified. Near the region where the two facial veins join to form the external jugular, a **transverse vein** will be seen that passes across the neck and connects the right and left jugular veins.

Drawing 22. The Heart and the Thoracic Veins—Ventral View. This drawing should include all veins anterior to the diaphragm. In case of duplicate branches on the two sides, only one branch need be labeled. **Labels:** right auricle, right ventricle, left auricle, left ventricle. Veins—postcaval, precaval, phrenic (if seen), azygous, intercostal, sternal, right vertebral, innominate, left vertebral, external jugular, internal jugular, subclavian, ventral thoracic, subscapular, long thoracic, axillary, thoracodorsal, brachial, transverse scapular, transverse, anterior facial, posterior facial.

The pulmonary veins will be located later.

Before study of the venous system of the cat is set aside, a few homologies should be re-emphasized, and some additional remarks made in this connection. The origin of the postcaval vein has already been discussed. It has also been previously noted that, in the cat embryo, two precaval veins are formed. This stage corresponds to the condition found in the adult turtle; also, some mammals have two precaval veins in the adult. In other mammals, including the cat and man, however, a cross vein develops, the left innominate vein, which passes from the distal end of the left precaval vein across to the right precaval. The left precaval vein then degenerates, except for a portion that remains as the coronary sinus. Thus in the adult only a single precaval vein remains, formed from a combination of the two innominate veins. Aside from the changes that are correlated with the degeneration of the left precaval vein, the homologies of the anterior vessels are essentially the same as those found in the turtle. The precaval vein of the cat is comparable to the common cardinal and anterior cardinal veins in the dogfish on the right side, while the internal jugular veins of the cat represent the distal ends of the anterior cardinal veins of the same animal.

It should be emphasized again that the renal portal system, which in some reptiles is becoming somewhat degenerate, is absent, as such, in the cat. A portion of the renal portal veins (embryonic posterior cardinal veins) persists to form a part of the postcaval vein of the adult cat, which drains the kidneys in mammals.

The Arteries. The arteries are the vessels that transport the blood away from the heart. In most cases, they carry aerated blood, but the pulmonary arteries passing to the lungs carry unaerated blood. The arteries of specimens that are to be used for a study of the circulatory system should be injected. They will then appear yellow or red, depending upon the color of the injection mass that is used. In most cases, the animals are injected through one of the large arteries of the leg. The injection usually destroys some of the blood vessels in this region, and for that reason, the arteries and veins of the opposite leg should be studied. Injections are sometimes made through one of the carotid arteries in the neck; in such a case, the arteries of the opposite side of the neck should be studied.

The Arteries of the Thorax. While this study is being made, keep in mind the general scheme of circulation in the region of the thorax. There are two main arteries that arise from the heart, the **pulmonary trunk,** which carries unaerated blood from the right ventricle to the lungs, and the **aorta,** which transmits aerated blood from the left ventricle over the body by way of its numerous branches. It is to be noted that the terms ventral aorta and dorsal aorta are no longer used in the cat. In the embryo, these two vessels form as rather distinct structures, but in the adult they are no longer separable, since both have contributed to the formation of the aorta. More details of these changes will be mentioned in a later discussion of the aortic arches.

Both the pulmonary artery, or trunk, and the aorta have been identified in a previous study. It will be remembered that the aorta is the larger of these vessels and that it passes somewhat anteriorly before curving dorsally and to the left. The pulmonary artery extends more nearly straight dorsally, so that it occurs somewhat posterior to the aorta. Trace both these vessels toward the left. Shortly anterior to the bases of these arteries, it will be observed that they are bound together by a piece of tissue. This piece of tissue is the **ligamentum arteriosum,** or the ligament of Botallus, which is the remains of the ductus arteriosus, or the ductus Botalli. During embryonic life, the ductus arteriosus forms a complete vessel between the aorta and the pulmonary artery. Since the lungs are not functional in the embryo, there is no necessity for the blood to enter the lungs to receive oxygen. Most of the blood from the pulmonary artery, therefore, passes to the aorta by way of the ductus arteriosus instead. At birth, or shortly thereafter, the ductus arteriosus degenerates and only the ligamentum arteriosum remains. This allows the pulmonary circulation to become established.

Trace the pulmonary trunk and observe that it divides into **right** and **left pulmonary arteries,** one of which passes to each lung. The pulmonary veins occur somewhat dorsally and thus should not be located until later. Return now to the base of the aorta. On the surface of the heart find the **coronary arteries,** rather small vessels that supply the wall of the heart with blood. They arise from the base of the aorta, but their origin is sometimes difficult to see. Trace the aorta forward, cleaning away the fat or other material that may be present. The portion of the aorta in the thoracic region is called the **thoracic aorta.** Since most of the arteries can be identified without destroying the main veins, it is suggested that these vessels be saved for review. The first branch that arises from the aorta is the large **brachiocephalic artery.** After locating this vessel, continue around to the left until another somewhat smaller artery is encountered that also arises from the aorta. This is the **left subclavian artery,** which supplies blood to the left arm and other structures in that region. The **right subclavian artery** also arises from the brachiocephalic, but the secondary branches of the subclavian arteries are similar.

Trace the brachiocephalic artery anteriorly. This vessel soon gives rise to three large arteries. From left to right these are the **left common carotid,** the **right common carotid,** and the **right subclavian artery.** The point of origin of these three vessels varies somewhat; the left common carotid usually arises independently from the brachiocephalic artery, while a common trunk then extends anteriorly a short distance from the brachiocephalic and in turn gives rise to the right common carotid and the right subclavian artery.

Trace the right subclavian artery into the right shoulder and arm, and identify its four branches. The first noticeable branch of this vessel is the **internal mammary artery,** which springs from the ventral surface of the subclavian and passes ventrally and posteriorly close to the mid-ventral line of the chest, parallel to the sternal and internal mammary veins. This artery was previously noted in the study of the veins and may have been cut to facilitate that study. It continues through the thorax and on into the abdomen, where it is called the **superior epigastric artery.**

Three other arteries in addition to the internal mammary originate from this region of the subclavian, but their bases typically arise from the dorsal or lateral edges of the subclavian. There may be some individual variation in these vessels. With forceps pick away the tissue that surrounds the subclavian in this region until these three arteries are located; it may also be necessary to remove some of the ribs that obscure them. The **vertebral artery** is normally the most proximal. It comes from the dorsal surface of the subclavian artery, usually runs anteriorly for a very short distance, and then turns sharply dorsally. It supplies blood to some of the neck muscles and also enters the vertebrarterial canal and furnishes some of the blood to the spinal cord and the ventral surface of the brain. The **costocervical axis** also arises from the dorsal surface of the subclavian artery, usually somewhat proximal to the vertebral artery, but very close to it. It can be identified rather easily in most cases because it divides into two branches almost immediately after its origin. One of these branches, the **superior inter-costal,** passes posteriorly a short distance along the ribs and then turns dorsally. The other branch of the costocervical axis passes almost straight dorsally and divides into two branches. These vessels supply the muscles of the back and neck but need not be traced further. The fourth main branch of the subclavian artery in this region is the **thyrocervical axis.** It typically arises as the most lateral of the four branches and comes from the anterior or anteriodorsal surface of the subclavian artery. It should be traced as it runs anteriorly parallel to the external jugular vein. It gives off several branches to the neck and shoulder regions.

Distal to the four branches just identified, the subclavian artery is called the **axillary artery.** Trace it laterally. The next branch arising from this vessel is the **ventral thoracic artery,** which comes from the anterior, or ventral, surface of the axillary and passes to the pectoral muscles. It is typically in close association with the ventral thoracic vein. Somewhat lateral to the ventral thoracic artery, the **long thoracic artery** arises. It originates considerably nearer to the body than does the long thoracic vein. This vessel passes along the pectoral muscles in this region, and a branch from it goes to the latissimus dorsi. Distal to the long thoracic artery, the axillary gives rise to the **subscapular artery.** This vessel is relatively large and in most cases comes from the dorsal edge of the axillary. It has several branches, only one of which is important from the present standpoint. The first branch of the subscapular is the **thoracodorsal artery,** which runs posteriorly alongside and sometimes dorsal to the thoracodorsal vein. It supplies blood to the latissimus dorsi and teres major muscles. The subscapular artery continues out into the upper arm and shoulder and supplies blood to the structures in this region. Lateral to the subscapular, the axillary is called the **brachial artery,** which continues out into the arm. This vessel need not be traced farther.

Return now to the common carotid arteries. Since the branches of the two arteries are identical, only one of them need be followed. It is suggested that the right carotid be traced, unless the injection was made through this vessel, since the right side was used in previous dissections. Trace this vessel anteriorly, cleaning away tissue and muscles. At this point, the **thyroid gland** should be observed again. It consists of two small masses of tissue, one on each side of the trachea. The two masses are connected by a small strand of tissue that passes ventral to the trachea. In some specimens, this gland does not show up well; in such cases, the identification is helped by observing the position of the superior thyroid artery, as described below. In man, the thyroid gland is an important gland of internal secretion. The common carotid does not give rise to any branches until it attains the level of the anterior end of the thyroid gland. Here it gives off two arteries. The **superior thyroid artery** runs ventrally and medially and sends a twig to the anterior end of the thyroid gland and other branches to the ventral neck muscles. On the opposite side of the common carotid, the **muscularis artery** originates from its dorsal side, passes dorsally and laterally, and supplies the muscles of the neck. In some instances, the muscularis artery may have more than a single root. Anterior to the muscularis artery close to the angle of the jaw, the common carotid gives off the **occipital artery** from its dorsal side. This vessel passes dorsally and supplies some of the neck muscles. The small **internal carotid** also arises in this region; but unless the specimen is well injected, it is difficult to find. The internal carotid may arise as a separate branch from the common carotid, or it may be given off from the trunk of the occipital artery. It passes somewhat anteriorly and dorsally and enters the skull, where it helps to supply the brain.

Anterior to the internal carotid, the common carotid becomes the **external carotid artery,** which very shortly gives rise to other branches. The first branch is the **lingual artery,** which passes along the lower surface of the lower jaw and eventually reaches the tongue. Shortly anterior to the lingual artery, the external carotid gives off the medial **external maxillary artery,** while the external carotid itself continues laterally and dorsal around the angle of the jaw. The external maxillary artery soon divides and sends off branches to the masseter muscle, the submaxillary salivary gland, and other regions of the jaw and face. Near the angle of the jaw, the external carotid divides into several branches, which supply blood to the structures in this region. One of the branches enters the skull and passes to the brain.

Turn back to the aorta, and trace it as it runs to the left and dorsally along the middorsal line of the thorax. In order to see it better, push the heart and the left lung over to the right. As the aorta proceeds posteriorly, it supplies paired **intercostal arteries** to the ribs. In well-injected specimens small **esophageal arteries** to the esophagus and **bronchial arteires** to the bronchi and lungs may be seen.

Drawing 23. The Heart and the Thoracic Arteries—Ventral View. Show only the bases of the pulmonary and the smaller arteries. Draw in the branches on both sides, but label the branches of the subclavian arteries on one side only and the branches of the carotids on the other. **Labels:** right auricle, right ventricle, left auricle, left ventricle. Arteries—right and left pulmonary, brachiocephalic, aorta, pulmonary trunk, right subclavian, left subclavian, right common carotid, left common carotid, internal mammary, vertebral, costocervical axis, thyrocervical axis, axillary, long thoracic, subscapular, thoracodorsal, brachial, superior thyroid, muscularis, occipital, internal carotid (sketch in, if not seen), external carotid, lingual, external maxillary, intercostal, esophageal (if seen), bronchial (if seen).

The **pulmonary veins** should now be found. These vessels carry aerated blood from the lungs to the left auricle, several passing from each lung. Push the heart and one of the lungs apart, and find the veins as they pass toward the left auricle from the lung. Some of them combine to form common trunks before they join the left auricle near its dorsal side.

Before the study on the abdominal cavity is continued, the aortic arches in the cat will be considered briefly. It should be remembered that the typical, or primitive, number of aortic arches is six, although some primitive vertebrates have more. These six aortic arches, connecting the ventral aorta with the dorsal aorta, form in the embryo of most vertebrates. In most fish, these arches are divided into two parts by gill capillaries, and these two divisions are called the afferent and efferent branchial arteries. It should be recalled that, in the dogfish, aortic arch 1 is greatly modified, while aortic arch 2 is only partly present in the typical condition. In Necturus, only arches 3, 4, and 6 remain complete, and arch 6 gives rise to the pulmonary artery. No common carotid artery is present in either the dogfish or Necturus, while the external and internal carotids are formed, respectively, from the ends of the ventral and dorsal aortas. In the turtle, arches 3, 4, and 6 are represented. Arch 3 and the ventral and dorsal aortas form the carotids; arch 4 remains as a complete arch, and its two sides combine in the abdominal cavity to form the dorsal aorta; arch 6 contributes to the pulmonaries. Thus, only arch 4 remains as a fairly typical aortic arch. In the cat, the six arches form as usual in the embryo, but in the adult they are considerably modified. Arches 1, 2, and 5 completely degenerate. Arch 3 and the ventral and dorsal aortas form the carotid arteries, and arch 4 persists on the left side only as a portion of the aorta. The right half of arch 4 partly degenerates, but it may contribute to the formation of the subclavian artery on that side. The ventral aorta and the conus are not present, as such, in the adult but have become split into the bases of the aorta and the pulmonary. The term dorsal aorta is seldom used with respect to the cat, since there is no sharp division between this vessel and the ventral aorta as found in lower forms. The aorta in the adult cat is thus seen to be a composite of several embryonic vessels, including the ventral aorta, the left portion of aortic arch 4, and the dorsal aorta. The pulmonary arteries are as usual derived from aortic arch 6.

Arteries of the Peritoneal Cavity. Loosen the diaphragm on the left side, and trace the aorta into the abdominal cavity. In the abdominal region, the aorta is frequently called the **abdominal aorta.** The first large branch from the aorta is the **coeliac artery,** which gives off branches to the anterior end of the digestive tract and the digestive glands. This vessel arises from the ventral surface of the aorta near the level of the stomach, and its origin is frequently somewhat obscured by fat and mesenteries. Pull the digestive tract over to the right, and trace this vessel. It soon breaks up into three vessels, which vary somewhat in the way they arise. These vessels, the **hepatic, left gastric,** and **splenic arteries,** may arise from the coeliac quite close together or in the sequence in which they are now discussed.

The hepatic artery may originate near the base of the coeliac; or if the coeliac divides into the three vessels near the base, the hepatic artery is the most anterior branch. It passes anteriorly from the anterior edge of the coeliac artery and is normally surrounded by tissue, which should be cleared away. It continues anteriorly dorsal to the stomach. Its branches can best be identified by pushing the liver anteriorly, the stomach posteriorly, and looking into the lesser omentum just ventral to the hepatic portal vein. Slightly anterior to the lesser curvature of the stomach, the hepatic artery gives off a large branch that turns sharply posteriorly. This is the **anterior pancreatico-duodenal artery,** which in turn sends branches to the duodenum, the pancreas, and the greater curvature of the stomach. The hepatic artery then continues on into the liver.

The second (or middle) branch of the coeliac is the left gastric artery passing to the stomach. There may also be other small arteries arising directly from the coeliac near the base of the left gastric and likewise passing to the stomach.

The third (or posterior) branch of the coeliac, the splenic, appears to be a direct continuation of the coeliac artery. It soon splits into two branches that pass to the spleen. Small twigs from the splenic artery also enter the stomach, the great omentum, and the pancreas.

Just posterior to the coeliac artery the **superior mesenteric artery** takes origin from the abdominal aorta and passes somewhat posteriorly, where it supplies branches to the posterior end of the digestive tract. If the superior mesenteric vein has not been destroyed, it should be seen that its branches somewhat parallel the tributaries of the superior mesenteric artery. Trace the superior mesenteric artery, and identify its branches. The first branch is the **middle colic artery,** which arises from the side of the superior mesenteric and runs posteriorly in the mesocolon, ordinarily in company with the inferior mesenteric vein. It supplies blood to the transverse and descending colon. The other branches of the superior mesenteric vary somewhat in their point of origin, but in most cases they arise from the main vessel rather close together. The distribution of these vessels furnishes a more positive means of identification than their origin. The **posterior pancreaticoduodenal artery** passes laterally and anteriorly in company with the posterior pancreaticoduodenal vein to the posterior part of the duodenum and the pancreas. On the opposite side of the superior mesenteric (usually) the **ileocolic artery** arises and gives off branches to the posterior part of the ileum, caecum, and ascending colon. The superior mesenteric artery then breaks up into a large number of **intestinal branches** supplying the intestine.

Posterior to the origin of the superior mesenteric artery, the abdominal aorta gives off a pair of **adrenolumbar arteries** laterally, which send branches to the adrenal glands and the body wall in this region. In well-injected specimens, small **phrenic arteries** can be seen arising from the anterior edge of the adrenolumbar arteries and passing to the diaphragm, although in many specimens these vessels will not appear. The **renal arteries,** slightly posterior to the adrenolumbar, pass directly to the kidneys. Some distance posterior to the renal arteries, **gonadal arteries** arise and pass to the reproductive organs. In the male, these are the **internal spermatic arteries** and are usually quite small. They run posteriorly along the dorsal body wall in company with the internal spermatic veins and into the testes. In some instances, the internal spermatic arteries may arise from the renal arteries. The **ovarian arteries** of the female are in most cases somewhat larger than the internal spermatic arteries of the male.   They pass more laterally across the body to the ovaries and the anterior end of the reproductive tract.

The **inferior mesenteric artery** branches from the ventral surface of the aorta, passes into the mesocolon (mesentery), and divides into an anterior and a posterior branch.   The anterior branch, supplying the anterior end of the descending colon, is the **left colic artery;** the posterior branch, the **superior hemorrhoidal,** passes to the posterior part of the descending colon and the rectum.

Posterior to the inferior mesenteric artery, a pair of **iliolumbar arteries** arise, one from each side of the aorta, and proceed into the muscles of the body wall.   In addition to these branches to the body wall, the abdominal aorta gives off small **lumbar arteries** along its length from its dorsal surface.   Frequently, dissection has to be made somewhat dorsally for locating some of these vessels.

Near the posterior end of the abdominal cavity, the aorta splits into five parts.   In order to see these branches, it may be necessary to disconnect the mesocolon from the body wall and pull the digestive tract over to one side.   The largest of these arteries are the two outside branches, the **external iliac arteries.** The **internal iliac arteries** are medial to the external iliac arteries and run somewhat parallel to them.   The fifth branch of the aorta in this region is the **caudal artery,** which arises between the internal iliac arteries and continues out into the tail.

First trace one of the external iliac arteries.   If the specimen has been injected in the leg, the vessels in this region should be studied on the opposite leg.   About 1 inch posterior to the origin of the external iliac artery, the **deep femoral artery** arises from its inner edge and passes somewhat posteriorly and medially. The origins of the branches of the deep femoral artery are somewhat variable in different specimens and therefore will not be studied in detail.   There are usually three main branches, but two of these may originate from a single main trunk, which in turn has arisen from the deep femoral artery.   One of the branches passes anteriorly into the abdominal cavity onto the surface of the rectus abdominis, continues anteriorly, and eventually anastomoses with the superior epigastric artery from the anterior part of the body.   This branch is the **inferior epigastric artery.** It is sometimes quite small, and the chances are that the anterior portion has been cut in previous dissections, which causes the connection with the superior epigastric artery to be difficult to find. If the arterial injection has been well done, however, a portion of the inferior epigastric artery can normally be seen on the rectus abdominis muscle within the abdominal cavity. There is apparently no agreement as to the names that should be given to the other two branches of the deep femoral. One branch passes toward the median part of the thigh and gives off twigs to this part of the thigh and to the bladder. The other branch passes distally, somewhat parallel to the distal end of the femoral artery.

Distal to the region where the deep femoral artery arises, the main artery passing along the leg is called the **femoral.** Just distal to the deep femoral, a rather large branch arises from the outer surface of the femoral artery. This is the **lateral femoral circumflex artery.** The main branch of the femoral artery then continues along the leg, giving off branches to the lower thigh and shank.

The internal iliac artery sends branches to the muscles of the thigh, the bladder, and the reproductive organs. Its branches need not be traced out.

Drawing 24. Abdominal Arteries—Ventral View. Sketch in some of the organs so that the relationships of the vessels will be indicated. **Labels:** Arteries—aorta, coeliac, hepatic, left gastric, splenic, superior mesenteric, middle colic, posterior pancreatico-duodenal, ileocolic, intestinal, adrenolumbar, phrenic (if seen), renal, gonadal, inferior mesenteric, left colic, superior hemorrhoidal, lumbar, external iliac, internal iliac, caudal, deep femoral, femoral.

The Posterior Branches of the Postcaval Vein. As was previously indicated, the posterior branches of the postcaval vein occur dorsal to the arteries in that region; thus, it was necessary to study the arteries first. If care is exerted, these veins may now be studied without destroying the arteries, and an attempt should be made to proceed in such a way that the arteries will be preserved for review.

Just dorsal to the posterior end of the abdominal cavity, where the aorta splits into five parts, the postcaval vein is formed by two large veins, one coming from each leg. Each of these large vessels is a **common iliac vein.** Between these two veins is a small **caudal,** or sacral, **vein** from the tail. It may join one or the other of the iliac veins. Trace one of the common iliac veins distally, preferably on the leg that was used for the study of the arteries. It passes undivided for about ½ inch or so and then divides into an **internal iliac** (hypogastric) and an **external iliac vein.** (It should be remembered that blood in the veins is actually flowing toward the heart rather than away from it.) The internal iliac usually comes into the common iliac on the dorsal side; it is thus easily overlooked. It somewhat accompanies the external iliac artery and collects blood from the bladder and the posterior region of the intestine as well as from the muscles in that region. The external iliac vein is more or less of a direct continuation of the common iliac. Just posterior to the internal iliac vein, the external iliac receives the **deep femoral vein** from the medial side of the leg. This vessel is closely associated with the artery of the same name and receives blood from the thigh muscles in this region. Posterior to the deep femoral, the main vein is called the **femoral vein.** Some distance distal to the deep femoral, the femoral vein is joined by a branch from the anterior surface of the thigh. This vessel is the **lateral femoral circumflex vein,** which is near the lateral femoral circumflex artery. The femoral vein then continues on into the distal portion of the leg, from which it conveys blood toward the heart. Add the branches of the postcaval vein to drawing 21, page 201.

THE NERVOUS SYSTEM

The nervous system is divided into three primary divisions: the **central nervous system,** composed of the brain and the spinal cord; the **peripheral nervous system,** which includes the cranial and spinal nerves; and the **autonomic nervous system,** to which belong the sympathetic and parasympathetic fibers. Some of the parts of the nervous system of the cat are difficult to study except for demonstration; consequently, these portions will not be considered in detail.

The Brain and the Cranial Nerves. Since the cat's skull is so hard, the dissection of the brain and the cranial nerves is difficult; but, with care, a successful study can be made. Remove the skin, muscles, and fascia from the dorsal and lateral surfaces of the skull. Then, with bone forceps or a bone saw, make an opening through the skull. Using this opening as a starting place, carefully chip away the bone from the dorsal surface of the skull, being careful not to get any of the chips in your eyes.

There are several membranes associated with the brain and the spinal cord, and the general term **meninges** (singular, meninx) is applied to them. The outer membrane next to the skull is the

dura mater, a tough membrane that should be removed. Closely applied to the brain surface and following all its contours is the delicate **pia mater,** which in injected cats will probably be seen to contain blood vessels. A third membrane associated with the brain, the **arachnoid,** is somewhat difficult to find. It occurs between the dura mater and the pia mater and is best found at the depressions in the brain surface. The pia mater follows the brain surface into these depressions; the arachnoid, on the contrary, passes across the depressions. Thus any delicate membrane covering a depression is a portion of the arachnoid. In the living cat, the cerebrospinal fluid fills the spaces between the membranes. Both the pia mater and arachnoid in the cat are probably derived from the pia mater as found in the turtle. The pia mater in the two are, accordingly, not entirely the same.

In contrast to the brains previously studied, the brain of the cat is striking in the extreme development of the cerebral portion. By far the largest part of the brain is composed of the anteriorly located **cerebral hemispheres,** which alone make up more than half the dorsal brain surface. At the anterior ends of the cerebral hemispheres are the small **olfactory lobes.** In lower forms, in which the olfactory lobes and the cerebral hemispheres are primarily olfactory in function, the term telencephalon is applied to them. Posterior to the cerebral hemispheres, and having a surface even more convoluted, is the **cerebellum.** Posterior to the cerebellum and partly covered by it is the **medulla oblongata.** Raise the cerebellum slightly so that the anterior end of the medulla may be seen. There is no morphological division between the medulla and the **spinal cord,** but the division is considered to occur at the foramen magnum of the skull. There are two additional divisions of the brain, the diencephalon and the mesencephalon; but since they cannot be seen from the dorsal view, they will not be identified until later.

Return now to the cerebral hemispheres. The surfaces of these structures are thrown up into folds, between which are depressions. The folds are the **gyri** (singular, gyrus), while the depressions are the **sulci** (singular, sulcus). A large sulcus is sometimes called a **fissure.** The two hemispheres are separated by a deep fissure that passes longitudinally, the **longitudinal fissure.** The dorsal surface of each hemisphere is divided into three gyri. The **marginal gyrus** is the most median and borders on the longitudinal fissure. Lateral to the marginal gyrus is the **supra-Sylvian gyrus.**   The most lateral is the **ecto-Sylvian gyrus.**   These gyri are separated by deep sulci.   Other gyri occur laterally, but these will not be identified.

The cerebellum consists of three lobes, a middle **vermis** and two lateral **hemispheres,** or lobes.   Push the cerebellum slightly forward so that the medulla can be seen better.   As in lower vertebrates, the medulla contains a cavity, the **fourth ventricle.** The roof of this cavity is covered by a membrane, the **medullary velum,** which contains a mass of blood vessels, a **chorioid plexus.**

Drawing 25.   Dorsal Surface of the Brain.   Place in center of page.   Make drawing before the covered portions are identified. **Labels :** cerebral hemisphere, olfactory lobe, cerebellum, medulla, longitudinal fissure, marginal gyrus, supra-Sylvian gyrus, ecto-Sylvian gyrus, vermis (cerebellum), hemisphere of cerebellum, fourth ventricle.

The other divisions of the brain should now be identified. Gradually separate the two cerebral hemispheres, and look into the longitudinal fissure.   As the cerebral hemispheres are separated, look for a broad white connection between them near the ventral portion of the fissure.   This connection is the **corpus callosum;** it consists of masses of nerve fibers connecting the two cerebral hemispheres.   It is maintained by some that intelligence is dependent in great measure upon the proper structure and functioning of the corpus callosum.

The **diencephalon** can be found if the hemispheres are pushed farther apart.   It appears as two small bodies just posterior to the region where the cerebral hemispheres are attached to the nerve cord.   In the roof of the diencephalon, there occurs a **chorioid plexus** composed of blood vessels.   Under the plexus in the diencephalon is the **third ventricle** of the brain, which is quite narrow distally.   Posterior to the diencephalon are two pairs of rounded elevations, one pair anterior to the other. These are the **corpora quadrigemina,** which correspond to the optic lobes of lower forms.   Since in lower vertebrates there are only two divisions to the optic lobes, these are sometimes called the corpora bigemina.   The corpora quadrigemina compose the dorsal region of the mesencephalon, or midbrain.

The ventral surface of the brain and the cranial nerves should now be studied.   Remove the brain from the skull; in so doing, clip the attached cranial nerves so that stubs will remain attached to the brain.   As indicated previously, the cranial nerves make up part of the peripheral nervous system.   Study the ventral region, and start at the anterior end in making the identification. Note again the two olfactory lobes ventral to the anterior end of the cerebral hemispheres. From each of these lobes, an **olfactory nerve** (cranial nerve I) passes anteriorly to the lining of the nose. This nerve is sensory.

A short distance posterior to the olfactory lobes is the **optic chiasma,** the region where the two optic nerves cross. The **optic nerves** are cranial nerves II, which innervate the retinas of the eyes. They pass into the orbit through the skull by way of the optic foramen. They are sensory nerves. Just posterior to the optic chiasma is a ventral projection, the **infundibulum,** to which is attached the **hypophysis.** The infundibulum is a ventral portion of the diencephalon, and the hypophysis is a gland of internal secretion, sometimes called the pituitary gland. Cranial nerve III, the **oculomotor,** arises from the ventral portion of the mesencephalon just posterior to the hypophysis and usually extends anteriorly on each side of it. These nerves pass to some of the muscles of the eye and send small branches (ciliary) into the eye itself. The oculomotor nerve penetrates the skull by way of the orbital fissure. It innervates the following eye muscles: the superior, medial, and inferior recti and the inferior oblique. This nerve is a motor nerve.

Behind the infundibulum and the hypophysis, there occurs a group of cross fibers that pass dorsally on each side. These fibers constitute the **pons** of the metencephalon, the dorsal part of which is the cerebellum. Along the outer edge of the pons, the **trochlear nerve** (IV) arises and passes through the orbital fissure and to the superior oblique muscle of the eye. This nerve is motor.

The ventral surface of the medulla is posterior to the pons. Cranial nerve V, the **trigeminal,** originates toward the posterior region of the pons and passes anteriorly. It is a large nerve and soon branches into several smaller nerves. Some of the fibers pass through the orbital fissure; other branches pass through the foramen rotundum and the foramen ovale. This nerve is distributed to the muscles and the skin of the sides of the head and face. A branch, the inferior alveolar nerve, passes into the lower jaw and sends off twigs to the teeth. It enters the mandible by the mandibular foramen and passes to the outside by way of the mental foramen or foramina, if two are present. The trigeminal nerve is a mixed nerve.

Cranial nerve number VI, the **abducens,** arises from the ventral surface of the medulla and passes through the orbital fissure to the lateral (posterior) rectus muscle of the eye.   This nerve is motor.   The **facial nerve** (VII) arises lateral to the abducens. It is composed of both motor and sensory fibers.   It passes through the skull by way of the stylomastoid foramen and is primarily distributed to the muscles of the head and the face. Some of its fibers become mixed with those of the trigeminal. The **auditory nerve** (VIII) is sensory.   It passes to the inner ear and arises posterior and lateral to the facial.

The **glossopharyngeal nerve** (IX) and the **vagus** (X), or pneumogastric, originate in sequence from the sides of the medulla posterior to the auditory nerve.   Both are mixed nerves, and both leave the skull through the jugular foramen.   The glossopharyngeal sends branches to the pharynx and the tongue. The vagus proceeds posteriorly in close association with the common carotid artery.   The vagus nerve sends off branches to the heart, lungs, and organs in the peritoneal cavity.

The **spinal accessory nerve** (XI) is formed from a combination of many small roots that arise from both the medulla and the spinal cord, although the roots from the spinal cord will probably not be seen.   A single fiber formed from the spinal roots passes anteriorly into the skull and combines with the roots from the medulla to form the complete nerve.   The medullary roots of this nerve occur just posterior to the vagus.   The spinal accessory nerve passes from the skull by way of the jugular foramen. It runs posteriorly and innervates several muscles, including the cleidomastoid and the three trapezius muscles.   It is a motor nerve.

Cranial nerve XII, the **hypoglossal,** arises by several roots from the medulla of the brain posterior to the medullary roots of the spinal accessory nerve.   It passes from the skull through the hypoglossal foramen and sends some branches to throat muscles, but the principal fibers innervate the muscles of the tongue.   The hypoglossal is a motor nerve.

As was mentioned in Chap. VI, The Turtle, cranial nerves XI and XII are characteristic of reptiles, birds, and mammals. There is evidence that the spinal accessory nerve is partly derived from the vagus and that the hypoglossal is a former spinal nerve which in reptiles, birds, and mammals becomes included in the skull as a cranial nerve.

Drawing 26.   Ventral Surface of Brain.   Place in center of page.   Since many of the cranial nerves are sometimes hard to locate, they are not included in the required list of labels. All that are located, however, should be included and labeled. **Labels:** olfactory lobe, cerebral hemisphere, optic chiasma, optic nerve (II), mesencephalon, infundibulum, hypophysis (if seen), pons, medulla.

The Spinal Nerves. The spinal nerves are also part of the peripheral division of the nervous system. In the cat there are approximately 38 pairs of these nerves passing laterally from the spinal cord through the intervertebral foramina to the various muscles and the skin. They are divided into groups. From anterior to posterior there are 8 pairs of **cervical,** 13 pairs of **thoracic,** 7 pairs of **lumbar,** 3 pairs of **sacral,** and 7 to 8 pairs of **caudal spinal nerves.** Not all these nerves will be studied, but a few will be observed.

Opposite each limb, several nerves combine to form a mass of nerve fibers called a **plexus.** This combination is doubtless correlated with the fact that the complicated musculature of each limb requires several nerves for proper coordination. The nerve fibers opposite the front limb form the **brachial plexus.** Opposite the hind limb, there occurs the **lumbosacral plexus.** In the latter case, two plexuses are involved, the lumbar plexus and the sacral plexus; but since there are connections between the two, they will be discussed together.

The Brachial Plexus. The spinal nerves are white cordlike structures, sometimes difficult to separate from the connective tissue. However, they are considerably tougher than most of the surrounding material and not so likely to break. Locate the brachial artery and the brachial vein. If no previous dissection has been made on the arm of the specimen, cut longitudinally through the pectoral muscles near the sternum and separate them from the ribs. When the two blood vessels are found, some of the nerves should be seen running parallel to the vessels. After locating the nerves near the blood vessels, trace them toward the body, and locate the plexus near the region where the arm joins the body.

The plexus is formed from interconnections between cervical nerves 5, 6, 7, 8, and thoracic nerve 1. Find the region where all these nerves show connections. Cervical nerve 5 is quite small and is sometimes hard to find. It is frequently difficult to identify all the different connections between the various nerves, and in some cases even the bases of the main nerves are not evident. Nerves from this plexus pass to the shoulder and the forelimb and thus innervate the muscles and the integument. The branches listed below are perhaps the most important and are easier to find than the others. There is likely to be considerable individual variation among the different specimens.

THE PHRENIC NERVE. The **phrenic nerve** passes to the diaphragm and is derived chiefly from cervical nerve 5, although it also receives some fibers from cervical nerve 6. It passes posteriorly across and at right angles to the roots of the spinal nerves and is probably best located between the lung and the pericardial cavity. Look between the point of entrance into the lung of the bronchus and the pericardial cavity. Trace the nerve posteriorly to the diaphragm and then anteriorly to its origin.

A somewhat larger nerve paralleling the phrenic nerve may also be found in this region. This is the vagus, cranial nerve X, which continues posteriorly and supplies various abdominal organs. It also sends branches to the heart and the lungs.

THE RADIAL NERVE. Remove enough material from the median portion of the upper arm, so that the branches of the nerves can be seen. The **radial nerve** is the largest nerve passing into the upper arm. It extends distally and somewhat anteriorly, passes under the edge of the biceps brachii, and proceeds distally along the posterior edge of this muscle. It continues out into the arm and supplies many of the arm muscles. This nerve is derived primarily from the seventh and eighth cervical nerves, with a small contribution from the first thoracic nerve.

THE MUSCULOCUTANEOUS NERVE. The **musculocutaneous nerve** contains fibers from the sixth and seventh cervical nerves. It is best located along the posterior edge of the biceps brachii.

THE MEDIAN NERVE. The **median nerve** is somewhat posterior and ventral to the radial nerve. It has three roots, the anterior of which may be intimately associated with the musculocutaneous nerve near its origin. The median nerve passes distally into the arm parallel to the brachial artery. It is derived primarily from the fibers of the seventh and eighth cervical nerves and the first thoracic nerve. It passes through the supracondyloid foramen of the humerus and down to the forearm. This nerve and the next to be mentioned are the principal nerves of the forearm.

THE ULNAR NERVE. The **ulnar nerve** occurs just posterior and parallel to the median nerve. It typically runs just posterior to the brachial artery, while the median nerve is anterior to it.

This nerve is an interesting one physiologically. Trace it distally to the arm joint, and note that at this point it is quite near the surface. In man this region is called the "funny bone." Relatively light blows in this unprotected region cause intense pain if the nerve is hit. The ulnar nerve is derived primarily from the first thoracic nerve.

In addition to the nerves described above, there are a number of other branches connected to the brachial plexus. They are, however, quite variable and difficult to identify.

The posterior **thoracic spinal nerves** pass to the muscles and skin of the thorax and the back. Portions of these nerves may be located by removing the tissue along the posterior borders of the ribs. In this region, the nerves pass along the ribs near the intercostal arteries. If the specimen has been injected, this should be an aid in identification.

The Lumbosacral Plexus and Associated Nerves. As indicated previously, there are seven pairs of lumbar spinal nerves in the cat. The first three pairs pass independently from the spinal cord to the abdominal wall, where they supply the muscles and the integument. Lumbar nerve 1 is best located about 1 inch posterior to the last rib in the dorsal region of the abdominal cavity. With forceps, pull away the peritoneum and muscles in this region until this nerve is found. Posterior to this nerve are lumbar nerves 2 and 3.

The last four lumbar nerves and the three sacral nerves are interconnected to form the lumbosacral plexus. The relation of this plexus to the hind limb is comparable with that of the brachial plexus to the forelimb. Only the main branches of this plexus will be studied. The **sciatic nerve** is the largest nerve to originate from the plexus; in fact, it is the longest nerve in the body. It should be located and traced toward the body. Turn the cat on its belly, and disconnect the biceps femoris for its entire length from the underlying muscles. The sciatic nerve is just under the biceps and appears as a broad white band passing lengthwise of the thigh across the adductor femoris toward the lower limb. Near the distal end of the biceps, the sciatic nerve divides into a lateral **peroneal branch** and a medial **tibial nerve.** These branches continue down into the lower leg and innervate muscles in that region. Trace the sciatic nerve toward the body, picking away any tissue that covers it. Note the small branches it gives off to the surrounding muscles. Near the base of the tail, a rather large nerve may be seen between the sciatic and the base of the tail.   This nerve extends parallel to the sciatic for a time and frequently is so closely associated with it that it appears to be a branch of the sciatic.   Closer examination will reveal that the two are separate.   This is the **posterior cutaneous nerve,** which supplies the tissue near the base of the tail and the biceps femoris.   It is derived primarily from sacral nerves 2 and 3.

Completely remove the two gluteus muscles, if this has not been done already.   Near the region where the leg is attached to the body, the sciatic nerve passes ventrally and into the peritoneal cavity.   Take a blunt probe, and push it through the muscles alongside the sciatic nerve until it emerges into the abdominal cavity.   Dissect in this region until the sciatic nerve and the other nerves of the lumbosacral plexus are found.   These connections are quite complicated, and no attempt will be made to study them in detail.

One additional nerve passing into the leg should be identified. Look on the inner surface of the thigh and find the **femoral nerve,** which passes distally between the sartorius and gracilis muscles. If these two muscles have been cut or removed, the nerve may be difficult to find.   Near the posterior end of the thigh, the nerve passes across the gracilis muscle and into the lower leg as the **saphenous nerve.**   This is primarily derived from the fifth and sixth lumbar nerves.

A number of other nerves that arise from the lumbosacral plexus will not be identified.   A formal drawing is not required, but sketches are suggested.

The **autonomic nervous system** will not be studied in detail. The system consists of a series of small fibers and ganglia, which, in turn, are connected to the spinal and cranial nerves.   One large division of this system is composed of a pair of sympathetic trunks, one on each side of the vertebral column.   These trunks consist of a series of ganglia that are connected to form chainlike cords.   Another important portion of the system consists of the several plexuses in association with the various organs.   One of these, the solar plexus, occurring in the region of the stomach, is in man a favorite target for prize fighters.

Generally speaking, nervous impulses passing over this complex network of fibers aid in the regulation of many of the organs of the body, including such important actions as the heartbeat, respiration, glandular secretions, and peristalsis.

CHAPTER VIII

THE PIGEON

Phylum—Chordata
Subphylum—Vertebrata
Class—Aves
Order—Columbiformes
Genus—Columba

Birds are of considerable interest anatomically because many of their systems are highly adapted for flight. Pigeons are used for this study, as a rule, because of their comparatively large size and because they are easily obtained. Detailed studies of the circulatory system will not be made, and consequently uninjected specimens are quite satisfactory for this work. It is suggested that the skeletal system be studied first, since a knowledge of this system will be helpful during the dissection for a study of the internal anatomy. Directions for drawings have been omitted because the procedures used for studying the pigeon differ widely in different courses.

THE SKELETAL SYSTEM

The skeletal system of birds, like that of most vertebrate animals, is composed of three divisions, the **axial,** the **appendicular,** and the **visceral.** The axial skeleton consists of the skull, the vertebral column, the ribs, and the sternum. The notochord, which is present only in the embryo of birds, is also considered to be a part of the axial skeleton. The appendicular division includes the bones of the wings and the legs and the pectoral and pelvic girdles to which these structures are attached. The visceral division of the skeleton is not well represented in the bird, but one or two structures derived from it will be noted. This visceral division, it is to be recalled, supports the gills and forms the jaws in the dogfish (page 58). In higher vertebrates, which do not have gills, the visceral skeleton develops in the embryo, but these various elements become highly modified during subsequent development. In the adult bird parts of the visceral skeleton form the hyoid apparatus which serves to

225

support the tongue, and certain elements also develop into the bones of the middle ear.

The Axial Skeleton. The **skull** of the pigeon is remarkable in several respects. Observe the almost complete absence of **sutures,** lines which indicate where two bones are fused together. Observe that the **upper** and **lower jaws** are modified into a horny **beak.** Just posterior to the beak, on each side is a large cavity. During life, each of these cavities contains an eye. They are the **orbits,** each of which is almost as large as the cranial cavity. in which the brain lies, and the two are separated by only a very thin membrane. This structure is correlated with the comparatively enormous size of the eyes of birds.

The bony portion of the **tongue** will be present in some skulls. It is a sharp projection lying between the two parts of the lower jaw and best seen from a ventral view. Passing from the base of the tongue ventral to each angle of the lower jaw is a small threadlike bone that attaches to the lateral surface of the skull. This framework is the **hyoid apparatus,** which may not be present in some specimens. It forms a support for the tongue and is derived embryologically from a part of the visceral skeleton.

Examine the jaws, and observe that no teeth are present. "Scarce as hen's teeth" is an appropriate way of describing rare or nonexistent objects since no teeth occur in any living bird.

Turn next to the **vertebral column,** or backbone, upon the anterior end of which the skull is perched. There are several types of vertebrae in the pigeon and these are associated into groups which make up rather definite regions of the vertebral column. From anterior to posterior these groups of vertebrae are: **cervical,** or neck, **vertebrae; thoracic; lumbosacral** (fused lumbar and sacral); and the **caudal,** or tail, **vertebrae.** All of these except the cervical vertebrae are partially or completely fused together, and this causes the skeleton to be more rigid.

Study the cervical vertebrae, of which there are 13 or 14 in the pigeon. Birds do not have a constant number of cervical vertebrae, as do most animals (the typical number in mammals is seven), but the number varies widely. They have in general more cervical vertebrae than other vertebrates, and even a short-necked bird, such as a sparrow, has more than the long-necked giraffe.

Certain features of individual vertebrae should be observed although, unless a disarticulated vertebral column is available for study, some of the parts will be hard to identify. It should be noted that, since the neck of the pigeon is held in an upright position, the part of the vertebrae in front is really ventral while the opposite side is dorsal.

If individual vertebrae are not available for study, examine the dorsal surface of the backbone between the wings and in the neck region. The vertebrae in mounted skeletons are usually supported by a rigid wire that passes through a hole in the vertebral column. This wire can often be seen from the dorsal surface between some of the cervical vertebrae. The hole through which the wire passes is the **neural canal,** which contains the spinal cord in life. That portion of the vertebra that surrounds the neural canal dorsally is the **neural arch.** A bony dorsal projection from the neural arch, the **neural spine,** is more evident in the posterior vertebrae. These projections serve for muscle attachments. Study the region of articulation of two of the vertebrae. If they are correctly joined in the mounted skeleton it will be seen that an elongate posterior projection from each vertebra on each side fits over a shorter anterior projection from the vertebra posterior to it. The posterior projections are termed the **postzygopophyses,** while the anterior ones are the **prezygopophyses.**

The prezygopophyses project dorsally from larger lateral processes called **transverse processes.** Observe that there is a small hole through the base of each transverse process in the cervical vertebrae. These holes make up the **vertebrarterial canal** through which pass the vertebral artery, the vertebral vein, and certain nerves belonging to the autonomic division of the nervous system.

Ventral to the neural canal is a solid portion of the vertebra called the **centrum.** The ends of the centra articulate with each other and in birds these articulating surfaces are so shaped that great freedom of movement is permitted. The articulating surfaces are somewhat saddle-shaped, a situation that is not evident unless individual vertebrae are available for examination; a vertebra in which the articulating surfaces of the centra are of this shape is said to be a **heterocoelous vertebra.**

Examine the articulation between the skull and the vertebral column. The first and second cervical vertebrae differ somewhat from the posterior ones. The first cervical vertebra that articulates directly with the skull is short and ringlike. It is called the **atlas.** The **axis,** the second cervical vertebra, is considerably longer than the atlas. Look on the ventral surface and see if you can find an anterior projection from the axis that extends into the atlas.   This is the **odontoid process,** and it probably represents the centrum of the atlas, which has become secondarily fused to the axis.   Each of the posterior two cervical vertebrae bears a pair of lateral projections, or **ribs.**

The **thoracic vertebrae,** of which there are five, are more or less fused together and each has a pair of **ribs,** which will be discussed later.   Notice that the last thoracic vertebra is fused with a compact structure extending posteriorly, called the **synsacrum.** Studies have shown that the synsacrum is composed of **lumbar, sacral,** and a few of the anterior **caudal vertebrae,** in addition to the last thoracic.   Look on the ventral surface of the synsacrum, and observe that the transverse processes of some of the individual vertebrae can be distinguished.   The synsacrum is partially fused laterally with a flat bony structure on each side, about which more will be said later.   There are seven movable caudal vertebrae.   The last one, which is larger than the others and probably represents several fused vertebrae, is termed the **pygostyle.**

Ribs.   There are seven pairs of ribs in the pigeon, although on mounted skeletons some of these may be broken.   The first two pairs of ribs, as we have seen, arise from the last cervical vertebrae.   Their ventral ends are not attached; therefore they are called **floating ribs.**   (In mammals, including man, the floating ribs are posterior to the others).   Notice that the five posterior ribs are attached to the **sternum,** a large bone between the legs. These are called **true ribs.**   All the ribs attached to the thoracic vertebrae have two easily identified regions, the vertebral and the sternal portions.   Those of the vertebral portion are attached to the vertebrae and extend ventrally.   The sternal division of each rib extends anteriorly from the articulation with the vertebral part, and is attached to the sternum.   In many animals the sternal portion of the ribs is mostly cartilaginous, even in the adult, but in birds this region is almost completely ossified. This is doubtless a modification correlated with the ability to fly.   Projecting posteriorly and dorsally from the vertebral part of each of the five middle ribs is a flat bony process that fits closely over the rib posterior to it.   These are **uncinate processes** and they apparently function to strengthen the rib framework.

In addition to the seven pairs of definite ribs noted above, the pigeon has structures on the anterior cervical vertebrae which probably represent rudimentary ribs.   These are the transverse processes, plus the posteriorly directed spine on their ventral surfaces.

The Sternum. The **sternum** is the large ventral bone between the legs, to which are attached the ribs along the dorsal margin. The large ventrally projecting process is the **carina,** or keel, and it, as well as many other processes, serves for the attachment of powerful muscles of flight. This bone, together with the muscles, makes up the so-called breast of the chicken, a piece popular with lovers of white meat. In birds, such as the ostrich, that have lost the power of flight, the sternum is flat, without a median carina.

The sternum has several processes that can best be identified from the dorsal surface. Notice two holes near the posterior end of the sternum; in old skeletons the posterior rims of these holes may be broken. The **lateral internal processes** form the anteriolateral rims of these holes. Just ventral to the ribs near the middle of the sternum, a **lateral external process** extends posteriorly on each side. The notch along the edge of the sternum, between the external and the internal process on each side, is the **external notch.** The most anterior pair of projections on the sternum, the **costal processes,** project somewhat anteriorly just below the floating ribs. (NOTE: The lateral external process and the lateral internal process are sometimes called xiphisternal processes).

The Appendicular Skeleton. This skeletal division consists of the bones of the appendages and the pectoral and pelvic girdles, to which the bones of the limbs are attached. Examine first the pectoral girdle, which on each side is composed of a **clavicle,** or "collarbone"; a **scapula,** or "shoulder blade"; and a **coracoid.** The two clavicles are fused together at their ventral ends to form the well-known wishbone. Notice that this structure is attached to the anterior end of the carina of the sternum. The point of fusion ventrally of the two clavicles to form the wishbone is called the **interclavicle.** The ends of the clavicles extend dorsally and attach to the dorsal ends of the coracoids, one on each side, that extend obliquely downward and join the sternum at the costal processes. The third element of the pectoral girdle, the scapula, is a flat bladelike bone, extending posteriorly from the upper end of the coracoid, dorsal to the ribs. The coracoid, scapula, and clavicle join in the shoulder region to form a socket, into which the large bone of the upper wing fits. This socket is the **glenoid fossa.**

The proximal end of the wing is surprisingly similar to the fore-limbs of other vertebrates, although the distal portion is more modified. The **humerus** is the large bone that is inserted into the glenoid fossa. Observe that the proximal end, called the **head,** has a number of projections. These projections are called tuberosities and they serve for muscle attachments in life. The **lesser tuberosity** usually forms a dorsal projection on mounted specimens, and the end is somewhat pointed. A ridge, called the **deltoid ridge,** passes distally along the humerus from the lesser tuberosity. Pectoral muscles insert in this region. The **greater tuberosity** is on the opposite side of the humerus. Turn the skeleton so that you can see the posterior side of the greater tuberosity, and find a large depression here. This is the **pneumatic foramen,** which connects with an air space in the humerus.

Two bones make up the second wing division, the part that corresponds to the forearm of human beings. The smaller of these is the **radius;** the larger one, the **ulna.** Note the small posterior projection from the ulna. This is the **olecranon process,** or elbow.

The remainder of the wing skeleton corresponds to the wrist, hand, and fingers of man, and to this same general area of other mammals. This region has obviously been highly modified. It should be recalled that this part of the forelimb in an unmodi-fied vertebrate limb consists of several small bones, or **carpals** (wristbones of man); separate **metacarpals** (hand bones of man); and a series of bones called **phalanges** that make up the digits (fingers in man).

Considerable fusion and dropping out of parts has occurred in birds, so that there is still some confusion regarding the homol-ogies of the parts that remain. Only two free wristbones, or carpals, are present in the pigeon, and these are often hard to find in mounted skeletons. One of these occurs near the distal end of the ulna, and the other near the distal end of the radius. Although as indicated the homologies of these elements are debatable, the carpal at the end of the radius is often called the **radiole,** while the one near the end of the ulna is termed the **ulnare.**

Remnants of only three metacarpals and digits occur, and they probably represent the second, third, and fourth, the first and fifth being entirely absent. The second metacarpal and digit is represented by a short, spurlike structure on the anterior wing margin. Near the distal end of the radius and ulna posterior to this structure are two long bones which probably represent a fusion of carpal and metacarpal bones. This bony complex is often called the **carpometacarpus.** Some phalanges of the third and fourth digits are represented at the distal end of the carpo-metacarpus. The third digit is best developed and is represented by two large bones, each of which is about a half inch in length. The fourth digit has only a single phalanx. This is usually closely applied to the base of the proximal phalanx of the third digit, on its posterior surface.

Turn now to the pelvic girdle, to which the legs are attached. This structure is composed of several bones, but they are so tightly fused together that the sutures between the bones are almost obliterated. The pelvic girdle is also fused with the synsacrum, although in this case sutures mark the boundaries of the separate elements. Study one side of the pelvic girdle and observe the irregular suture by which the medial part of the girdle and the lateral edge of the synsacrum come together. Three separate bones are fused to form the girdle on each side. These are the **ilium,** the **ischium,** and the **pubis.** The ilium is the element that is fused with the synsacrum. It is an elongate bone extending from the last rib posteriorly to the base of the tail. Note that it is concave anteriorly and convex posteriorly. A tasty bit of muscle usually nestles in the concavity of the ilium, which somewhat makes up for the disappointment experienced by a person who is served the back of a chicken. This is larger in turkeys than in chickens and is often called the "oyster."

The ilium forms the dorsal rim of the socket into which the leg articulates. The ischium and the pubis also contribute to the formation of this socket, which is called the **acetabulum.** The large upper bone of the leg that joins the pelvic girdle is the **femur.** The ischium is posterior and ventral to the upper end of the femur, and in its anterior end it has a large hole—the **ischiatic foramen.** The ischium extends posteriorly from the ischiatic foramen and is fused for the remainder of its length with the posterior part of the ilium. The pubis is the long slender bone that is ventral to the ischium.

Near the anterior margin of the ischiatic foramen is a smaller hole that separates the anterior ends of the pubis and the ischium. This is the **obturator foramen.** Posterior to the obturator foramen, the ischium and the pubis are separated by a slitlike opening for much of their lengths. This slit is the **foramen oblongatum.** Each half of the pelvic girdle, made up of the fused ilium, ischium, and pubis, is often called the **innominate bone.**

An important difference between the pelvic girdle of the bird and that of most other land-inhabiting vertebrates is that in the bird the pelvic girdle is open ventrally and not fused to form a complete bony ring. This feature is doubtless correlated with the fact that birds lay hard-shelled, comparatively large eggs.

When compared to the hind legs of other vertebrates, the legs of birds are in a situation similar to that in the wings. That is, most modifications occur distally. We have noted that the femur is the large bone that articulates with the pelvic girdle. In the chicken, this is sometimes called the thigh, or second joint, a favorite with people who prefer dark meat. The part that fits into the acetabulum of the pelvic girdle is the **head** of the femur. Lateral to the head is a ridgelike process called the **great trochanter,** which in mounted skeletons usually projects somewhat dorsally and posteriorly. Distally, the humerus articulates with two bones, a large one and a very slender one, forming the knee joint. On the anterior surface of this joint is a small rounded bone, sometimes absent in mounted skeletons, termed the **patella,** or kneecap. This small bone is characteristic of birds and mammals, but does not occur in other vertebrates.

Distal to the knee joint is that part of the leg called the drumstick in the chicken, which corresponds to the so-called "shank" of man. Two bones occur here, a large median **tibiotarsus,** and a much smaller slender **fibula.** The fibula is on the lateral surface of the tibiotarsus and partially fused with it. It is atrophied distally. Note the two large ridgelike **crests** on the anterior surface of the tibiotarsus near the knee joint. These are for muscle attachments. The tibiotarsus is so called because it represents a fusion of the tibia with some of the tarsal or ankle bones. That part of the leg from the distal end of the tibiotarsus through the toes corresponds to the foot. Observe that it is highly modified. There is a single large bone extending from the end of the tibiotarsus to the base of the toes. This is the **tarsometatarsus,** and represents a fusion of some ankle bones (tarsals) and three foot bones (metatarsals). There are thus no free tarsal or ankle bones in the bird, but all have either fused with other elements or have disappeared. The three metatarsal bones that fuse to form the tarsometatarsus are thought to be the second, third, and fourth, the first and fifth having been lost or in some cases being represented only by remnants.

Four **digits,** or toes, are present, one of which is directed posteriorly. This backward-projecting digit represents the first digit, or great toe. Look at its base and observe that it articulates with a projection that is partly fused with the tarsometatarsus. This projection is a remnant of the first metatarsal bone. Examine the distal end of the tarsometatarsus where it joins the anterior digits. The three partial divisions of this bone at this point are the ends of metatarsal bones two, three, and four, which together make up the tarsometatarsus.

Count the number of **phalanges** in each digit, and observe the **claw** on the end of each. The inner digit on each foot is number two.

EXTERNAL ANATOMY

One of the most obvious features of the external anatomy of the pigeon is that the body is covered with **feathers.** This one characteristic is sufficient to distinguish a bird from any other animal, since feathers occur only in this group. Other rather noticeable external features of birds include the **wings,** which are modified front limbs, and the presence of a horny **beak,** which is formed from both upper and lower jaws.

The body of the pigeon is divided into four general regions: the **head,** the **neck,** the **trunk**—to which the neck, wings, and legs are attached—and a short stumpy **tail.** The general position of the tail can be seen because the group of large **tail feathers** at the posterior end of the body is attached to it.

Examine the head. Observe the upper and lower jaws modified into a beak and the eyes posterior to the base of the upper jaw. Note the slitlike external **nares,** or nostrils, at the base of the upper jaw. Three protective structures occur about the eye. These are the upper and lower **eyelids** and a semitransparent membrane, called the **nictitating membrane.** In preserved specimens the eyeball and the membrane are often opaque and the eyes are partially open. The nictitating membrane is attached near the anterior corner of the eye and will probably be partially over the eye in the specimens. The lower eyelid is the one most movable in birds and in most other vertebrates, except mammals. The upper lid is the more movable in mammals, including man. Human beings do not have a nictitating membrane, although the small bit of skin in the inner corner of the eye may be the remnant of one. This membrane occurs in many mammals, including the cat.

Birds have an **external ear,** although they do not have any pinnae, the large cartilaginous structures surrounding the external ear opening in mammals.   Locate the ear, ventral to the posterior edge of the eye.   It is more or less covered by feathers and there are a number of protective, bristlelike feathers concentrated about the opening.   The opening is the **external auditory meatus,** which as in other vertebrates with this structure is formed from the first pharyngeal cleft of the embryo.   The external auditory meatus, together with the small folds of skin about it, constitutes the external ear.   The external auditory meatus is in contact with the middle ear, as in mammals.

It is now time to study the wing, keeping in mind the knowledge gained from a study of the skeleton.   Turn the specimen on its back and, by moving the wing, identify the three divisions. The part attached to the body corresponds to the **upper arm** in man.   In the preserved specimen, it usually extends obliquely posteriorly from its point of attachment.   The middle section, the **forearm,** extends obliquely anteriorly from its attachment with the upper arm to the anterior wing margin.   The most distal division, which corresponds to the **wrist** and the **hand,** or the front foot, of mammals, extends posteriorly, parallel with the upper-arm division.   It should be recalled from the study of the skeleton that the upper arm has a single large bone, the humerus, that the forearm has the radius and the ulna, while the distal section, or the hand, contains carpals, metacarpals, and phalanges. Several of these latter elements are considerably modified for flight.

The flight feathers are the largest feathers in the wing; they are attached along the posterior border, and as a group are called the **remiges.**   Those attached to the hand are **primary flight feathers,** those attached to the forearm are **secondaries,** while the flight feathers arising from the upper arm are the **tertiaries.**

With your finger feel the breast, and find the hard ridge near the center.   This is the keel, or **carina,** of the sternum, the large ventral bone that was seen in the skeleton.   The firm tissue on each side of the carina is composed of pectoral muscles, of importance in flying.

The hind limbs, or legs, consist of three divisions: **thigh, shank,** and **foot.**   The thigh is attached to the trunk and is so enclosed in tissue that it is hard to distinguish as a definite division.   It contains a single large bone, the humerus.   The shank, or "drumstick," is the leg division that passes from the distal part of the thigh to the foot.   It is completely covered with feathers.

The foot and ankle, which are combined in the pigeon, form the most distal section of the leg. At the proximal end, this division is partly clothed with feathers on the anterior surface, and the line of demarcation between it and the shank is sometimes hard to see anteriorly. On the posterior surface of the leg, however, the joint is easy to distinguish because the feathers are usually confined to the shank. Observe that only four **digits** are present, each of which bears a large **claw.** These digits represent digits one through four of the typical vertebrate foot, the fifth having been lost. The toe directed backward is the great toe, or digit number one. The scales that cover the foot and the digits are epidermal derivatives and are considered to be homologous with the scales of reptiles.

Examine the tail. It bears many large feathers, called **rectrices.** That part of the tail in which the tail feathers are inserted is often termed the **uropygium.** It contains seven caudal vertebrae, but it is so enclosed in tissue that it does not protrude very far from the body. Separate the feathers on the dorsal side, just anterior to the uropygium, and find a small nipplelike structure. This is the **uropygial gland,** a structure that secretes oil used in preening the feathers.

Just ventral to the tail is a rather large transverse opening. This is the **cloacal opening,** the common opening to the outside for the digestive tract and the urogenital system.

Feathers. We have noted that feathers occur only in birds. They are epidermal in origin and are considered to be homologous to scales. Feathers function to insulate the bird's body, thereby helping in the maintenance of a high body temperature; they help to keep the body dry and protect the integument or skin from injury; and finally they make flight possible, a distinctive feature of most birds. Three kinds of feathers occur in adult birds: **contour feathers, down feathers,** and **filoplumes.** The contour feathers, as the name implies, are the ones mostly responsible for the contours or shape of the bird. They include most visible body feathers on the body, as well as the feathers of the wings and tail. Both down and filoplumes are quite small and occur among the bases of the contour feathers.

Remove one of the large flight or tail feathers and study it. It is best to pull the feather out with a quick jerk, rather than with a steady pull, to prevent the feather from breaking. Note the hole that remains in the skin. This is known as a **feather follicle.** Two general divisions of the feather are easily seen.

The bare proximal portion, the end of which was inserted in the skin, is the **quill** or calamus. The distal, expanded part of the feather is the **vane.** Examine the end of the quill that was in the skin. The small hole in the tip is the **inferior umbilicus.** During embryonic development of the feather, a bit of tissue called a papilla extended through this opening and into the quill, which is hollow. This papilla is from the dermal layer of the skin and it apparently helps to stimulate the epidermal cells to develop into a feather. When the feather is mature, the papilla withdraws from the quill, leaving the feather as a dead structure, derived entirely from the epidermis.

The vane is composed of two parts: a central axis continuous with the quill and known as the **shaft,** and the **web,** made up of many small hairlike structures extending from each side of the shaft. The individual units that form the web are **barbs.** Note that one side of the shaft is rounded, while the opposite side has a longitudinal groove. The side of the feather with the groove is sometimes called the ventral surface; the opposite side is dorsal.

The individual barbs that compose the web are more complex than they appear to the unaided eye. A dissecting microscope is necessary to study them in detail. Each barb bears a series of side branches called **barbules,** and on each barbule is a large number of small **hooklets.** The barbules interlock by means of these hooklets, which causes the web to have a continuous smooth, strong surface. This continuous surface is not as evident in the wet feathers of preserved specimens as they are in dry feathers, in which the barbs are more nearly in their normal position.

Look among the bases of the contour feathers and find a down feather. The down feather will probably impress you as being an undeveloped contour feather. It has a large basal part, or **quill,** and the **barbs** spring directly from the end of the quill. Most young birds are covered at first with down feathers.

Filoplumes are also called pinfeathers and hairfeathers. They appear as slender hairs among the bases of the other feathers, and details are hard to see without using a dissecting microscope. Many of the filoplumes remain on the body after the bird or chicken has been "picked," and not infrequently they appear unappetizingly on pieces of fried chicken. One of these feathers consists of a long basal part, usually called the **shaft,** and a few short **barbs** from the terminal end of the shaft.

INTERNAL ANATOMY

For a study of the internal anatomy, removal of many of the feathers is necessary. This is a thankless chore at best, and the method to be used should be indicated to you by the instructor. If the instructor does not care to have the skin preserved, the feathers may be pulled off in large groups. Patches of skin will often stick to the bases of the feathers if this method is used, and the pigeon may be partially skinned. This method usually destroys the feather follicles, which are arranged in definite lines called **feather tracts**. If the feather tracts are to be studied, only a few feathers should be removed at a time and care should be taken that the skin does not remain attached to the bases of the feathers.

Do not allow the feathers to become scattered about the room and *do not* put them in the sink. The feathers should be placed in the waste cans provided for that purpose. Remove the feathers from the body, and from a wing and a leg on the same side.

When the bird has been plucked, place it ventral side up in the dissecting pan. Examine the neck. If the skin is still in place, make a longitudinal mid-ventral incision through it from the base of the lower jaw to the anterior end of the sternum. Then pull the skin away from the incision on each side.

Two longitudinal tubes occur in the neck region and, if the skin was removed with the feathers, one or both of them will be visible without any incision being made. Pick away the tissue obscuring these tubes. They may occur side by side, or one may be dorsal to the other. The **trachea,** or windpipe, is the one the walls of which show numerous small rings. These are of cartilage, which holds the cavity of the trachea open so that air can pass through. The **esophagus** is the other tube, which passes from the pharynx to the stomach.

Trace these tubes anteriorly, pulling away concealing tissues. Note that the esophagus passes dorsal to the trachea near the head. Remove the skin from underneath the lower jaw and from the angle of the jaw on one side. Then, with forceps, pick away the tissue. You should very shortly note a slender transverse piece of bone that passes from the base of the tongue toward the rear of the head, just under the lower jaw. This is a part of the **hyoid apparatus** which may have been observed in a study of the skeleton. This portion is one of the **posterior horns** of the hyoid, another of which occurs on the opposite side of the head. Trace this structure anteriorly and note that it passes into the base of the tongue. Here it fuses with the horn from the opposite side and eventually forms a structure inside the tongue called the **entoglossal.** The general function of the hyoid apparatus is to support the tongue. It is composed of remnants of the pharyngeal arches, or visceral skeleton, which are homologous with the gill arches of fishes. At the anterior end of the trachea is an enlargement, the **larynx,** which is partly concealed by the hyoid apparatus. The larynx is connected to the pharynx by an opening, the **glottis,** which will be observed later. The larynx of birds is homologous with the larynx, or voice box, of other vertebrate animals; but the sounds of birds are made by another structure, to be seen shortly.

Trace the esophagus posteriorly and observe that it opens into a large sac just anterior to the sternum. This sac is the **crop,** or craw, and it is considered to be a modification of the esophagus. This structure functions in many birds as a storage place for the food, which is swallowed without chewing.

Additional dissection to expose the internal organs should now be made, starting in the abdominal region. This is the soft area just posterior to the sternum. With a scalpel carefully make a longitudinal incision slightly to the right of the mid-ventral line. Care must be exerted, since the skin and muscles in this area are thin. The incision should be an inch or so in length. Pull the edges apart, and the coiled mass of **intestines** can be seen inside. The thin membrane which may be observed partly obscuring the intestines is the **peritoneum.** This membrane lines the cavity in which lie the internal organs.

Continue the incision anteriorly through the muscles of the sternum. Use the scalpel to cut through the pectoral muscles until you reach the dorsal flattened part of the sternum. Then with scissors cut anteriorly through the sternum. Follow the incision through the pectoral muscles, and be careful not to cut any internal organs. Hold the right edge (pigeon's right) of the incision with the left hand and, as the sternum is cut, pull the incision apart. This will help to prevent injury to the organs. Continue the dissection to the anterior end of the sternum. Just dorsal to the posterior end of the sternum is the **liver,** a dark-red organ. Now with a scalpel, make a transverse incision through the abdominal wall, just posterior to the tip of the sternum and beginning at the original longitudinal incision. Carry this around the end of the sternum to the left and continue dorsally for an inch or so. The triangular area of abdominal body wall thus formed should now be pulled to the left (pigeon's). Note that membranes attach some of the organs to the body wall. The most obvious of these occurs on the left side. This tissue is made of **mesenteries,** which attach the liver and the gizzard to the ventral body wall. Disconnect these mesenteries so that the internal organs can be examined. Place the thumb of the left hand under the edge of the sternum and, holding the body of the pigeon with the right hand, pull upward gently on the sternum. This will enlarge the cavity so that more details can be seen. Note the mesentery that passes from the liver to the inner surface of the sternum. This is the **falciform ligament.**

Observe that the liver has two lobes, a large right one and a smaller left lobe. No gall bladder occurs in the pigeon, although many birds, including the domestic chicken, have gall bladders. With scalpel and scissors make a second longitudinal incision through the sternum to the left of the keel. Carry this anteriorly until the middle portion of the sternum can be loosened and removed.

Now study the internal organs. The **heart** lies just anterior to the liver and the posterior part is partially enclosed within the liver lobes. Note that a thin membrane surrounds the heart. This is the **pericardial sac.** The space between the sac and the heart is the **pericardial cavity,** and it is a part of the coelom. The cavity in which the visceral organs lie is the **peritoneal,** or abdominal, **cavity.** This too is a part of the coelom. The **pleural cavities,** anterior divisions of the coelom, will be noted presently.

Turn back to the organs in the peritoneal cavity. The **gizzard** lies just dorsal to the left lobe of the liver, at the level of the thigh. It is a rounded, hard organ that corresponds to a part of the stomach of other vertebrates. Raise the lobes of the liver and note a mesentery passing between the left lobe of the liver and the gizzard. This is the **gastrohepatic ligament.** Break this and locate the **proventriculus,** anterior to the gizzard. Break off a part of the left liver lobe if necessary. The proventriculus is a tubelike structure that enters the anterior surface of the gizzard. It connects anteriorly to the crop by way of the esophagus. The proventriculus and the gizzard make up the stomach. The proventriculus secretes digestive juices, while the gizzard grinds up the food which is swallowed whole by its toothless owner. Many birds swallow small stones from time to time, which pass to the gizzard and are used in the grinding of the food.

The anterior end of the **small intestine** is, as usual, known as the

duodenum. It is attached to the right side of the gizzard near the latter's junction with the proventriculus. Trace the duodenum posteriorly and note that it passes over to the right, loops back upon itself, and curves to the left and anteriorly. Between these two loops of the duodenum is the **pancreas,** an elongate lobed grayish digestive gland.

Bile ducts arise from the liver and pass into the duodenum. These can sometimes be seen near the anterior end of right and left duodenal loops. The pancreas also connects to the duodenum by **pancreatic ducts,** through which pass pancreatic juices. Some of these can often be seen by spreading the two loops of the duodenum and looking in the mesentery that binds the two loops together.

The duodenum passes over to the right and is continued posteriorly as the **ileum,** a tightly coiled mass of intestine, bound together by the intestinal mesentery. It is quite difficult to trace the intestine through all of its complicated loops without getting lost in a maze. Pick away some of the mesentery binding the loops together, disconnect the mesenteries from the body wall, and pull some of the intestinal loops out of the peritoneal cavity. Observe the numerous blood vessels passing through the mesenteries. When the intestinal coils have been pulled to one side sufficiently, locate the cloacal opening. Then in the peritoneal cavity find where the posterior end of the intestine joins the cloaca. This part of the intestine is the **large intestine.** Trace the large intestine anteriorly in the midline for about an inch, until you find two small lateral projections, of variable size in different specimens. These are blind pouches called **colic caeca,** and they mark the point of junction between large and small intestine. It should be recalled that both the intestine and the urogenital system, to be studied presently, open to the outside through the cloacal opening.

The pigeon, as well as many other birds, has an extensive system of structures called **air sacs.** These sacs have membranous walls, and they are easily destroyed. The air sacs are connected with the lungs, and they are considered to be a part of the respiratory system. An attempt should be made at this point to find some of these air sacs although, as indicated, some of them have probably already been destroyed. However, in some cases, the space which they occupied or remnants of them can be seen.

Examine the heart and notice a sheet of tissue extending from the pericardium on each side laterally and posteriorly to the body wall. This is the **oblique septum,** which divides the coelom into a posterior peritoneal division and two pleural divisions, to be seen shortly. The oblique septum is a double-walled structure, and the two walls enclose the **posterior intermediate air sac.** Part of the posterior wall of the septum has probably been broken at this stage of the dissection. Probe anterior to it, and observe the cavity in which the air sac was enclosed.

A large **abdominal air sac** occurs in the peritoneal, or abdominal, cavity, somewhat dorsal to the visceral organs. Look in this area, and see if you can find remnants of the membranous walls. Most of the sac has probably been destroyed.

THE HEART AND ASSOCIATED VESSELS

Before the heart can be studied, a little more dissection will probably be necessary at the anterior end of the organ. The two coracoid bones, parts of the pectoral girdle, join with the sternum near the anterior end of the heart, and if these have not already been cut through, they will probably obscure the blood vessels and the anterior end of the heart. Cut through the coracoids, if they have not already been cut, and take out a section of tissue on each side. Then work anteriorly with forceps. Just anterior to the heart is another air sac, the **anterior intermediate air sac.** Look for the thin membranous walls of this sac as you clear away the tissue in front of the heart.

With forceps carefully remove the pericardial sac from the heart. The space between the heart and the sac, it should be remembered, is the pericardial cavity. Since the pigeon is not injected, we will study only the divisions of the heart and a few of the major blood vessels.

The heart of the pigeon has four complete chambers: two **ventricles** and two **auricles.** The structure is, roughly, cone-shaped, with a posterior point called the **apex** and an anterior **base.** The **right** and **left ventricles** form the major part of the posterior region of the heart. Externally, the division between the two ventricles is obscure, except that on the right side a shallow oblique groove marks the division between right and left ventricles in this area. Look at the base of the heart, and find the **right** and **left auricles.** They are rounded caplike structures—usually darker in color than the ventricles—that fit over the anterior ends of the ventricles.

Two main arteries arise from the two ventricles.   These are the **pulmonary trunk** and the **aorta.**   The pulmonary arises from the right ventricle and almost immediately divides into **right** and **left pulmonary arteries,** each of which passes to a lung.   The aorta comes from the left ventricle, and from it arteries spring which supply the organs and tissues with blood.   In uninjected specimens, the arteries will appear as white cords.   The bases of the aorta and the pulmonary are in contact and they arise from the ventricles between the two auricles.   Locate these vessels. A vessel will be seen arching over to the left (pigeon's).   This is the left pulmonary artery.   The right pulmonary, also derived from the pulmonary trunk, passes almost straight dorsally, and it probably cannot be seen as yet.   The aorta arches over to the right and in this region is called the **aortic arch.**   It very shortly gives rise, from its anterior surface, to two arteries that pass forward toward the crop.   These are the **brachiocephalic arteries,** which supply blood to the anterior regions of the body, including the wings and the brain.   The aorta then passes on to the right and into the abdominal cavity, where it gives off branches to the visceral organs.

Blood carried over the body by the aorta and its branches is returned to the right auricle by three large veins and smaller vessels which combine to form them.   These are two **precaval veins** and one **postcaval vein.**   The precaval veins enter the right auricle near its anterior surface, and the points of entrance are often partly obscured.   With forceps pull away the tissue just posterior to the aortic arch.   A large vein should soon be seen here entering the auricle.   This is the **right precaval vein,** and some of the veins which combine to form it are obscured by the aortic arch.   The **left precaval** enters the right auricle somewhat dorsally and cannot be seen at this time.   The branches of these two vessels are the same.   These vessels return blood from the anterior end of the body which is carried there by the brachiocephalic arteries and their branches.

The postcaval vein enters the right auricle dorsal to the ventricles.   Raise the tip of the heart and push it somewhat anteriorly, so that the space between the liver and the heart can be seen.   Pick away the membranes in this area with forceps and find the postcaval.   This vessel returns blood from the posterior region of the body.

Aerated blood is returned from the lungs to the left auricle by **pulmonary veins,** of which there are several.   Push the heart over to the right and see if you can find some of these veins entering the left auricle.

The aortic arches and other embryonic vessels from which the major arteries of the pigeon are derived are similar to the condition found in the cat (page 211). There is, however, one major difference between the two relative to the origin of the aorta. In both the pigeon and the cat, the aorta is derived from the embryonic ventral aorta, the dorsal aorta, and a portion of aortic arch number 4. In the pigeon and other birds, the aortic arch on the *right* side persists; in the cat the *left* arch contributes to the formation of the aorta, while the right arch degenerates.

THE RESPIRATORY SYSTEM

Part of the respiratory system has already been seen. It consists of lungs, air sacs, and several sets of interconnected tubes and chambers. Start at the head for this study. The **external nares,** or nostrils, have already been observed. Insert one point of the scissors into the angle of the mouth on one side and cut posteriorly ventral to the eye. Repeat on the opposite side, so that the mouth can be widely opened. Note the pointed **tongue** on the floor of the **oral cavity,** or mouth cavity. Notice that the **hyoid apparatus,** previously seen, passes into the base of the tongue. The external nares open into the roof of the mouth but these internal openings are hard to see.

The mouth cavity is continued posteriorly by the **pharynx,** the region where the respiratory and digestive systems come together. The pharynx can be readily found by passing a probe posteriorly along the tongue. In the floor of the pharynx find a small hole. This is the **glottis,** the opening through which air passes through the **larynx** and into the **trachea.** Pass a small probe through the glottis and notice that it enters the trachea, the ringed tube lying near the mid-line and previously identified. A passage can be seen extending posteriorly from the pharynx. This is the **esophagus,** which leads to the crop.

The larynx is the enlarged end of the trachea into which the glottis opens. This structure is partly concealed by the hyoid apparatus and muscles. Cut the horns of the hyoid, grasp it with forceps, and pull. This will often remove the tongue, revealing the larynx and the glottis in more detail. The larynx is composed of several units or cartilages, but they are small and hard to identify. Trace the trachea posteriorly and observe again that its walls are strengthened by a series of cartilaginous rings, which prevent the tube from collapsing. The trachea passes dorsal to the crop.

Carefully disconnect the crop from the surrounding tissue on the left side. Just dorsal to the crop and in contact with it and somewhat enclosed by the two arms of the wishbone is the **interclavicular air sac.** It may be collapsed, but the remnants of its membranous walls can probably be seen. Look for this sac as you loosen the crop. Pull the crop over to the right, so that the posterior extension of the trachea can be seen. Observe at this time that the esophagus continues posteriorly from the crop and leads directly into the proventriculus. Just dorsal to the heart, the trachea divides into two **bronchi,** each of which passes to a lung.

Clip through the large arteries and veins attached to the heart, and loosen the pericardial sac so that the heart can be pulled to one side. The division of the trachea into two bronchi will now be revealed. Observe that the trachea expands slightly at the point where it divides into the bronchi. This expansion forms a chamber called the **syrinx.** The syrinx is a structure found only in birds. It, rather than the larynx, is responsible for sound production.

Trace one of the bronchi to its entrance into a **lung** and pull away the membranous tissue to reveal it. During the dissection note again the oblique septum. The space between its two walls, which in life is occupied by the anterior intermediate air sac, is often quite evident at this stage of the dissection.

The thin membrane on the ventral surface of each lung is called the **pleura.** It also occurs between the lungs, forming **right** and **left pleural cavities.** The pleural cavities, as noted previously, are also divisions of the coelom, or body cavity. The coelom of a bird has four divisions: the peritoneal cavity, containing the abdominal organs; the pericardial cavity around the heart; the two pleural cavities, each of which encloses a lung. It should be recalled that this division of the original pleuroperitoneal cavity into anterior pleural and posterior peritoneal divisions is somewhat anticipated in the turtle (page 122).

The **lungs** are reddish, flattened structures closely applied to the undersurface of the dorsal body wall. Examine the lungs and see if you can find air sacs connected with them. Air sacs are of considerable importance in the functioning of birds. When filled, they help to decrease the weight, or specific gravity, of the body. They also make possible more complete aeration of the lungs than is attainable in other animals.

At this stage of the dissection, the lateral regions of the large pectoral muscles should be intact, the central portions and keel of the sternum having been removed. Examine the cut edges of these muscles on one side. This mass of muscle consists of two muscles, a large ventral **pectoralis major,** and a smaller **pectoralis minor** under the pectoralis major and in contact with the sternum. Manipulate the cut edges of these muscles and note that these two muscles are easily separated. In fact, near the anterior end of the sternum a definite space can usually be seen between them. This space is occupied by the **axillary air sac,** which is connected to the interclavicular air sac previously seen. The membranous walls of the axillary air sac are often still partially intact.

Many of the bones of birds are hollow, and these hollow spaces are often connected with air sacs. The axillary air sac communicates with the end of the **humerus** on each side, the large bones of the upper wing. Break the ventral membranous wall of the air sac, and look on the dorsal side of the cavity near the anterior end for this connection. Nerves, small muscles, and other tissue occur here, some of which may need to be pulled away with forceps. A rather large opening into the humerus can usually be found. This is the **pneumatic foramen,** which was also observed in the study of the skeleton.

THE UROGENITAL SYSTEM

The urinary, or excretory, system and the genital, or reproductive, system are intimately associated together in birds as in other vertebrates. For this reason, they will be studied together as the **urogenital system.**

One important organ unrelated to the urogenital system should be seen during the dissection. Loosen the mesentery that attaches the gizzard to the dorsal body wall, and cut across the proventriculus just anterior to the gizzard. Turn these organs to the right and find a small reddish, oblong organ in the mesentery between the proventriculus and the gizzard. This is the **spleen,** an organ which is considered to be a part of the circulatory system. Cut the small intestine at the anterior end of the peritoneal cavity where it becomes applied to the dorsal body wall, and remove the visceral organs from the body. Leave the posterior end of the small intestine and the large intestine intact. The organs of both sexes should be studied.

Female. The appearance of the genital part of the urogenital system will vary, depending upon the maturity of the bird at the time of its untimely demise.   Only the left **ovary** and **oviduct** are functional in the pigeon and in most birds.   The right ovary and oviduct occur in the embryo, but these disintegrate before development is complete, or remain as remnants.

In some birds, the ovary will be easily found near the anterior end of the peritoneal cavity.   It is an irregular-shaped mass containing eggs of various sizes, and it partly conceals the left **kidney,** which is closely applied to the dorsal body wall.   In immature specimens, the ovary is small and sometimes difficult to differentiate from surrounding tissue.

Passing posteriorly from the ovary is the left oviduct, or Müllerian duct.   In mature specimens it is coiled, but is comparatively straight in immature birds.   It passes along the ventral kidney surface and opens into the cloaca on the left side. There is no direct connection between the oviduct and the ovary, a situation characteristic of most vertebrate animals.   The anterior end of the oviduct is expanded into the **ostium,** a funnel-shaped opening that occurs close to the ovary.

Observe that each kidney is three-lobed and that the kidneys are closely applied to the dorsal body wall.   Here they fit into a depression in the pelvic girdle.   Their undersurfaces are covered by the peritoneum, the membrane that lines the peritoneal cavity.   A straight white tube may be seen through the membrane against the posterior kidney lobe on the ventral surface.   If the oviduct is enlarged, this tube will be partly concealed on the left side. It is the **ureter,** or metanephric duct.   Pull the peritoneum away with forceps and trace the ureter anteriorly to its connection with the kidney.   The ureter collects waste products from the kidney and passes posteriorly, where it empties into the **cloaca.**

Male.   The **testes,** the reproductive organs of the male, will vary in size, depending upon the season in which the pigeon was killed.   They are light-colored oval bodies near the anterior dorsal region of the peritoneal cavity.   Each of them is just ventral to the anterior end of a **kidney.**   Look dorsal to a testis and find the kidney, a three-lobed reddish structure closely applied to the dorsal body wall.   The kidneys are dorsal to the peritoneum, the thin membrane that lines the peritoneal cavity.

Manipulate one of the testes with forceps and note that a white tube passes from the posterior end backward toward the cloaca. This is the **vas deferens** (plural, vasa deferentia), the duct that transmits sperm cells from the testes to the cloaca. The vas deferens proceeds posteriorly over the ventral kidney surface and near the center becomes associated with a tube arising from the kidney. This duct is the **ureter,** or metanephric duct, which transports excretory products to the cloaca. The ureter and the vas deferens continue posteriorly, often so closely opposed that they have the appearance of a single duct. The vas deferens is often lateral to the ureter and, where the tubes are not in contact, the two can be distinguished. The vas deferens is greatly convoluted, while the ureter is straight. Trace the tubes to their entrance into the **cloaca.**

Note that the male pigeon does not have a penis—a structure that is absent in most birds. Transfer of sperm cells to the female occurs when the cloacas of the two sexes are brought into contact with each other. A few birds, including the ostrich and the duck, have a penis in the male.

The kidneys of birds are metanephric kidneys, the same type as in reptiles and mammals; and the ureter is known as the metanephric duct, an almost entirely new attainment that started with reptiles. The vasa deferentia, as in the turtle (page 128) and the cat (page 196), are derived from the embryonic mesonephric duct. Note that in the pigeon no bladder is present, an accessory excretory structure that occurs in both the turtle and the cat.

INDEX

A

Accessory bladder of turtle, 115, 126, 127
Adam's apple, 168
Adrenal gland of cat, 200, 213
Air sacs of pigeon, 240, 241, 244, 245
Amphibia, emergence of, on land, 87
  as "typical vertebrates," 86
Amphioxus, circulatory system of, 13
  classification of, 6
  coelom of, 12
  cross sections of, 10–13
  external anatomy of, 6
  gonads of, 8
  internal anatomy of, 6
  muscles of, 7–8
  reproduction in, 12
Ampullae, of inner ear, 44
  of Lorenzini, 29
Aortic arches, of cat, 211–212
  discussion of, 78–79, 122–123, 211–212
  of dogfish, 70–72, 74–78
  of lamprey, 22
  of Necturus, 102–103
  of pigeon, 243
  of turtle, 122–123
Aponeurosis, definition of, 160
Arteries, of Amphioxus, 13
  of cat, of heart, 187–188
    in peritoneal cavity, 212–215
    in thorax, 206–210
  of dogfish, afferent branchial, 71–72
    anterior to transverse septum, 69–72
    efferent branchial and associated vessels, 74–76
  of lamprey, 22, 23
  of Necturus, afferent branchial, 100, 102
    efferent branchial, 102–104

Arteries, of Necturus, of heart, 99–100
  in pleuroperitoneal cavity, 98–99
  of pigeon, of heart, 242–243
  of turtle, anterior, 118–123
    brachiocephalic and branches, 120–121
    systemic arches and associated vessels, 121–124
Artery, definition of, 63
Atlas, of cat, 135–136
  of pigeon, 227–228
Atriopore of Amphioxus, 7
Atrium of Amphioxus, 10
Autonomic nervous system, of cat, 224
  of dogfish, 56
  of Necturus, 107
  of turtle, 131
Axis, of cat, 135–136
  of pigeon, 227–228

B

Beak of pigeon, 226, 233
Bladder, accessory, 115, 126, 127
  gall, 32, 83, 92, 111, 190, 239
  swim, of perch, 83
  urinary, 84, 93, 105, 111, 126, 127, 189, 192, 195
Blood circulation, in Amphioxus, 13
  through heart, of cat, 189
    of turtle, 119–120
Brain, of cat, 216–221
  of dogfish, 45–48
  of lamprey, 19
  membranes of, 46, 106, 129–130, 216–217
  of Necturus, 106–107
  of turtle, 129–130
Brain region of Amphioxus, 9
Branchial basket of lamprey, 20

249